Thomas F.

197

The Difference of Man
and the
Difference It Makes

Books by Mortimer J. Adler

The Conditions of Philosophy 1965
The Idea of Freedom (VOLUME II) 1961
The New Capitalists (with LOUIS O. KELSO) 1961
The Idea of Freedom (VOLUME I) 1958
The Capitalist Manifesto (with LOUIS O. KELSO) 1958
The Revolution in Education (with MILTON MAYER) 1958
How to Think About War and Peace 1944
A Dialectic of Morals 1941
How to Read a Book 1940
Problems for Thomists: The Problem of Species 1940
What Man Has Made of Man 1938
Saint Thomas and the Gentiles 1938
Art and Prudence 1937
Crime, Law, and Social Science 1933
Dialectic 1927

The Difference of Man and the Difference It Makes

MORTIMER J. ADLER

Based on the Encyclopaedia Britannica Lectures delivered at the University of Chicago, 1966

HOLT, RINEHART AND WINSTON

New York Chicago
San Francisco

Published simultaneously in Canada by Holt, Rinehart and Winston of Canada, Limited.

Library of Congress Catalog Card Number: 67-19054

First Edition

A portion of Chapter 12 has appeared in *The New Scholasticism.*

Grateful acknowledgment is made to Little, Brown and Company for permission to reprint excerpts from YOU SHALL KNOW THEM *by Vercors, copyright 1953 by Jean Bruller.*

Designer: Ernst Reichl

8655201

Printed in the United States of America

TO

MARK AND MICHAEL

Contents

Part Three

The Difference It Makes

Preface

IN *The Conditions of Philosophy*, based on the first series of Encyclopaedia Britannica Lectures delivered at the University of Chicago in 1964, I called attention to certain difficult questions that cannot be satisfactorily answered by scientific investigation or by philosophical thought alone. I called them mixed questions because they require, for satisfactory answers, the fullest cooperation of both scientific research and philosophical inquiry. How man differs from everything else in the universe is such a question. It cannot be adequately formulated, much less resolved, without our bringing philosophical insight and analysis to bear upon all the scientific data and hypotheses that we now have concerning the constitution and behavior of man as a living organism. The second series of Britannica Lectures delivered at the University in the Spring of 1966 undertook to discharge that task.

Based on these lectures, the present book exemplifies the spirit and method of the philosophical enterprise as it is conceived in *The Conditions of Philosophy*. In writing this book, as in writing its predecessor, I had before me not only the notes that I had prepared for the lectures, but also a record of the questions raised by an audience that included laymen as well as faculty and students. The experience of giving the lectures and the memory of the discussions that ensued helped me to find the language and structure for presenting the complex argument of this book in a manner intelligible to the general reader and at the same time effective for the specialist who is expert in one or more of the fields of learning relevant to the question about man. For this experience, I am grateful to the auspices provided by the University, and to Encyclopaedia Britannica, Inc. for sponsoring the lectureship.

The Difference of Man and the Difference It Makes is, in a sense, also the product of the work of the Institute for Philosophical Research, of which I am Director. It employs the method developed by the Institute to clarify the discussion of basic ideas —first of all, by formulating with precision the questions at issue, and then by discovering in the literature of the subject the conflicting views that constitute the various positions taken on these issues, together with the evidences appealed to and the arguments advanced that bear on the matters in dispute. The Institute's method was first exemplified, as well as outlined and explained, in *The Idea of Freedom*, the two volumes of which were published some years ago. The further applicability of the method to other ideas is exemplified in four books being published this year: *The Idea of Love*, by Robert Hazo; *The Idea of Progress*, by Charles Van Doren; *The Idea of Justice*, by Otto Bird; and *The Idea of Happiness*, by V. J. McGill.

Like these other books, *The Difference of Man and the Difference It Makes* represents a collaborative effort, in that its formulations have been subjected to critical examination and discussion by the Institute's staff and have profited from the contributions of many minds. Responsibility for the final product lies, of course, with the author, but whatever merit attaches to the results achieved must be shared with others. On this last point, I am deeply sensitive to the debt I owe my colleagues at the Institute. I wish to express my gratitude especially to Arthur L. H. Rubin, Charles Van Doren, and Otto Bird for the hours they spent in reading and discussing with me the outlines of my lectures and the manuscript of this book, as well as for the guidance I derived from their critical and constructive suggestions.

Mortimer J. Adler

Chicago
April 22, 1967

Introduction

BY THEODORE T. PUCK

Professor of Biophysics and Director of the Eleanor Roosevelt Institute for Cancer Research at the University of Colorado

Two hundred years ago it was widely believed that the continued growth of science would usher in a golden age of reason and human fulfillment. Some of these hopes have indeed been fulfilled. The growth of physics and engineering has produced a mastery over matter and energy, and a level of productivity that far surpasses the most optimistic of the informed opinions of the past. Many of the diseases which scourged mankind throughout the ages have been conquered. Numerous inexplicable natural phenomena have been rationally understood, so that the force of superstition (and of those who would exploit it) has been considerably weakened. Nevertheless, it is obvious from a look at any newspaper that the human condition throughout the world still has a long and weary road to travel before anything even approaching a civilized ideal is within reach.

This state of affairs derives in part from the continuing failure to solve some of man's age-old problems—such as the achievement of a consensus on how material goods should be allocated among the members of society, or the elimination of force as a means of settling disputes. But new and deep-seated problems have also arisen as a consequence of the growth of science and its attendant technology.

Some of these new problems are simple and direct. For example, the population explosion now threatening the planet is a mathematical consequence of the alleviation of some of the lethal processes affecting human populations without an equivalent change in their birth rates. Others are more abstract and elusive, and involve changing conceptions of man and his value systems in a world that has altered both radically and rapidly. It is with some of these latter problems that Dr. Adler's book is concerned.

The unsettling effects on traditional human value systems that appeared with the phenomenal growth of science and technology have been of two different kinds. One of these has been indirect in nature—a consequence of the changes in the pattern of daily living brought about by industrialization. The tremendous increase in communication between previously isolated cultural groups has produced a mutual confrontation of value systems with different historical developments; as a result, questions have been raised as to the validity of goals and attitudes previously taken for granted. Many of the current value systems had their origins within religious or other frameworks whose form may be inharmonious with modern rationalistic attitudes, or whose application to the problems of man in modern society may be ambiguous. The huge increase in numbers of people in each community has itself contributed further complications. It becomes necessary to deal with people and their problems on a statistical basis, a procedure which makes all too easy the confusion of the person with the statistic representing him in a particular computation.

These are examples of problems that operate mechanically to produce blurring or even disintegration of traditional value systems. The difficulties they pose in themselves are great. However, those difficulties are enormously intensified by the second more direct category of problems, problems which are basically conceptual and have risen out of the newest developments of modern science. These new scientific achievements have raised fundamental questions about man's essential nature, and might be interpreted to mean that the whole question of human values is hardly worth bothering about, simply because man himself is not all that important.

What are these scientific developments? They occur in the fields of biology and physics. Ever since Linnaeus, biologists have been uncovering more and more resemblances between all living forms, and therefore between man and other organisms. In the last two decades there has been a revolution in the understanding of life processes, a revolution that has given biology a new conceptual dimension and brought to culmination the idea of biological relatedness. Arising out of this development has been the realization that *all* of the innumerable living forms of the earth that have so far been studied conform in the most intimate detail, at the level of the molecules themselves, to the same basic pattern of structural and functional organization.

Both the most simple and the most complex living forms utilize the same molecular code to store information and the same molecular machinery to translate this information into the actions that make up their living processes. Different forms differ from each other in the number of elements in their basic gene complement, and in details of their intimate structure and regulatory arrangements. But from the smallest bacterium to man, the underlying pattern by which all life processes are carried out is so overwhelmingly similar as to leave no doubt about its essential identity in all living forms. In addition, the intricate mechanisms by which living things manipulate molecules to carry out the phenomena of life, including functions as complex as biological reproduction, have now been understood in considerable detail. This understanding seems to have eliminated in the minds of modern biological scientists the ability to entertain any longer the hypothesis of the existence in living organisms of a mystical component which can evade or contravene the laws of physics, chemistry, and mathematics.

Similarly, physics has produced some new advances with a bearing on man's conception of himself. The nature of information theory has been clarified in fundamental ways, and it has become possible to construct powerful electronic computers with astonishing capabilities. These machines can now mimic and indeed enormously improve upon certain highly specific human mental operations. But with the current understanding of the theory of informational manipulation, it has also been projected that machines will eventually be built with abilities to equal or exceed human mental powers in much broader areas.

This situation raises difficult conceptual questions. A superficial examination might yield the following conclusion: If man is essentially no different from a pig or an ape, except that he has a more powerful mind, and if man-made machines are more powerful mentally than man, man is neither unique among living forms nor different from man-made machines in any way that is truly significant. From this point it is an easy step to denying the validity of almost any human aspirations, however widely and deeply they may be held.

It has been said that two questions should always be asked of any scientific assertion: First, "Is it true?" and second, "If it is true, is it *really* true?" The sense of the second question is, of course, that even if the specific facts are correct, their implications on many different levels constitute an independent set of problems, whose difficulty and importance require the initiation of a wholly new analytical investigation.

It is just this kind of analysis which Dr. Adler has carried out in re-examining the problem of man's nature in the light of these newer scientific developments. He poses the question: "Is man unique, and if so what are the implications for humanity of this uniqueness?" He has produced a careful, reasoned and highly readable analysis in which the data and methods of science and philosophy are jointly brought to bear. He has carefully examined the validity of the conclusions possible now, and the ways in which future developments may bring new elements into the situation. Finally, he has discussed the theoretical implications, and the practical moral decisions connected with the various possible positions that are logically defensible.

This excellent book presents a philosophic examination of problems arising out of the newer scientific developments, and illuminates problems of the deepest human significance. It demonstrates the need to end the artificial separation between science and philosophy in our society—a separation which has already been costly to our understanding of the meaning of past accomplishments and to our ability to plan future goals wisely.

Part One

The Modes of Difference

CHAPTER I

The Question About Man

(1)

IN 195–, living specimens of *Paranthropus erectus* were discovered in New Guinea. Their almost-human qualities recommended them to Australian industrialists, who announced plans for using them as factory slaves. This aroused Douglas Templemore, a British journalist, who had accompanied the scientific expedition that discovered the *Paranthropus*. He conceived a dramatic way of determining which these creatures were—apes or men—in order to decide what action should be taken, if any, to thwart the plans being made for them in Australia. Was the civilized world going to allow the "tropis," as members of the species were affectionately called by the scientists who discovered them, to be unjustly exploited, their rights violated, their dignity transgressed? Or should it acquiesce in their being used, like horses and oxen, as beasts of burden in the service of man?

To get a legal decision on these matters by putting the status of the species to the test, Templemore arranged to have a captured female *Paranthropus erectus* impregnated, by artificial insemination, with his own sperm. He took care of the pregnant tropi, whose name was Derry; and when she gave birth to a male offspring, he brought the mother and "child" back to London, along with thirty other members of the species, for scientific study. While the mother was housed in the Zoo with the other tropis, Templemore kept the little one in his home. To carry out the plan which he had initiated with the artificial insemination of Derry, Templemore, not without anguish, killed his and her offspring with a shot of strychnine chlorhydrate and called in a physician to certify the death.

Informed of the circumstances of the case, the perplexed Dr. Figgins notified the local constabulary. When the inspector arrived on the scene, the following conversation took place between him and Douglas Templemore.

"You are the father, I gather?"

"I am."

"Your wife's upstairs?"

"Yes, I can call her if you like."

"Oh no," the inspector hastened to assure him. "I wouldn't ask her to get up in *her* condition! I'll go and see her presently."

"I'm afraid you are under a misapprehension," said Douglas. "The child is not hers."

"Oh . . . oh . . . well . . . is the—er—the mother here, then?"

"No," said Douglas.

"Ah . . . where is she?"

"She was taken back to the Zoo yesterday."

"The Zoo? Does she work there?"

"No. She lives there."

"I beg your pardon?"

"The mother is not a woman, properly speaking. She is a female of the species *Paranthropus erectus*."

With this revelation, Dr. Figgins then examined the dead infant more closely and declared it to be a monkey, not a boy. In response, Douglas Templemore produced an affidavit testifying to the infant's peculiar origin. Written on the stationery of the Australian College of Surgeons, it read as follows:

> I hereby certify that this day at 4:30 A.M. I have delivered a pithecoid female, known as Derry, of the species *Paranthropus erectus*, of a male child in sound physical condition; and that the said birth took place as a result of an artificial insemination carried out by me in Sydney on December 9, 19— for the purpose of scientific investigation, the donor being Douglas M. Templemore.
>
> Selby D. Williams, M.D., K.B.E.

The police inspector was flabbergasted. "Mr. Templemore," he said, "what exactly do you expect us to do?"

"Your job, Inspector."

"But what job, sir? This little creature is a monkey, that's plain. Why the dickens do you want to . . ."

"That's my business, Inspector."

"Well, ours is certainly not to meddle . . ."

"I have killed my child, Inspector."

"I've grasped that. But this . . . this creature isn't a . . . it doesn't present . . ."

"He's been christened, Inspector, and his birth duly entered at the registry office under the name of Garry Ralph Templemore."

"Under what name was the mother entered?"

"Under her own, Inspector: 'Native woman from New Guinea, known as Derry.'"

"False declaration!" cried the inspector triumphantly. "The whole registration is invalid."

"False declaration?"

"The mother isn't a woman."

"That remains to be proved."

"Why, you yourself—"

"Opinions are divided."

"Divided? Divided about what? Whose opinions?"

"Those of the leading anthropologists, about the species the *Paranthropus* belongs to. It's an intermediate species: man or ape? It may well be that Derry is a woman after all. It's up to you to prove the contrary if you can. In the meantime her child is my son, before God and the law."

The foregoing conversations, as well as the circumstances under which they occur, are taken from the opening scene of a novel by Vercors entitled *You Shall Know Them.* The main narrative focuses on a series of trials to determine whether Douglas Templemore is guilty of murder—infanticide, to be specific. The case finally goes up to the High Court of Parliament for adjudication, and before that august tribunal an impressive array of scientists, philosophers, and theologians present expert testimony bearing on the criteria for determining whether the *Paranthropus erectus* is or is not human. Listening to the debate of the experts on the pros and cons of each criterion, the Law Lords are greatly bemused by the question of fact whether Derry, the female tropi, is a woman; but they remain quite clear on the legal question involved: whether, if as matter of fact Derry must be considered a woman, Douglas Templemore should be legally—and morally—condemned as a murderer, to be convicted of one or another degree of homicide.

(2)

Those who have read the novel will know how Vercors solves both problems. I do not propose to give his secret away to those who have not read it. [1] My purpose in citing it is not to endorse the conclusions the novel reaches, but rather to call attention to the questions that perplex its leading characters. They are the very questions that will occupy us in the pages to follow. I would not be writing this book if I did not regard them as among the most serious questions with which we can be concerned. I have been in search of the right answers to them over many years, as a teacher of psychology and of philosophy, and as a student of the biological sciences, especially of the facts and theories of evolution in their bearing on man. My efforts to resolve the question of how man differs from other animals have, in recent years, been seriously complicated by technological achievements with computers that have persuaded many to call them "thinking machines," and by the promises of future wizardry that will produce mechanical artifacts—robots—capable of simulating any human performance.

If I could be sure that all readers of this book had intellectual experiences similar to those that I have had in trying to make up my mind just where man stands in the scheme of things and how, in consequence, he should be treated; or if I could be sure that they, for reasons of their own, shared my estimate of the theoretical and practical importance of the questions raised in Vercor's novel and dealt with in this book, I might dispense with these preliminaries and launch at once into an analysis of the problem itself, an examination and interpretation of the relevant scientific evidence, an assessment of conflicting philosophical arguments, and finally a consideration of the difference it makes whether we settle on one or another solution of the problem. In the absence of such assurances, I will spend a moment more trying to develop a concern comparable to my own about the difference of man and the difference it makes. Vague feelings about these matters are, I believe, at work in most members of the human race, and need only be brought into focus in order to be transformed from feelings into thoughts.

Imagine yourself on the tribunal trying the case of Douglas Templemore, I would say to such readers. What signs would you look for to determine whether the tropis were human or not? What sort of observable behavior on the part of the tropis would prove decisive in your mind, one way or the other? And if, by these signs or evidences, you knew them to be on this or that side of the line that divides men from other animals, would you take action accordingly not only in the case of Douglas Templemore, but also with respect to the Australian industrialists? Would your finding that the tropis are on the human side of the line be the sole, the indispensable, and the sufficient reason for convicting Templemore of murder and for crusading against the industrial exploitation of the tropis as chattel slaves?

If this is the way you would think about the matter, does it lead you to say that the killing of non-human animals cannot be called murder; or that, while it is possible for men to mistreat them in a fashion that is inhumane and morally reprehensible, no injustice is done to them simply by owning them as one owns tools or by using them as beasts of burden or as implements of work? Would you go so far as to say that non-human animals have no rights that must be respected, or at least no rights that, if respected, would secure them from being owned and used as chattels? And if you would say this, what would have to be the character of the difference between men and other animals to justify your policy of treating men and other animals so differently, assuming for the moment that you thought your policy needed justification?

Suppose that you were convinced that men and other animals differed only in degree, or that such differences in kind as might appear to put a chasm between them could be shown to arise from underlying or bedrock differences in degree? Would that type of difference—a difference merely of more and less of the very same traits or capabilities possessed to some degree by all animals, human and non-human—supply the ground for exonerating Douglas Templemore as a murderer and the Australian industrialists as enslavers, if it were ascertained, as a matter of fact, that the tropis, while possessing the same traits and capabilities that we find in human beings, possessed them to a degree distinctly less than the least competent man?

Give an affirmative answer to this question, and you would then be confronted by a whole series of other questions that might perplex you. Men differ from one another in degree, sometimes quite remarkably if one considers the extremes of superior endowment at one end of the scale and of subnormal deficiency at the other. If a difference in degree suffices to justify a difference in treatment, why would not superior men be justified in treating inferior men in whatever way men think they are justified in treating non-human animals because the latter are inferior in degree?

Rightly or wrongly, the ancient Greeks conceived themselves as vastly superior to the barbarians; the African slave traders and the American slaveowners of the seventeenth and eighteenth centuries regarded the Negroes as barely human; in this century, the Nazis looked upon Jews and Slavs as racial inferiors. In each case, the inferior human beings were treated as a despised or hated animal is treated by men. If you think that the Greeks, the Negro enslavers, and the Nazis were wrong; if you think that their policies were morally reprehensible violations of the dignity of man, do you charge them with being wrong as a matter of fact (*because* barbarians are not inferior to Greeks, Negroes to white men, or Jews and Slavs to Germans), or do you maintain instead that if the facts were as they claimed them to be, they would still be morally wrong (*because* a difference in degree, no matter how large the gap between superior and inferior individuals, groups, races, or for that matter, species, does not justify a difference in treatment)?

If you give the latter answer and do not limit it to differences in degree *within* the species that biologists classify as *Homo sapiens*, do you have any way of separating yourself from the philosophical vegetarian who regards the eating of animal flesh with the same moral repugnance that most men now regard cannibalism? Carry that point of view to its logical conclusion, and ask yourself whether the men who hunt inferior forms of animal life are murderers when they kill, or enslavers when they capture and cage, their prey. Eliminate the instances in which the killing is in self-defense because the animal attacks, or, as in the case of certain insects or vermin, it is disease-bearing and so is a threat to human health. Think instead of killing animals for the enjoyment of the sport; or, in another context, of killing them for the purposes of vivisection in the course of medical research. Now, if these actions can be justified by nothing more than a difference in degree between human and non-human animals, why is not the same justification available for the actions of Nazis or other racists?

It will not do merely to point out that, as a matter of fact, Jews are not racially inferior to Nordics, or Negroes to white men; for it is also a matter of fact that substantial differences in degree separate the upper from the lower limits in the scale of human endowment. At some future time when overpopulation threatens the survival of the human race, suppose that the truly superior men, regardless of race or nationality, band together to exterminate their inferiors and have the means of doing so at their disposal. Would this, in your eyes, be a morally acceptable solution of the problem of overpopulation?

If these questions bother you, perhaps you would like to return to the point of their origin and see what happens when you embrace the opposite point of view; namely, that only a difference in kind between human and non-human animals can justify the difference between the kind of treatment that we accord men and the kind of treatment that we accord other animals. Adopting this point of view, you can invoke the moral, juridical, and theological distinction between persons and things (which rests on a difference in kind, not a difference in degree); you can attribute to men and men alone the dignity that attaches to persons, not things, as well as the rights that inhere in persons, not things; you can explain why things, even though they can be misused in various ways and even destroyed, can never be murdered, slandered, enslaved, lied to, stolen from, or otherwise injured—for only persons can suffer injustice.

In spite of the undeniable facts of individual differences in degree, which often place a wide gulf between one human being and another, you can hold onto the truth that is contained in the statement that all men are born equal because, being born human, they have the equality of persons, an equality or sameness in kind that overrides their various inequalities in human endowment or accomplishment. And understanding this truth that way will carry you to its corollary—that the inequality, or difference in kind, between things and persons exempts us from treating things as we are required to treat persons.

You and I know, of course, that the history of mankind right down to the present century is replete with the most grievous violations of the dignity of man. We may even suspect, taking human history as a whole, that the violations—the injustices perpetrated on men by men—have been the rule rather than the exception. But we also know that, since the beginning of civilized life on earth, the small voice of conscience has also been heard denouncing these atrocities; and that with the passage of time and, especially in recent centuries, it has spoken out with increasing vigor, gained the attention of more and more men, and inspired crusading reforms for human rights and against human injustices. Will it eventually prevail, establish the just treatment of persons as the rule in human affairs, and make mass criminality as much the exception as individual criminality is the exception within the confines of most civilized societies? We may not be able to answer that question, which calls for a prediction difficult to make, but each of us, it would seem, should be able to answer another question, one that calls only for an expression of preference on our part. Do we want justice to prevail in human affairs? Or would we be equally pleased to have the voice of conscience gagged, and to have men in the mass persist in their treatment of other men as if they were not different in kind from—and no better than—non-human animals?

That question, unfortunately, throws you right back to the very center of the problem with which you started to grapple when you assumed a seat on the tribunal trying the case of Douglas Templemore. You have explored it in various directions and in widening circles, but you cannot get away from a central question of fact—the question of how man differs from other animals. Basically in kind or basically in degree? Inseparable from that question is the question about the practical consequences that follow—the question about the difference it makes whether the difference between men and other animals is one of kind or of degree. Both questions, on closer examination, involve complications that I have either not touched on or barely indicated. In ways that I cannot explain until the latter part of this book, the question of fact is complicated by the simulation of distinctively human performances by computer-like machines—machines that, at some time in the not so distant future, may assume the guise of persons by virtue of their performances and may, in consequence, command the respect and treatment that we accord only to persons. The question of practical consequences, whether with respect to men and other animals or with respect to men and machines, is itself further complicated by a number of considerations that I have not mentioned or made clear, again because to do so effectively is possible only at the end of this book, not at its beginning.

The reader will appreciate, I hope, that in these opening pages I have sought, mainly by questions, to solicit his agreement with my own sense of the importance of the problems with which this book deals. If he thinks he can detect, here and there, in the way the questions have been asked, that I have assumed answers to certain questions in order to ask others, he may be right; but I can promise him that if certain answers have been assumed, the assumptions will not go unchallenged. They will be subject to critical scrutiny later, at points where it is more appropriate or feasible to do so.

(3)

The question about man has been asked in a variety of ways. We are all familiar with the ways in which philosophers and theologians have traditionally posed it: *What is man? How shall man's nature be defined? What is the essence of humanity?* And, recently, existentialist thinkers have appeared to strike out in another direction by asking, *Who is man?* In all these forms the question tends to bypass or ignore the contributions of the biological and behavioral sciences to the study of man. No scientist who understood his business would attempt to answer questions couched in such terms, though he would, quite rightly, suspect that much knowledge in his possession and still more within his competence to acquire would have critical relevance to any answer that might be given to questions thus formulated. As thus formulated, the question about man has a philosophical or theological cast that tends to protect it from the intrusion of scientific evidence and tends to elicit only the kind of answers that theologians have given in the course of explicating the dogmas of religious faith, or that philosophers have discovered by intuition, propounded by reason, or framed within the systematic context of an over-all view of the world.

That is why it seems to me preferable to pose the question in another way and ask how man differs from everything else on earth—from inert bodies, from other living things, especially the higher forms of animal life, and from machines, especially such mechanical contrivances as computers or robots invented to simulate human intelligence in operation. Asked in this way, the question calls for a multitude of comparisons—comparisons of the sort that biological and behavioral scientists have carefully and patiently made. Asked in this way, the question becomes impossible to answer without consulting all the available scientific evidence, the relevance of which cannot be doubted or discounted by evasive tactics on the part of philosophers or theologians. For all that, the question thus formulated, is, as we shall see, not a purely scientific question. Philosophical analysis plays an indispensable part in clarifying the question by indicating the range of the possible answers and also by determining the criteria for interpreting the relevance of particular items of evidence. In addition, it helps us to evaluate the probative force of the scientific data —to see, with regard to this or that piece of evidence, which of the possible answers it tends to support and the extent to which it approximates being decisive in the resolution of the problem.

At the same time, the comparative question about how man differs from everything else on earth underlies the traditional philosophical and theological forms of the question about man that, on the surface at least, appear to be non-comparative. To know man's quiddity, to define human nature or to understand its essence, and even to speculate about man's identity—who he is —presupposes that one knows and understands how man differs from everything else. This presupposition, unfortunately, was often overlooked when the question was traditionally asked by philosophers in its non-comparative form. They often appeared to proceed as if they could, by contemplating or by examining man in isolation from everything else, reach a definitive answer about his nature, essence, or identity. Nevertheless, whether they were aware of it or not, the answers they did give always contained one or another of the possible answers to the question about how man differs, bearing out the point that the latter question is the inescapable underlying one in any approach to the consideration of man.

In *The Conditions of Philosophy*, [2] I tried to show that there are some purely philosophical questions, just as there are some purely scientific questions—the former being questions that philosophers alone are competent to answer, just as the latter are questions that scientists alone are competent to answer, the answers in both cases having the same character as knowledge (i.e., reasonable and criticizable opinion, testable and falsifiable by experience). The comparative question about man is neither a purely philosophical nor a purely scientific question. It is instead what I have called a mixed question, a question that cannot be adequately answered either by scientists alone or by philosophers alone, but only by their collaboration—by combining the findings of scientific investigation with the contributions of philosophical analysis and criticism.

To say that philosophy and science are knowledge in the same sense is to say that both are empirical knowledge: their theories or conclusions are falsifiable by experience. They have the status of testable and corrigible opinions, capable of some relative degree of truth, but never attaining certitude or finality. But while both are empirical by virtue of submitting their theories or conclusions to the test of experience, the experience that philosophy appeals to is the common experience of mankind, experience that is possessed without any effort of investigation, whereas the experience that science appeals to is special experience, experience that can be obtained only by deliberate and methodical investigation. Science, in other words, is investigative knowledge about that which is or happens in the world; philosophy, insofar as it is knowledge of that which is or happens, is non-investigative, precisely because it relies on and appeals to the experience that all men enjoy and share without any effort of investigation on their part. [3]

By virtue of the fact that philosophy, employing common experience, has a method of its own, it also has certain questions of its own—questions that it and it alone is competent to answer, questions that cannot be answered by scientific and historical research because they are questions on which investigation, no matter how ingenious or extensive, is unable to throw light. Similarly, there are questions that can be answered solely by investigation and in the light of the data of special experience that results from investigation. These are purely scientific or historical questions, to the solution of which philosophy can make no direct contribution. But there are certain questions which, while subject to investigative efforts, cannot be adequately solved by investigation alone. These are the questions that I have called "mixed" to indicate that the solution of them depends upon some combination of philosophical knowledge with other forms of empirical knowledge obtained by investigation, whether by scientific inquiry or by historical research. [4]

Though this book will, in my judgment, amply demonstrate that the question about man is a mixed question, it has not always been recognized to be one. On the contrary, it has been treated for almost twenty-five centuries of Western thought as if it were a purely philosophical question. This is partly because the question was traditionally posed in a non-comparative form, and partly because until recently little scientific evidence was available for answering the comparative question about how man differs. Most of the philosophers who proposed answers did so entirely in terms of philosophical theories, hypotheses, or conclusions based on common experience alone. A few philosophers showed some awareness of scientific evidence—evidence obtained by investigation—that had some bearing on the question, but at the time this evidence was either so slight or so indecisive that even they treated the question as if it were a purely philosophical one. It is only in the last hundred years, at the most, that the mixed character of this question has forced itself upon our attention; and it is only in the last hundred years, or even less, that the mounting masses of scientific evidence from a wide variety of research pursuits have come to play a critical role in the consideration of how man differs from everything else on earth. Yet even now there are philosophers who persist in ignoring the scientific evidence, just as there are scientists who fail to recognize its philosophical dimensions and proceed as if their data could solve it without the help of philosophical analysis.

(4)

A philosophical clarification of the mixed question about man will, I hope, be achieved in Chapter 2, where I will try to set forth, exhaustively, the range of possible answers to a more general question; namely, how any object that we can consider differs from any other. The various possible ways in which any two comparable things can be said to differ exhaust the ways in which man can be said to differ from everything else on earth.

Everyone is familiar with the usual alternative answers that we give when we are asked how two things differ: either we say that they differ in degree or we say that they differ in kind. But though the words "degree" and "kind" are frequent and familiar in everyday speech, they are seldom understood by the persons who use them in ordinary discourse; nor, as we shall see, is the distinction between these two modes of difference adequately grasped by the scientists who use these words. In addition, the alternatives thus far mentioned—difference in degree and difference in kind—by no means exhaust the possible modes of difference. A difference in kind may be only apparent, as compared with one that is real. Since an apparent difference in kind reduces to a difference in degree, we need only consider differences in kind that are real; among these, some are superficial, and some radical. Hence there are three basically distinct modes of differences: (1) difference in degree, (2) superficial difference in kind, and (3) radical difference in kind.

These distinctions will, I hope, become clear in the following chapter, both as they apply to any two comparable things and also as they apply to the comparison of man with anything else. Here I wish only to point out that unless these distinctions are made and understood, the various answers that the philosophers have given to the question about man cannot be seen as constituting the opposed positions in a three-sided controversy; nor, without this philosophical clarification of the modes of difference, can the scientific literature bearing on the question be read critically.

With this philosophical analysis set forth in Chapter 2, clarifying the question of man's difference by reference to a framework of possible answers, I will, in Chapter 3, consider the different types of evidence that bear on the question and the conditions under which a decisive resolution of it may be reached, or at least something closely approximating a decision in favor of one as against the other two modes of difference. And since Chapter 3 will conclude the introductory part of this book, I will try there to prepare the reader for the series of chapters that constitute Part Two, by outlining the course of the argument that lies ahead —the sequence of steps that will bring us to the appraisal we can make at this time of the state of the mixed question about man. Then, in Part Three, we will be concerned with the theoretical and practical differences it makes how the question about the difference of man is answered.

When the conflicting answers to a question do not make a significant difference to us—either a difference to the way we think about things and to what we believe or a difference to the way in which we act and to the practical policies we adopt— the question is academic in the worst sense of that term. William James and the pragmatists were quite right to dismiss such questions as trivial and to call upon philosophers and men generally to concentrate on what James called "vital options"—questions to which the conflicting answers make a significant difference. The question about man, with which this book is concerned, is far from being an academic or trivial question; it is a vital option in James's sense of that term. How we answer it makes a great difference to us—both to the principles and policies governing our actions and to many of our fundamental beliefs and disbeliefs. We tend to be impatient with extended analyses, elaborate arguments, and thoroughgoing examinations of evidence, unless we can foresee that the effort will be repaid in the form of important practical or theoretical consequences. A brief preview of the consequences to be discussed in Part Three may persuade the reader to be patient with all the steps of thinking through which he must go in order to have a clear and solid foundation for assessing the difference it makes how man differs from other things.

We will find, on the one hand, that it makes a great practical difference whether we say that man differs only in degree from other things or that he differs in kind as well. And, on the other hand, we will find that regarding *all* of man's differences in kind as only superficial or regarding at least some of them as radical has serious theoretical consequences—for science, for philosophy, and for religion.

The practical consequences of regarding man as differing only in degree from other animals all turn on the abrogation of the distinction we make between persons and things—a distinction that involves a difference in kind. The dignity of man is the dignity of the human being as a person—a dignity that is not possessed by things. Precisely because we do not attribute to them the dignity of persons, we feel justified in treating things —other animals or machines—as means, as instruments to be used or exploited. The dignity of man as a person underlies the moral imperative that enjoins us never to use other human beings merely as means, but always to respect them as ends to be served. The condemnation of slavery and other forms of human exploitation as unjust is an immediate corollary of this basic normative principle. Hence, it would appear to make a great practical difference whether we can preserve the distinction between men as persons and all else as things, or must abrogate it because men differ from all else only in degree.

What are the opposite theoretical consequences of asserting a superficial or a radical difference in kind between man and other things? We will find, on the one hand, that the view that man differs radically in kind harmonizes with certain fundamental beliefs in all orthodox forms of Judaism and Christianity: for example, the belief that man and man alone is, as a person, made in the image of God; the belief that man and man alone is a special creation of God; the belief that man and man alone has an immortal soul or is destined for personal immortality; the belief that man alone has free will and carries the burden of moral responsibility. But this view of man does not harmonize with the fundamental principle of continuity in nature, to which almost all natural scientists subscribe. More specifically, it challenges the principle of developmental or phylogenetic continuity, which is central to the theory of evolution and which evolutionists think is as applicable to man as it is to other living organisms. In addition, the view that man differs radically in kind, entailing as it does the conception of man as having a non-physical factor in his make-up, is embarrassing, to say the least, to the new theology that rejects the traditional tenets of orthodox Christianity.

We will find, on the other hand, that the view that man differs in kind, but *only superficially*, harmonizes with the principle of continuity in nature. It also harmonizes with the main tenets of materialism and naturalism in philosophy, and gives support to the fundamental disbeliefs of the prevalent secularism. By the same token, it challenges and tends to repudiate the traditional dogmas of orthodox Judaism and Christianity. The philosophers who have held this view have been, for the most part, anti-religious. Far from concealing their antagonism to religion, they have outspokenly espoused the adverse effects of their views of nature and of man upon traditional religious beliefs. In addition, this view, entailing as it does the denial of anything non-physical in the nature of man, raises serious if not insuperable difficulties for the metaphysical theory of the will's freedom, as well as for the philosophical doctrine that freedom of choice is the *sine qua non* of moral responsibility.

This must suffice as a sketchy preview of the consequences for action and for thought of the answers we give to the question about man. These matters will be more thoroughly treated in Chapters 17 and 18. We shall then have explored all angles of the question about the difference of man and be in a position to examine with thoroughness the difference it makes.

CHAPTER 2

The Possible Answers

(1)

THE simplicity or complexity of a question derives from the range of answers that can be given to it. When we ask how man differs, the first pair of opposed answers that we can think of leaves the question in a relatively simple condition. Let me begin with that first pair of answers and then subsequently complicate the question by introducing variations on each of the two answers.

The two initial answers that we tend to give when we ask how any two things differ are that they differ in *kind* and that they differ in *degree*. To explain these answers in principle, I will first use mathematical objects as examples.

In the series of regular plane figures, distinguishable figures—a triangle and a quadrangle, let us say—differ in kind. So, too, in the series of integral numbers, odd and even numbers differ in kind. What are the properties of this mode of difference? They are twofold: (1) One of the objects compared possesses a defining characteristic *not possessed by the other*—three-sidedness or four-sidedness, in the case of triangles and quadrangles; divisibility by two or indivisibility by two, in the case of even and odd numbers. (2) There is no intermediate object possible—nothing which is a little more than three-sided or a little less than four-sided, nothing which is somehow in between odd and even numbers.

Intermediates are, of course, possible in the series of plane figures differing in kind; for example, a quadrangle is intermediate between a triangle and a pentagon; as, in the series of whole numbers, four is intermediate between three and five. But in such series, intermediates are not possible between proximate members —between triangle and quadrangle there is no three-and-one-half-sided figure; between three and four there is no other whole number. Odd and even represents a distinction between kinds of whole numbers without regard to their serial order; and so in this case we can say that intermediates are impossible without reference to serial order.

The impossibility of intermediates constitutes the discontinuity or discreteness of kinds: only things that differ in kind differ discretely or discontinuously. Another way of saying this is to say that the law of excluded middle holds for things that differ in kind and *only* for things that differ in kind. Thus, for example, a whole number is either odd or even. There is no third possibility or *tertium quid*.

So much for difference in kind. Let us now consider the following examples of difference in degree: a series of straight lines differing in length, or the achromatic series of light intensities from white to black through all shades of gray. The properties of this mode of difference are also twofold; and they are also exactly opposite to the aforementioned two properties of difference in kind. (1) Both of the objects being compared *possess a common characteristic, but one has more of it and the other less.* Both a two-inch line and a three-inch line have length, but one is longer and the other shorter; one has more, the other less, of their common property—length. Of any two light intensities that we select in the achromatic series from white to black, one is brighter and the other duller; one is more, the other less, intense. (2) Between any two straight lines or any two light intensities, no matter how proximate, no matter how small the difference in quantity, an intermediate is always possible.

The possibility of an intermediate—in fact, of an indefinite number of intermediates—between any two objects that differ in degree confers upon things that differ in this way the trait of continuity. Two things that differ in degree differ continuously, not discretely. Here the law of excluded middle does not apply. We cannot say of light intensities that they must be either white or black, or this shade or gray or that. The light intensity may be neither white nor black, but gray. It may be neither this nor that shade of gray, but a shade intermediate between them.

When, in what follows, I speak of a continuum of degrees, I will not be using the word "continuum" in the mathematical sense, but rather to signify continuous variation—the mode of difference to which the law of excluded middle does not apply—as contrasted with discrete differences, to which it does apply.

Let me now summarize the distinction between difference in kind and difference in degree by reminding you of their opposite properties. In doing so, I will replace the mathematical or physical examples used above with biological ones.

Two things differ in *kind* if one possesses a characteristic totally lacked by the other, or if one can do something that the other cannot do at all. Thus, vertebrate and invertebrate animals differ in kind, for the one has a bony skeletal structure totally lacked by the other. Similarly, viviparous and oviparous animals differ in kind, for the one gives birth to living offspring and the other reproduces itself by laying eggs; and since these two methods of reproduction exclude each other, it follows that viviparous animals cannot lay eggs and that oviparous animals cannot give birth to living offspring. Two things differ in *degree* if, with respect to some characteristic that they both possess, one has more of it and the other less. Thus, one species of bird may differ in degree from another with respect to the speed with which it can fly; or to shift the comparison, one species of reptile may differ in degree from another with respect to length (e.g., the python and the garter snake).

Whenever, with respect to two things being compared, it is said that *only* one of them has a certain property or is capable of a certain performance, a difference in kind is being asserted. Just as the word "only" is indicative of difference in kind (whenever it is said of two things that *only* one of them has a certain characteristic), so the words "more" and "less" are indicative of difference in degree. Aristotle made this elementary observation centuries ago when he pointed out that "the difference between ruler and subject is a difference of kind, which the difference of more and less never is." [1] Darwin, who manifests an admirable and exceptional consistency in his defense of the position that all the differences between men and other animals are differences in degree, always accompanies any reference to what looks like a unique characteristic of man, such as propositional speech, by adding the qualification that other animals have rudimentary forms of the same characteristic, and so it cannot be said that *only* man has any characteristic not possessed in some degree, however slight, by other animals.

When two things differ in *kind*, no intermediate is possible; the law of excluded middle applies; and the two things can be said to differ discretely or discontinuously. Thus, for example, an animal either is able to fly or not; there is no intermediate between flying and not flying. When two things differ in *degree*, intermediates are always possible; the law of excluded middle does not apply; and the two things can be said to differ continuously. Thus, for example, between any two species of reptile differing in length, a third species, having an intermediate length, is always possible. The fact that no fossil or extant species may have this intermediate length does not remove the possibility of there being one.

(2)

Before I complicate this analysis of the modes of difference by introducing distinctions subordinate to that between difference in degree and difference in kind, let me apply what I have said so far to the case of man.

If man differs in degree from all other physical things, he does so with respect to whatever characteristics are common to man and these other things; and, in each of these respects, man has either more or less of the common trait. If man differs in kind from all other physical things, he does so by virtue of possessing one or more characteristics totally absent from or lacking in these other things.

The two modes of difference, as thus far stated, are not exclusive. Man can differ in both ways from other things. A triangle and a quadrangle differ in kind with respect to many-sidedness; but, with respect to plane area, a given triangle can also be larger or smaller than a given quadrangle, from which, then, it differs both in degree and in kind, though in different respects. The important point to note here is that when things differ both in degree and in kind, the two concurrent modes of difference have reference to distinct respects in which the two things are being compared.

It is, of course, possible to say that man does not differ at all from other physical things—neither in degree nor in kind—but, in the history of Western thought, *this extreme view is seldom if ever seriously held.*

The distinction between difference in kind and difference in degree is neutral with respect to the question of superiority or inferiority—the status of being higher or lower in a scale or gradation of beings. To say that man differs in degree from other things leaves open the question whether he is superior or inferior to them in all the respects in which he is compared with them in degree—or superior in some respects and inferior in others. To say that man differs in kind from other things similarly leaves open the question whether he is superior or inferior in kind to them, i.e., whether he stands higher or lower in the scale or gradation of beings.

It is, of course, possible to say that man is inferior in degree to other things in all respects, *but no one has ever said this; as no one has ever said that man is superior in degree in all respects.* It is also possible to say that man is inferior in kind to other things, *but, in fact, no one (except, perhaps, a few satirical poets) has ever said this; on the contrary, everyone who has asserted that man differs in kind from other things has also asserted that man is superior in kind.*

It is now necessary to complicate the question of how man differs by introducing, first, a minor distinction between two ways in which things can differ in degree; and second, a major distinction between two ways in which things can differ in kind.

(3)

The first and minor distinction turns on the recognition that some differences that are treated as differences in kind are only *apparently* so, and are *really* masked or concealed differences in degree.

When, between two things being compared, the difference in degree in a certain respect is large, and when, in addition, in that same respect, the intermediate degrees which are always possible are in fact absent or missing (i.e., not realized by actual specimens), then the large gap in the series of degrees may confer upon the two things being compared the *appearance* of a difference in kind.

Thus, for example, the chromatic spectrum is thought to be a continuous series of chromatic qualities, and one, moreover, that is correlated with a continuous series of degrees of wave length. But when interference bands or blackouts are introduced into the spectrum, the colors separated by the interference bands *appear to differ in kind*, i.e., discontinuously. However, we know that this is only apparent, because we know that the discontinuity can be removed by removing the interference bands or blackouts, thus reinstating the continuum of chromatic qualities differing in degree of wave length.

Another and more pertinent example is afforded by the classification of plants or animals, in which—both before and after the eighteenth century—it was thought that the real order of nature was a continuum of forms differing only in degree. Nevertheless, the absence of intermediate forms, introducing gaps or breaks in the continuum, permitted the taxonomist to classify certain plants or animals as belonging to different kinds. If all the *possible* intermediate forms were *actually* to co-exist with the forms being classified, the differences in kind among the latter would be abolished, for they only obtain when the possible intermediates are absent or non-existent.

I will henceforth refer to this mode of difference as an *apparent* —and *only apparent*—difference in kind. When two things are said to differ in this way, they really differ in degree, and *not* in kind. Hence, an apparent difference in kind is really a subordinate mode of difference in degree, not of difference in kind. Anyone who holds the view that, in the domain of living things, only differences in degree obtain, must regard all manifest differences in kind as apparent, not real.

The second and major distinction turns on what underlies and explains a manifest difference in kind that is recognized to be real, not merely apparent.

An observable or manifest difference in kind may be based on and explained by an underlying difference in degree, in which one degree is above and the other is below *a critical threshold* in a continuum of degrees. I will call such differences in kind "superficial" to indicate that what underlies and explains them is a difference in degree involving a critical threshold. I beg the reader to observe—and henceforth remember—that the word "superficial" is here being used in a purely descriptive sense, *with no pejorative connotation.*

An observable or manifest difference in kind may be based on and explained by the fact that one of the two things being compared has a factor or element in its constitution that is totally absent from the constitution of the other; in consequence of which the two things, with respect to their fundamental constitution or make-up, can also be said to differ in kind. I will call such difference in kind "radical" to indicate that the observable or manifest difference in kind is itself rooted in an underlying difference in kind. Like the word "superficial," the word "radical" is also here used in a purely descriptive sense, *not eulogistically.*

A superficial difference in kind is, as a manifest or observable difference, no less a real difference in kind than a radical difference in kind. If one does not go below the observable differences to explain them in terms of the factors from which they arise, all real differences in kind are alike. It is only when we do try to explain them in terms of underlying factors that they can be distinguished and recognized as superficial or as radical differences in kind.

The words "apparent" and "superficial" have enough affinity of meaning in ordinary speech to cause confusion. I, therefore, beg the reader to observe—and henceforth remember—that the distinction between superficial and radical difference in kind applies only to manifest differences in kind that are real, not apparent (i.e., not reducible to differences in degree by the introduction of intermediate forms to fill the gap or break in the series that made the things being compared appear to differ in kind). The fact that a superficial difference in kind is one that can be explained by an underlying difference in degree does not reduce that difference in kind to a difference in degree. Even when so explained, the difference in kind remains; for between the two things being compared, one of which has certain property totally lacked by the other, no intermediates are possible with respect to the property in question. The fact that intermediates are always possible in the underlying series of degrees that makes this real difference in kind superficial does not alter the picture; for a given degree is either above or below the critical threshold and so is correlated with either the possession or the lack of the property in question, and it is this that constitutes the superficial difference in kind. If this is remembered, the reader will not be likely to confuse a superficial difference in kind, which is really a difference in kind, with an apparent difference in kind, which is really a difference in degree.

A few examples, illustrating this distinction, may help to fortify our understanding of it.

Consider the three states of matter: solid, liquid, and gaseous. We all recognize that ice has certain manifest physical properties lacked by water and by steam; that water has certain manifest properties lacked by ice and steam; and that steam has certain manifest properties lacked by ice and water. By virtue of the fact that each possesses certain observable characteristics lacked by the others, we would therefore say that they differ in kind. But when we know that the difference in kind can be explained by an underlying quantitative difference in the motion of molecules and further, when, by measurement, we ascertain the critical threshold in the continuum of degrees at which ice turns into water, or water into steam, we must regard this difference in kind as superficial, not radical. We need not be concerned here with the problem of determining the boiling point or freezing point. Suffice it to say that such points exist and function as critical thresholds in a continuum of degrees.

Consider the difference between inert or inanimate bodies and living organisms. We all recognize that living organisms manifest certain behavioral characteristics not to be found in the behavior of inert or inanimate bodies. By virtue of this fact, we would, therefore, say that they differ in kind. But according to the way in which this observable difference in kind is explained, it is regarded either as a radical or as a superficial difference in kind. If, for example, we accept the explanation of the vitalists, that there is a soul or vital principle in the make-up of living organisms, totally lacking in the constitution of inert bodies, then we treat the difference in kind as radical. But if we accept the explanation of the mechanists, that living organisms are merely more complex organizations of matter and that the degree of their material complexity lies above a certain critical threshold, then we treat the difference in kind as superficial. Thus we see that the same manifest difference in kind may be regarded as radical or as superficial according to the way in which it is interpreted; that is, according to the explanation given of it, or according to the underlying factors or conditions posited to explain it.

(4)

Now let us apply this distinction between superficial and radical differences in kind to the question about man. Let us suppose for the moment—without begging any questions about matters later to be discussed—that we find one or more observable differences in kind between man and other things, and that we regard them as real differences in kind, not as merely apparent. If any of these differences can be explained, let us say, in terms of the magnitude and complexity of the human brain and by the fact that in a continuum of degrees of magnitude and complexity the brain lies above an ascertainable critical threshold, then that difference in kind is seen to be superficial. But if there is an observable difference in kind that cannot be so explained—if, in other words, the explanation of the given difference in kind requires us to posit a factor in the constitution of man that is totally absent from the things with which he is being compared—then that difference in kind must be regarded as radical.

Looked at one way, we have four possible answers to the question of how man differs from everything else on earth: (1) in degree only; (2) apparently in kind as well as in degree; (3) really in kind as well as in degree, but only superficially in kind; (4) really in kind as well as in degree, but, in some if not all respects, radically in kind. Looked at another way, we have only three irreducible alternatives, since all the apparent differences in kind always mask or conceal differences in degree and are—in principle at least—reducible thereto. With apparent differences in kind thus dismissed, we are left with three possible answers about the real state of affairs; and these three answers are, in my judgment, both exhaustive and exclusive. If one of these answers is true, the other two are false; and one of these answers must be true, for beyond these three there are no other answers to consider.

Of the three possible answers to the question, the first and second—difference in degree and superficial difference in kind—are compatible with the general continuity of nature, and with the special evolutionary principle of phylogenetic continuity. To understand human traits and human behavior, no additional explanatory factors or causes are needed over and above those employed to explain the traits and behavior of all other living things. It is true that the second answer—superficial difference in kind—involves both continuity and discontinuity; for here we have an underlying continuum of degrees together with the manifest discontinuity, or difference in kind, that it explains. But while this is true, it also remains true that a superficial difference in kind is compatible with the general principle of continuity in nature and with the special principle of phylogenetic continuity precisely because the manifest discontinuity, or difference in kind, is only superficial and can be explained by an underlying continuum of degrees in which a critical threshold is operative.

Of the three possible answers, only the third—radical difference in kind—makes man fundamentally discontinuous with the rest of nature, not in all respects, of course, but in whatever respect he differs radically in kind. To understand distinctively human traits and distinctively human behavior then requires our having recourse to additional explanatory factors or causes that are not needed in the explanation of the traits and behavior of all other living things.

The three modes of difference can be concurrent. It is possible for man to differ from other things in all three ways, but, of course, *not in the same respect.* If in a particular respect, man differs from other things in degree, he cannot, *in that respect*, also differ from them in kind. Similarly, if, in a particular respect, man differs from other things in kind, that difference must be either superficial or radical; it cannot be both *in that one respect.*

While it is possible for man to differ from other things in all three modes of difference, conflicts of opinion can arise, as we have just seen, in a number of ways. The assertion that man differs *only* in degree conflicts with the assertion that, while differing in degree, man *also*, in certain respects, differs in kind. The assertion that in whatever respect man differs in kind, the difference in kind is superficial conflicts with the assertion that in one or more respects, if not in all, the difference in kind is radical.

The possible conflicts of opinion just stated project the possibility of a three-sided issue about the difference of man, in which one side takes the position that man differs only in degree; a second side takes the position that, in addition to differing in degree, man also differs in kind, but only superficially; a third side takes the position that in one or more respects man differs radically in kind, in addition to differing in degree and whether or not he also differs superficially in kind in certain respects.

The three-sided issue about man (that I have just projected as a formal possibility) involves, as a corollary, a basic dispute about the continuity of nature. Those who maintain either that man differs only in degree or that man differs in kind as well, but only superficially, affirm the continuity of nature. Those who, on the contrary, maintain that however else man differs, he also differs radically in kind from other things, deny the continuity of nature; for in the respects in which man differs radically in kind, he is discontinuous with the rest of nature.

(5)

Tables I and II provide a convenient summary of the distinctions that we have been considering, and of the corollaries or consequences that follow from making them. In Table I, I have retained the fourfold division that results from regarding an apparent difference in kind as a minor variant of what is really a difference in degree. In Table II, I have stressed this point and indicated the bearing of all these distinctions on continuity or discontinuity in nature. (See pages 30–31.)

In the chapters of Part Two, I will, of course, be at some pains to fill in this abstract picture of the formal possibilities by citing the views of philosophers and scientists that correspond to one or another of these conflicting positions on the difference of man and on the continuity of nature. Projecting the three-sided issue in this formal or abstract way enables us to delineate the kind of evidence required to support each of the possible answers, and to determine the conditions under which evidence might some day decisively favor one answer as against the other two. I will attempt to do this in the next chapter, where I shall also be concerned with the history of the question—its past, its present state, and its likely future.

I have another reason for presenting a purely formal picture of

TABLE I. THE FOUR MODES OF DIFFERENCE

I. *Difference in degree*

X .... Y
less alpha — more alpha

(1) where both X and Y have the property *alpha*, and X has less of it, Y more,

(2) and where an infinite number of Zs are possible between X and Y, the alpha of each being more than the alpha of X and less than the alpha of Y.

II. *Apparent difference in kind*

X .... Y
non-alpha [really less alpha] — more alpha

(1) where the manifest difference in kind with respect to alpha is due to the absence of intermediate forms or qualities, which, if they were present, would continuously fill the gap between X and Y that is made by their absence,

(2) and where, if the absent intermediates were introduced to fill the gap, the difference between X and Y would cease to be one in kind and become one of degree or only a difference between individuals rather than between kinds.

III. *Superficial difference in kind*

X || Y
non-alpha — alpha

X ..../........ Y
less beta — more beta

(1) where the underlying difference between X and Y with respect to beta occurs in a continuum of degrees of beta with a threshold or critical point, (/), X being below the threshold in its degree of beta, and Y being above the threshold,

(2) and where the operation of this threshold or critical point accounts for the manifest difference in kind between X and Y with respect to alpha.

IV. *Radical difference in kind*

$$\begin{cases} X_{\text{non-alpha}} \quad \parallel \quad Y_{\text{alpha}} \\ X_{\text{non-beta}} \quad \parallel \quad Y_{\text{beta}} \end{cases}$$

(1) where the difference in kind between X and Y is duplex rather than simplex,

(2) and where the manifest difference in kind with respect to alpha is rooted in the underlying difference in kind with respect to beta.

TABLE II. COMPARISON OF THE FOUR MODES OF DIFFERENCE

A. *Modes of difference I and II*

are really differences in degree,
I manifest,
II latent or concealed.

B. *Modes of difference III and IV*

are really differences in kind,
III simplex, and combined with an underlying difference in degree,
IV duplex, and combined with an underlying difference in kind.

C. *Modes of difference I, II, and III*

are manifestations of
an underlying continuity in nature.

D. *Mode of difference IV*

is the manifestation of
an underlying discontinuity in nature.

the possible answers in advance of documenting the possibilities by reference to positions actually taken by scientists and philosophers who have concerned themselves with the difference of man. Most, if not all, of them have approached the question with too few distinctions explicitly in mind. They use the words "degree" and "kind" without qualifying them by such critical modifiers as "real" and "apparent," "superficial" and "radical." The reader will find that the philosophical and scientific literature on the subject of man's difference is simply not intelligible without these distinctions, especially the distinction between a radical and a superficial difference in kind. He will see that if the only distinction available were the one between difference in kind and difference in degree, the scientists who acknowledge that man differs in kind but who also maintain the continuity of nature and the evolutionary principle of phylogenetic continuity would be unable to do so without contradicting themselves. And he will also see that the failure to employ the distinction between radical and superficial difference in kind leads many writers, philosophers as well as scientists, into the contradiction of asserting, on the one hand, that man differs only in degree from other animals, while acknowledging, on the other hand, that man is able to do certain things that no other animal is able to do at all.

For example, in a recent book co-authored by a Nobel Prize winner in the field of genetics, we find the following statement:

> Not until 50,000 to 75,000 years ago was the biological job complete, and an individual whom we would recognize as kin today—*Homo sapiens*—walked and talked and used his hands and head much as we do. He did not differ from apes in kind (nor do we), but he differed greatly in degree. . . .

That statement appears on page 41. Less than two pages earlier, the same writers make the following observation, without any awareness that they will shortly contradict themselves: ". . . with the initial discovery that one can make tools, our species appeared on the evolutionary horizon. Apes can use tools, but only man can *fabricate* them." [2] The difference between merely *using* tools and *fabricating* them, which is here emphasized, combined with the assertion that *only* man can fabricate tools, plainly points to a difference in kind, flatly denied two pages later when it is said that men and apes do not differ in kind, however greatly they differ in degree. What the writers wanted to deny was not that man differed in kind from apes, but rather the view that man and ape are biologically discontinuous. Like most biologists and evolutionists, they are committed to the phylogenetic continuity of man with other members of the primate family. This they could have maintained while still acknowledging the difference in kind between man and ape that obtains *if* their observation concerning the uniqueness of man's tool-fabrication is correct; but *only if* they had also understood and employed the distinction between a superficial and a radical difference in kind. A superficial difference in kind, like a difference in degree, is compatible with phylogenetic continuity; a radical difference in kind is not.

Another recent book, this one by an eminent technologist who doubles as a philosophical commentator on the meaning of science, reveals the same unclarity about differences that leads to self-contradiction. The author tells us that his fundamental assumption is that "man is a part of nature" and that "there is no break in the continuity of nature." [3] This, he further explains, means that "man is not different in kind from other forms of life; that living matter is not different in kind from dead matter; and therefore that a man is an assembly of atoms that obeys natural laws of the same kind that a star does." [4] After saying this, he is still able to make the following statement without any sense that he has contradicted what he said earlier: "The gift of humanity is precisely that, unlike animals, we form concepts; and we express that gift in our thinking language." [5] The phrase "unlike animals" unmistakably indicates that the writer attributes to man and to man alone the ability to form concepts; yet he fails to see that *if* it is true that only man can form concepts, then what he said earlier must be false; namely, that "man is not different in kind from other forms of life." His fundamental assumption that there is no break in the continuity of nature tells us what the author is trying to say, but does not know how to say clearly: that while there is a difference in kind between man and other animals (viz., concept-formation), this difference in kind must be superficial, not radical, for only such a difference in kind, together with a difference in degree, is compatible with the continuity of nature.

Still another example is afforded by a philosophical treatise, one chapter of which is devoted to man. Its author, a professor of the history and philosophy of science, can be characterized as an avant-garde thinker, if a philosopher can ever be so described. What he has to say on the subject of man's difference from other animals and from machines appears to assert both that there are only differences of degree, and also that there are some differences in kind—some things that man and man alone can do. Consider the following passage in which both assertions are plainly made.

> Various distinctions between man and other animals have been put forward as the key difference that led to, or now proves, man's superiority. The number of real distinctions to have survived careful analysis is very small. Something can be made of the opposed thumb but not very much of its necessity for tool-using or toolmaking. . . . Something can be made of the brain-weight–body-weight ratio but not enough to put us significantly ahead of the dolphins, and so on with the sense of humor and the use of language. The idea that we are the only rational animal either means that we alone are intelligent, in which interpretation it is false, or it means that only human beings can engage in explicit reasoning, in which case it is true, but it is then very doubtful whether it *explains* man's success.
>
> The fact is that man is just more intelligent than any animal and that his present technology is *highly* dependent upon his use of language in storing and communicating information. But whatever the combination of mutations and environmental stresses that led the strain of tree shrews that are our ancestors to develop that intelligence faster than the competing strains that led to the contemporary monkeys, all that developed was a neural network that is somewhat superior for problem-solving. The problem of communicating is one of the problems at which it has done slightly better than the bees. The use of fire, clothes, and tools to widen man's survival range presents other examples of problem-solving payoff. [6]

The inaccuracy of certain statements of facts in the passage just quoted does not alter the interpretation we must place upon it; namely, that the writer, applying the principle of phylogenetic continuity to the origin of man, holds that the fundamental differences between men and other animals are all differences in degree, e.g., that man is "just more intelligent," that his neural equipment is "somewhat superior for problem-solving," or that he is only a "slightly better" communicator than the bees. On the other hand, the author also acknowledges that "only human beings can engage in explicit reasoning." This plainly indicates a difference in kind. It does not by itself explain man's biological success in competition with other animals; it may, perhaps, explain the difference in kind between human language and the means of communication used by other animals, including the bees; though even here it must be noted that the author remarks that we are not "significantly ahead" of other animals in the use of language, a remark that is appropriate only with respect to a difference in degree. Add to this the remark with which his book concludes, that "man is not just an animal or a machine, but yet he is an animal and a machine," [7] and one is left in some doubt as to just where the writer does stand, though one is inclined to hazard the guess that he thinks man differs from other things (animal or machines) mainly in degree or, if at all in kind, only superficially in kind and in a manner that is explainable by underlying differences in degree.

The foregoing examples of self-contradiction or at least of unclarity and imprecision can be multiplied many times in the writing of biologists, psychologists, and philosophers who deal with the question of how man differs from other animals. It will be impossible to review and interpret the literature of this subject without calling attention to the inconsistencies or obscurities of statement and thought that arise from want of an adequate framework of analytical distinctions. The few examples given above should suffice to make the reader appreciate how indispensable a careful philosophical analysis of the modes of difference is for an understanding of the literature—an understanding of what scientists and philosophers are trying to say in spite of their inability to say it clearly or even when their use of words belies what they have in mind.

CHAPTER 3

The State of the Question, Past, Present, and Future

(1)

WE HAVE so far envisaged in formal and abstract terms a three-sided controversy about the difference of man. We have seen that there are three possible answers to the question about how man differs from everything else on earth. What are the criteria for judging the relevance and probative force of the evidence or arguments that are offered in support of each of these three answers? What is required in the way of evidence and arguments to resolve the question, or at least to approach a resolution?

Since we are concerned with the difference between man and other things, evidence to be relevant must be comparative; that is, it must involve observations of human and animal behavior, or of human and machine behavior. In order to be comparative, the evidence must be objective or public; it must consist exclusively of what can be observed about the external or overt behavior of the objects being compared. In other words, man must be treated as an object to be studied by the observation of his external or overt behavior in exactly the same way that other animals or machines are objects to be studied.

This excludes from consideration all evidence drawn from man's reflexive study of himself as a subject rather than as an object. Even if such evidence, drawn from elements common to man's self-consciousness, has the character of being inter-subjective, it is still irrelevant for the simple reason that it is not comparative. Much contemporary philosophical writing about the nature of man—that of the existentialists and the phenomenologists as well as that of more traditional philosophical sects, such as the Kantians and the Thomists—appeals almost exclusively to such reflexive or subjective evidence, consisting of what men universally discover about themselves from self-consciousness or close examination of their interior life. Evidence of this type would be relevant to the question of man's difference only if we had similar and comparable evidence from other animals and from machines. We do not at present have such evidence; and we cannot beg the question by assuming that it is unobtainable because it does not and cannot exist.

I am not saying that reflexive or subjective evidence is totally without significance. My sole critical point is that such evidence can have no bearing, probatively, on the comparative question with which we are concerned. It is inadmissible for that purpose, but that does not exclude it entirely from consideration. Once the question of how man differs from other things has been answered in the light of objective evidence, then it may contribute significantly to the understanding of whichever answer the objective evidence decisively supports. Yet even here it is of limited value, for it can never alter the purport of that answer. What we know about ourselves reflexively or through self-consciousness must itself be understood in a manner that is compatible with what we know about ourselves through objective and comparative evidence.

The evidence, to be relevant and probative, must not only be objective and comparative; it must also be as extensive as possible; therefore, common experience, on the very face of it, is woefully inadequate for answering the question with which we are concerned. Scientific investigations of every sort, experimental and clinical as well as studies in the field, are required to provide the data we need. When in earlier centuries the question about man was regarded as if it were a purely philosophical question—one that could be answered in the light of common experience alone —the question, as I have already pointed out, was usually framed in a non-comparative form. Its primary interest was not in how man differs, but in what man's nature or essence is. To answer a question so framed, philosophers relied mainly on the intersubjective common experience of man's self-awareness—his reflexive knowledge of his own interior life and processes. Having drawn from such self-knowledge an answer to the question about man's nature or essence, philosophers then illicitly begged the answer to the question of how man differs. Misled by the indications of common experience and by common-sense opinion, they assumed that what he knew himself to be, other animals were *not*.

The philosophers have not been the only offenders against the logical requirements of an adequate approach to the mixed question about man. The biological and behavioral scientists, especially contemporary ones, have for the most part assumed that they could answer the question in the light of scientific evidence alone and without the help of philosophical analysis and argument, just as the philosophers of an earlier day, and even some of recent date, have for the most part assumed that they could answer the question without the benefit of the detailed comparative evidence that only the most painstaking scientific investigation can amass.

In the three-sided controversy that is constituted by the possible answers to the question, philosophers—past and present—have taken and take all three positions: (1) that man differs only in degree from other things; (2) that man differs in kind, but only superficially; and (3) that man differs radically in kind from everything else on earth. Scientists have held and hold only the first two of these three views of man's difference, in the nineteenth century mainly the first, and in the twentieth the second as well as the first. It would, perhaps, be more accurate to say that no reputable scientist has held the view that man differs radically in kind from everything else on earth on the basis of scientific evidence alone, whereas scientists, on the basis of such evidence alone, have concluded—correctly or not—that man differs only in degree from other things or that, if he differs in kind as well, that difference in kind is only superficial. There have been a number of eminent scientists who have favored the third view, but they have done so on philosophical grounds or by engaging in philosophical speculation, to which they felt they had to have recourse because the available scientific evidence has seemed to them insufficient to establish either of the other two views.

In different ways, scientific evidence and philosophical analysis, criticism, and reasoning are involved in the attempt to support each of the three answers, or *should* be if that attempt is properly conducted in the light of the fact that the question is neither purely philosophical nor purely scientific, but mixed.

To support the answer that man differs only in degree, the evidence must show that *every* type of human performance is found in other living things and in machines as well, and that it is present either to a higher or a lower degree in man. Since the evidence never consists in the bare data of observation, but the data interpreted, the interpretations given must be checked against conflicting evidence from common experience and the interpretation put upon it by common-sense opinion; in addition, the methods of investigation employed in obtaining the data, the assumptions underlying such methods, and the soundness of the theoretical constructs used by the scientists in interpreting their data, must all be subjected to critical examination. This is the work of the philosopher; if the scientist engages in such criticism, he can do so competently only to the extent that he possesses the competence of a philosopher.

To support the answer that man differs in kind, but only superficially, the evidence must show that man's objectively observable behavior includes certain performances *not found at all* in other living things or in machines; this must be combined with evidence that clearly supports the explanation of these distinctively human performances by reference to a critical threshold in an underlying continuum of degrees of either psychological or neurological complexity. Everything that was said above about the interpretation of the scientific data supposed to be relevant and probative, and about the need for a critical examination of both the data and the interpretation, applies with even greater force here; and so, *a fortiori*, if philosophical competence is required in an effort to determine whether the first answer can be adopted as the right answer to the question, it is even more so required here.

To support the answer that man differs radically in kind, the evidence must show, as in the case of the second answer, that man performs certain acts *not performed at all* by other living things or by machines, combined with arguments that justify the positing of some power or factor in man's constitution that is *not present* in other things, animate or inanimate. The justification must always take a form that is in line with the principle of parsimony; i.e., it must take the form of arguing that the performances found in man's observable behavior but not found at all in the observable behavior of other things cannot be satisfactorily explained *except* by positing a power or factor in man's constitution that is not present in anything else. To advance such arguments is clearly the work of the philosopher, and just as clearly is it the work of the philosopher to advance arguments of a contrary tenor, similarly and equally in line with the principle of parsimony and trying to show that the behavior in question can be satisfactorily explained without positing any power or factor in man's constitution that cannot be found in other living things or in machines. Here, then, we cannot avoid the confrontation of opposed philosophical views bearing directly on the question of man's difference.

It would appear that the work of the philosopher is even more important in connection with an effort to determine whether this third answer—radical difference in kind—is right or wrong than it is in the case of the first two answers—difference in degree and superficial difference in kind. Nevertheless, surprising as it may seem, we shall see that, within the framework set up by these opposed philosophical views, we may have to await the future work of scientists for something approaching a decisive resolution of the philosophical dispute, though it should not be surprising that the philosophers, left to themselves, may never be able to resolve it.

(2)

Everything that has been said above indicates why it is necessary to separate two historical periods in the treatment of the question about the difference of man. The *first period* runs from the beginning of Western thought until the middle or end of the nineteenth century. During this time, the question was regarded as a purely philosophical question by all or most of the writers, mainly philosophers and theologians, who addressed themselves to it. The *second period* runs from the middle of the nineteenth century to the present. During this period, the question could no longer be so regarded, at least not by anyone who was aware of the obvious relevance of the data accumulated by the biological and behavioral sciences, and of the theories or hypotheses developed by scientists in the light of the evidence they had amassed. Though it ceased to be a purely philosophical question, it did not, in consequence, become a purely scientific one. There are, unfortunately, too many scientists who are still not aware that the question cannot be treated as a purely scientific one, in spite of the great achievements of the biological and behavioral scientists in obtaining critically relevant evidence.

The error that the philosophers made during the first historical period is at least excusable in view of the fact that there was little or no scientific evidence available for them to consider, even if they had had a mind to do so. If there are philosophers alive today who still persist in that error (as unhappily there are among the existentialists, the phenomenologists, and the scholastics), their blindness to the evidence that now confronts them on all sides is difficult to explain away or condone. It is as inexcusable as the opposite error that is made by the host of contemporary scientists who are blind to the philosophical aspects of the question, and proceed ineptly as if the question were one wholly within the competence of scientists to answer.

The second historical period, during which scientific investigations and theories based on scientific data have contributed to the solution of the problem, can itself be divided into three stages. (1) The initial entrance of science into the picture is represented by the obvious relevance of the theory of evolution in general and by the development of paleoanthropology in particular—by the finding of fossil remains and by the hypotheses concerning their significance for the origin of man on earth. (2) The second, and somewhat later, entrance of science is represented by the development of the behavioral sciences, especially in the area of comparative studies of human and animal behavior, and also by clinical and experimental research in neurology. (3) Last comes the stage that is represented by the work of computer technology and by the development of machines for the simulation of human performances, together with the mathematical and neurological theories underlying these technological and experimental efforts.

Whereas the first stage began 150 years ago, and the second 60 to 75 years ago, this third stage is of recent origin, a matter of the last 30 years at most. As I see it, it is to the future development of the efforts represented by this third stage that we must look for any significant alteration in the state of the question about the difference of man, rather than to any further discoveries in the field of paleoanthropology or to any new data that can be obtained by the ethologists, by the comparative study of human and animal behavior, by clinical and experimental neurology, or even by the revolutionary biophysics and biochemistry that are opening new vistas in physiology.

This may appear to be a rash prediction. The reasons for it are explained in Part Two. The reader, having examined the analyses and arguments there set forth, will be in a position to judge whether the reasons for my prediction are sound or not.

(3)

The analyses and arguments referred to above are developed in the following sequence.

Chapter 4 reviews the theories of the philosophers who treated the question about man as if it could be satisfactorily answered without investigation—by philosophical analysis in the light of common experience alone. It sets forth the state of the question during the first historical period when it was incorrectly treated. By doing so, it enables us to see where we would be now if scientific evidence had never been brought to bear on the question. Suppose that we had nothing but the assertions or arguments of opposed philosophical views about the nature of man, together with such evidence as is supplied by common experience but without any comparative study by investigative effort, of the behavior of men and animals. Which side in the three-sided issue that the philosophers disputed would we—should we—favor? Would the issue be resolved? Would it be resolvable?

Chapter 5 deals with the views of Darwin and his contemporaries and tries to explain why Darwin answered the question as he did, in the light of the evolutionary evidence that was available in his day; it also considers the advances in evolutionary theory as well as the extraordinary increase in significant data from his day to our own. Chapter 6 deals with the findings and theories of the paleoanthropologists, largely since the turn of the century. In addition, it tries to explain why they, with few exceptions, reject Darwin's answer that man differs only in degree from other animals, and take the position that man differs in kind as well as in degree. Though they themselves are not always explicit or definite on the point, it is nevertheless evident that they regard man's difference in kind as superficial, not radical. Together Chapters 5 and 6 cover what I have called the first stage of the entrance of science into the picture.

Chapter 7 turns to the work of the behavioral scientists, especially the comparative studies of human and animal behavior that began in the early years of this century and have multiplied progressively in the succeeding decades. It also considers the relevant findings of ethologists in the field and of experimental psychologists in laboratory studies of human behavior, many of them of very recent date. It undertakes a critical examination of the methodological postulates and the basic assumptions of psychological theory, particularly that of behaviorism in its various forms, in an effort to understand why the behavioral scientists in general, and the behavioristic psychologists in particular, tended to revert to Darwin's view that man differs only in degree from other animals. Here, then, we have what I have called the second stage of scientific work that has affected the state of the question about man.

Chapter 8 brings us to a point of decision. In the light of all the evidence now available, it appears to be the unanimous agreement of reputable scientists today, both the paleoanthropologists, on the one hand, and the behavioral scientists, on the other, that man and man alone possesses a propositional language or has the power of syntactical speech. When I say "appears to be unanimous," I mean, of course, just this: that in all the scientific literature that I have examined, I have found no dissenting voice to the contrary. There may be some, but I have not come upon them. In any case, I feel relatively sure that if there are dissenting voices, they are an almost inaudible minority. What needs to be explained, and Chapter 8 attempts it, is why, though agreeing with the paleoanthropologists that man alone possesses a propositional language, the behavioral scientists persist in saying that man differs only in degree from other animals, whereas the paleoanthropologists, in recognition of the same fact, assert that man differs in kind. It is plainly a contradiction to say, on the one hand, that only man has a certain trait or is capable of a certain performance, and to say, on the other hand, that man differs only in degree from other animals. With that contradiction resolved, as it must be, in favor of the observed facts and hence in favor of the proposition that man differs in kind from other animals, at least in this one respect if in no other, we are brought in Chapter 8 to the point of decision mentioned above.

Let me be clear on this point. All I am saying is that the data at present available together with the present state of scientific opinion on the subject appear to be decisive on the question whether man differs only in degree, or in kind as well as in degree. This must not lead us to conclude that this question is forever closed, or that it is finally and incorrigibly answered. New and contrary evidence may be discovered by further scientific investigation, such as the research now being done on the communicative powers of the bottle-nosed dolphin. The state of scientific opinion on the subject may change. These things being as they may, it still remains the case that, as this book is being written, it is impossible for anyone who understands the distinction between difference in degree and difference in kind to assert, in the face of the available evidence, that man differs only in degree from other animals.

With the question whether man differs only in degree or also in kind decided, for the time being, in favor of kind, we are left with the question whether man's difference in kind is radical or only superficial. Chapter 6, it will be recalled, will have pointed out that the paleoanthropologists tend to regard it as superficial because they think it can be explained by a critical threshold in a continuous series of degrees of brain magnitude and complexity. The behavioral scientists and especially the behavioristic psychologists do not disagree on this point; but, as Chapter 9 will show, they offer still another reason for thinking that the difference in kind between man and other animals, based on man's exclusive possession of a propositional language, is only a superficial difference in kind: namely, that the underlying psychological processes are exactly the same in men and other animals and that man's having propositional speech, lacked by other animals, can be accounted for simply by the much higher degree to which the same psychological processes are operative in him.

If this theory of the matter were established by the scientific evidence now available, we would have reached a second and final point of decision—at least for the time being; for, in addition to knowing that man differs in kind, not just in degree, we would also know that man's difference in kind is only superficial, not radical. The age-old question about how man differs would have been resolved—again let me say, for the time being. But, in my judgment, the explanation that is offered by the psychologists of why men possess and other animals do not in the least degree possess a propositional language cannot stand the test of criticism. When, in Chapter 9, the data offered by the psychologists is thoroughly reviewed and their interpretation of it carefully examined, their theory of human language will be found untenable. This will be followed in Chapter 10 by an analysis of language in relation to thought that, in my judgment, decisively establishes the opposite theory: namely, that the reason why man and man alone has a propositional language is that man and man alone has the power of conceptual thought. If that is the case, then the manifest difference in kind between man and other animals, in virtue of the fact that only man has a propositional language, is not shown to be a superficial difference in kind *by reference to a critical threshold in a series of degrees of the same psychological processes in both animals and men.*

With these two points of decision reached—*and they are the only points of decision reached in this book*—we are left in Chapter 11 with the one issue that still remains undecided: namely, whether the difference in kind between men and other animals is merely superficial or is, on the contrary, radical. Chapter 12 then describes the efforts of the philosophers to decide that issue, by arguments which either try to show, on the one hand, that conceptual thought cannot be adequately explained in neurological terms, or, on the other hand, that it can be. If the first line of argument were to prevail and become universally persuasive, the issue would be resolved in favor of the view that man differs radically in kind. If the second line of argument were to prevail and become universally persuasive, the issue would be resolved in the opposite direction, in favor of the view that man's difference in kind is only superficial. But, as we shall see, there is little chance that either set of arguments will ever become so cogent as to prevail and become universally persuasive.

Must the crucial issue, then, forever remain unresolved? Chapter 13 gives us some hope that a resolution is possible by other means than direct philosophical argument in support of one or the other of the competing theories. The other means take the form of a challenge laid down three centuries ago by Descartes, a challenge that we can now see has three prongs: one for the zoologists to meet; one for the neurologists to meet; and one for the computer technologists and experimenters with artificial intelligence to meet. Chapter 13 explains why the zoologists and the neurologists cannot resolve the issue even if they are able in the future, as they are not yet able, to offer evidence of the sort that is called for. This leaves for Chapter 14 the consideration of the evidence offered by the computer technologists and by the experimental work on machines designed to simulate human intelligent behavior. Here we come to the third and most recent stage of scientific work that bears on the question of how man differs from everything else on earth. And while Chapter 14 will show that the present achievements of this scientific effort do not meet the Cartesian challenge and resolve the crucial issue about superficial versus radical difference in kind, Chapter 15 will conclude Part Two by explaining why it is almost certain—as certain as anything can be on earth—that through the scientific effort that is now being made in this direction, the issue will be resolved at some future date—one way or the other. Which way, I, for one, do not dare to predict.

Part Two thus ends inconclusively, as in my judgment it must in view of the present state of the question. It leaves for Part Three a hypothetical exploration of the difference it makes how man differs from other animals and from machines. Since we do not now know the answer to the question whether the difference in kind is superficial or radical, we must consider what consequences follow, first, if one alternative turns out to be true, and then, if the other does. Though the evidence at present available and the present state of scientific opinion favor the proposition that man differs in kind from other animals and not just in degree, new evidence may be discovered in the future that changes the state of scientific opinion. We must, therefore, consider what consequences follow, on the one hand, if man differs in kind, whether superficially or radically, and, on the other hand, if man should turn out to differ only in degree.

Most readers expect a book that undertakes to deal with an important question to conclude with a definitive answer to it.

This book does not do that for the simple reason that no one knows the answer yet. The countless books that claim to give a definitive answer claim more than is known in the present state of scientific evidence and philosophical thought. The claim that this book makes may be just as presumptuous, but it is of a different sort: namely, that it provides the basis for understanding and criticizing all the writing that has so far been done on this subject, as well as whatever remains to be written in the future as new evidence accumulates and new theories or arguments develop. Anyone who tries to solve the problem of man's difference, either by research or by argument, would be well advised to consider the guidelines here laid down. Precisely because it offers a dialectically objective assessment of the research and thinking that has so far been done on the question of man, this book can fairly claim to be a prolegomenon to future research and thinking about the subject.

What do I mean by a dialectically objective assessment? I mean one that fairly examines a conflict of opinions without taking sides. The procedure of this book is dialectical in the sense just defined. It is an adaptation of the method developed and applied by the Institute for Philosophical Research in the studies it has completed of the ideas of freedom, love, progress, happiness, and justice, and the studies now in progress on the idea of equality, and on the problem of the relation of language and thought. In describing that method as dialectical, the Institute has stressed the restraints with which it approaches controversy about any subject. It tries to clarify the question or questions that constitute the issues of a controversy; it attempts to present or construct the positions that are taken in a controversy, so far as they can be found in or developed from the literature of the subject; it offers the evidence and the arguments that enter into the dispute of the issues, so far as these exist. Beyond this it does not go; it does not take sides; it makes every effort to exercise the restraints of dialectical neutrality. [1]

The reader may think that I have cast aside these restraints at two points—the point at which I found it necessary to resolve the contradiction into which the psychologists fall when they say, on the one hand, that man differs only in degree, and, on the other hand, that only man possesses a propositional lauguage; and the point at which I found it necessary to reject as untenable, in the light of the known facts, the theory that the same psychological processes are operative in animals and men, though to a different degree, and that it is this difference in degree that explains why animals lack a propositional language and men possess one. But that is not the case. I do not regard the criticism of illicit inferences or specious arguments, or the pointing out of patent inconsistencies and misleading equivocations in the use of words, as a violation of dialectical neutrality.

Part Two

The Difference of Man

CHAPTER 4

The Philosophers Give All the Answers and Establish None

(1)

IT HAS been remarked earlier that the philosophers have given all three of the possible answers to the question about how man differs. They have done so either as a conclusion drawn from the evidence of common experience or as a corollary of some more general principle in an elaborate philosophical doctrine. Let us now look a little more closely at the positions they take in the controversy about man, and at the doctrinal settings in which these positions occur.

The position that man differs radically in kind is the one held by the majority of the great philosophers in the history of Western thought, from the beginning to the middle or end of the nineteenth century. They share this view in spite of their many differences on other points of doctrine. This may account for the fact that some of the philosophers who affirm man's radical difference in kind do so at the expense of being inconsistent with other views they hold.

The position that man differs only in degree is held by a smaller number of philosophers, but philosophers who are much more homogeneous in doctrine, for most of the members of this group are classical materialists, whether ancient or modern.

The third position—the position that man differs not only in degree but also superficially in kind—is held by a smaller and even more homogeneous group: the Marxists or dialectical materialists. While the classical and the dialectical materialists part company on whether man differs in kind as well as in degree, they stand together in denying that man differs radically in kind. Their agreement on this point follows as a corollary of their commitment to the continuity of nature.

Before I comment on these three divergent philosophical positions, I would like briefly to consider, first, the relation of these philosophical views to common-sense opinion; and second, the bearing of scientific evidence on them.

1. *The relation of the three-sided issue to commonsense opinion.* The common-sense view of the difference of man, based on common experience, holds that man is not only superior to other living things, but that he differs from them in kind, not just in degree. The evidence that common experience provides in support of this opinion can be simply summarized. It consists of all the things that men do which, so far as our common experience goes, are done only by men and are not done in any way or to any degree by other animals. So far as common experience goes, only men make laws; only men make sentences; only men read, write, and make speeches; only men build and operate machines; only men paint pictures that have some representative meaning; only men engage in religious worship; only men cook their food; only men walk erect; and so on. If common experience includes any exceptions to these generalizations, they consist of the humanly trained performances of circus animals or domestic pets, and so do not seriously affect the commonsense view. But, working with such evidence, common sense is not subtle enough to distinguish between a superficial and a radical difference in kind; and so we can only say that common-sense opinion tends to reject the position that man differs only in degree.

Common sense grasps the distinction between person and thing as a distinction in kind, not degree. Acting in the light of common sense, men tend to treat human begins—at least some, if not all —as persons rather than things; conversely, they also tend to treat most animals as things rather than persons. The fact that commonsense opinion tends to reject the view that man differs only in degree does not mean that one or the other of the remaining views is nearer the truth of the matter. Since the question is not a purely philosophical question, but is also susceptible to investigation, common sense can be wrong and open to correction by the special data obtained by scientific investigation. As I pointed out in *The Conditions of Philosophy*, philosophy is obligated to defend common-sense opinion only about such matters as are not capable of being investigated, and then only against adverse philosophical views. [1]

2. *The bearing of scientific evidence on the three-sided issue in philosophy*. We must note at once that when the question about man ceases to be treated as a purely philosophical question and becomes a mixed question involving science as well as philosophy, the fundamental structure of the issue is not altered. The three answers to the question—degree, superficial kind, and radical kind—exhaust the possibilities. Those same three answers exhaustively represent the positions actually taken in the history of Western philosophy. The intervention of science in the consideration of the question has not increased the number of answers, nor has it in any way affected the structure of their opposition. This is not to say, of course, that a new and distinct type of answer cannot be found. I am only saying that it has not yet been discovered, adding thereto the confession that I cannot imagine what shape it would take.

Though science has had no effect as yet on the structure of the issue (i.e., on the range and character of the alternative answers), it has contributed considerable evidence that weighs heavily against one of the three philosophical answers to the question. None of the scientific evidence that has so far been amassed favors the view that man differs radically in kind. Nor is it likely that any scientific evidence to be obtained in the future will tend *positively* to support that side of the issue; though, as we shall subsequently see, the lack of certain scientific evidence may, *at least negatively*, have that effect.

It is certainly the case that the present mass of scientific evidence accords with the doctrine of the continuity of nature, and therefore either with the view that man differs only in degree or only superficially in kind. Here, as we shall see later, the weight of scientific evidence now tends to support the latter view: that man differs in kind superficially as well as in degree. The fact that scientific evidence and authoritative scientific opinion tend to support one position on the issue as against the other two is by no means yet a decisive indication of where the truth lies. Whether something more decisive will be forthcoming in the future remains to be seen.

With these preliminary observations made, let us turn now to a brief roll call of the philosophers, grouped by reference to the position they take in the three-sided controversy about man. In this inventory of eminent names, I have omitted reference to contemporary philosophers and to those scientists who vouchsafe to speak as philosophers on the question. Their voices enter the discussion more appropriately at a later stage since they, unlike the philosophers now to be considered, recognize that the question is a mixed one and that scientific evidence must be taken into account for all it is worth.

(2)

Philosophical exponents of the view that man differs radically in kind from other things. Holding this position are philosophers as diverse in their views as Plato, Aristotle, the Stoics (Marcus Aurelius and Epictetus), Augustine, Aquinas, Descartes, Spinoza, Pascal, Locke, Leibniz, Rousseau, Kant, and Hegel. [2]

With the one exception of Rousseau, for whom the difference between man and brute lies solely in man's free will, [3] all the others attribute man's difference to the fact that man alone among living things has the power of reason, intellect, thought, or understanding—manifested in the distinctively human activities of logical discourse, lawmaking, artistic production, scientific investigation, philosophical argument, the handling of general or abstract ideas, and so on. Along with Rousseau, many of the others—notably Aristotle, Augustine, Aquinas, Descartes, Pascal, Kant, and Hegel—ascribe free will or the power of free choice to man alone; and, except for Rousseau, they conceive that power as intimately related to man's rationality or intellectual power. Only Spinoza most emphatically denies this. [4]

Of the authors mentioned, some—notably Plato, Aristotle, Augustine, Aquinas, Locke, and Leibniz—picture the order of nature as a hierarchy involving at least four grades of perfection in being, involving three radical differences in kind: (1) between non-living and living things, and, in the realm of living things, (2) between plant life and animal life, and (3) between animal life and human life. [5] Here Descartes is the major dissenting voice; for he conceives infrahuman living things—animals and plants—as nothing more than elaborate mechanisms or automata. [6] For him, nature does not consist of a hierarchy of kinds, but a bifurcation into thinking and non-thinking beings—men and everything else. It is worth noting that Locke, Leibniz, and Kant expressly disagree with Descartes on this point. [7]

With the exception of Plato, Leibniz, and perhaps also Spinoza, all the remaining philosophers who affirm man's radical difference in kind attribute man's power of thought and free choice to his *possession of a non-physical or immaterial principle* (call it rational soul, mind, intellect, spiritual power, thinking substance, or divine spark) *that is not present in other physical things, even those that are alive, sensitive, and conscious.* [8] (This becomes a pivotal point in the controversy. It explains why materialists of all varieties deny man's radical difference in kind; for to affirm it is to affirm an immaterial factor or principle.) For these philosophers—notably Aristotle, the Stoics, Augustine, Aquinas, Pascal, Descartes, Leibniz, and Hegel—there is something peculiarly divine about man that is not present in other things. Only the Christian philosophers, of course, speak of man as being created in God's image, but the others speak of the special kinship between man and God, the traces of divinity in man, the fellowship of man and God, and so forth. [9]

A number of other writers should be mentioned as expressing views about man that associate them with the philosophers who affirm man's radical difference in kind. They are Harvey the physiologist, Montesquieu the political theorist, and Adam Smith the economist. [10]

It is necessary to point out that some of the philosophers in this group also hold views that are inconsistent with their affirmation of man's radical difference in kind or with their assertion of a hierarchy of distinct gradations of being in the order of nature. Locke, because of his difficulty about real definitions and the distinction between real and nominal essences, refuses to define man as a rational animal, even though he has, in other passages, declared that men alone have the power of abstract and rational thought. [11] There are passages in both Locke and Rousseau in which they maintain that men differ from the higher animals only in degree, even saying that some animals are superior to some men in intelligence. [12] Most important of all, both Leibniz and Locke become involved in self-contradiction by trying to reconcile a hierarchy of forms or kinds with the continuity of nature. The self-contradiction is compactly expressed in their reference to a continuum of forms or kinds. Understanding why this is a contradiction is of sufficient importance to justify a careful examination of the matter.

As I pointed out earlier, things that differ in degree differ continuously, whereas things that differ in kind differ discretely or discontinuously. If the difference in kind is radical, there is an underlying discontinuity as well. But even if the difference in kind is superficial and there is an underlying continuity, the observed or manifest difference in kind is a discontinuous difference. Hence it is self-contradictory to speak of an order or series of kinds as a continuum of forms, in which there are no gaps or breaks because between any two forms there are always intermediates.

Locke and Leibniz are the two most eminent figures in the group of seventeenth- and eighteenth-century writers who make this glaring mistake. Locke says that "in all the visible, corporeal world, we see no chasms or gaps." He pictures created nature, both corporeal and spiritual, as consisting of "numberless species in a continuous series or gradation." And he goes on to say that "the several species are linked together and differ but in almost insensible degrees." [13] Leibniz again and again asserts, as a necessary truth deducible from the principle of sufficient reason and the principle of plenitude, the law of continuity that nature does nothing by jumps, that nature abhors a vacuum of forms, and that all created forms, species, or kinds are linked together in a great chain of being, constituted by a continuous series of gradations from lowest to highest. [14] (To produce a necessary truth that is self-contradictory is quite a feat on Leibniz's part.)

If Locke and Leibniz and the others who subscribed to the great chain of being had denied the reality of kinds or species (as Locke almost does), their assertion of continuity in nature, constituted solely by differences in degree, would have been saved from self-contradiction. But, unfortunately, they insisted upon picturing the order of nature as a continuum of forms or kinds.

In the eighteenth century, Dr. Johnson and the French *philosophe* J. B. Robinet clearly pointed out the contradiction that is involved in saying *both* that distinct kinds exist in nature and *also* that they vary continuously from lowest to highest with no gaps or jumps. To resolve the contradiction and maintain the continuity of nature, Robinet came to the conclusion that nature consists of nothing but differences in degree. [15] Professor Lovejoy, whose large book on the great chain of being treats this idea, for hundreds of pages, as if it were to be taken seriously, finally concedes that a continuum of forms or kinds "is a contradiction in terms. Wherever, in a series, there appears . . . a different *kind* of thing, and not merely a different magnitude or degree of something common to the whole series, there is *eo ipso* a breach of continuity." [16] Differences in kind can, of course, be reconciled with the continuity of nature, but only by invoking the distinction between superficial and radical difference in kind—a distinction unknown to the writers we have been considering and also, apparently, to Professor Lovejoy.

(3)

Philosophical exponents of the view that man differs only in degree from other things. Here we have mainly philosophers whose fundamental doctrine is that of classical materialism.

The controlling principles of this doctrine are atomism and mechanism. As we shall see, when the Marxists try to distinguish their brand of dialectical materialism from this classical doctrine, they refer to it as "atomistic and mechanistic materialism." Associated with the classical materialists are a few others who, while not espousing their doctrine, concur in the view that man differs only in degree.

Among the atomistic or mechanistic materialists, those who speak most clearly and emphatically on the point at issue are Hobbes and La Mettrie. For Hobbes, man differs only in degree or, at most, only apparently in kind. He attributes understanding to men and brutes alike, and explains man's superiority in degree by reference to man's power of articulate speech, which is superior in degree to communication among animals. Brutes as well as men deliberate and exercise prudence, though men have more foresight—again because of their linguistic superiority. [17] La Mettrie—whose book, *Man a Machine*, treats men as automata in the same way that Descartes treats animals—explicitly declares that men differ only in degree from other automata. [18]

The other outstanding materialists in the history of Western thought—Democritus and Epicurus in antiquity; Holbach, Hartley, Helvétius, Feuerbach, Moleschott, and Büchner in the eighteenth and nineteenth centuries—all regard man as a purely physical thing operating according to the same mechanical laws of bodily motion that control the behavior of other physical things. Insofar as they treat sensation and thought, they reduce it to the action of matter—to the impact of bodies upon bodies or to the physical properties of bodies in motion. By implication certainly, if not by express declaration, they treat man as differing only in degree from other physical things, animate and inanimate. For all of them the continuity of nature is a fundamental doctrine. They view nature as a single continuum of degrees of complexity in the material organization of bodies. Their denial of anything immaterial entails their rejection of the view that man differs radically in kind. [19]

Associated with them in rejecting radical difference in kind and in asserting that man differs only in degree are a number of other writers. Two who are certainly not doctrinal materialists—Montaigne and Hume—are quite explicit on the point. Hume maintains that men and animals differ only in the degree of their inferential power or their power to reason. [20] Montaigne, in his "Apology for Raimond de Sebonde," plays with the alternatives that men and animals do not differ at all in the traits usually thought to be distinctive of men; or that, if they do, animals are superior in intelligence to men. It must be added that Montaigne, in another essay, also says with blatant inconsistency that God endowed man with reason so that, unlike beasts, he is not servilely subject to the laws of nature. [21]

The others that remain to be mentioned but whom I reserve for fuller treatment in the next chapter—Bolingbroke, Jenyns, Bonnet, and Robinet—have intellectual affinities with the materialist philosophers, as Hume and Montaigne do not. They are all as explicit as Hume in declaring that men differ only in degree from other animals. They go further; they definitely espouse the principle of a single continuum in nature, from the lowest to the highest degree, denying thereby the reality of kinds or species.

(4)

Philosophical exponents of the view that man differs superficially in kind from other things. Here we have the dialectical materialists—Marx, Engels, Lenin, and their followers—who reject the mechanistic materialism of the atomists, and of La Mettrie, Holbach, Büchner, and Moleschott. [22] With it they reject the proposition that man differs only in degree from other animals. They assert man's difference in kind, attributing to man alone the power of thought and the rational control of his environment through productive activity. [23]

As materialists, they affirm the continuity of nature, which they see as a single continuum of degrees of complexity in the organization of matter; and so as *materialists* they deny the existence of any immaterial principle that would make man radically different in kind. [24] But as *dialectical* materialists (and as followers of Hegel), they explain man's difference in kind by reference to the law of the transformation of quantity into quality or what they sometimes call the "law of leaping development." [25]

Since the operation of a critical threshold in a quantitative series or continuum of degrees is not confined to the production of a qualitative change, but extends to other respects in which things can differ in kind, the Hegelian formula—the law of the transformation of quantity into quality—while apparently apt, is on closer examination seen to be inadequate and inaccurate. As we have already observed, the explanation of a difference in kind by reference to a critical threshold in a continuum of degrees makes that difference in kind superficial, as distinct from radical. It is perfectly clear that the position of the dialectical materialists, divested of its Hegelian trappings and jargon, amounts to the assertion that man differs superficially in kind from other things. It is also perfectly clear that when they first adopted this position in the controversy about man, they did not have scientific evidence to support their view; they held it entirely as a matter of philosophical doctrine. It enabled them to maintain their conception of man as different in kind by virtue of being the only historical and technologically productive animal, and it also permitted them to reconcile that conception of man with the principle of continuity in nature—a principle that no materialist, classical or dialectical, can relinquish.

(5)

I have already called attention to the basic error made by certain philosophers, who tried to conceive the order of nature as a continuum of kinds or species. Not only did Locke and Leibniz commit this error, but they also tried to combine their assertion of a single all-embracing continuum in nature with the contradictory assertion that nature consists in a hierarchy of radically distinct kinds—inert bodies, plants, brute animals, and man. If a single all-embracing continuum in nature is incompatible with a hierarchy of kinds, and if a continuum cannot be a continuum of kinds, but must consist solely of variations in degree, *what are the philosophically tenable alternatives?*

Aware of the contradictions just pointed out, Kant answered this question in the following manner. On the one hand, he regarded the tendency to find continuity in nature as one of the regulative principles of reason in man's effort to understand the world. This tendency led the mind to find sameness in things and to allow only for differences in degree. On the other hand, he regarded the tendency to distinguish things as different in kind as another regulative principle of reason, governing man's efforts to understand the order of nature. This tendency led the mind to find otherness in things and to introduce discontinuities into nature.

For the mind to operate in accordance with either one of these regulative principles to the exclusion of the other, would, in Kant's view, result in the error of a half-truth's being treated as if it were the whole story. But Kant also held that to apply both principles without limitation must result in a contradiction; for the order of nature cannot be both a single all-embracing continuum and a set of distinct kinds. Kant thought that we were saved from this antinomy only by the fact that we could not *empirically support* either principle applied without limit—to the exclusion of the other. We must, in short, look for continuity in nature, on the one hand, and we must try to discover distinct kinds, on the other; but we must not suppose that either of these regulative principles can be converted into the one and only objective truth about nature. [26]

While I think that Kant's insight into the problem is in part correct, I do not think that his statement of the antinomy is correct, nor that we are obliged to accept his resolution of it. I would express what is correct about Kant's insight in the following manner. No universe, real or possible, is intelligible unless it contains some samenesses and some differences. For any two things that exist or any two objects of thought, it must be true that they are the same in one or more respects and that they differ in one or more respects. They cannot be utterly the same and be two; they cannot be utterly different and yet both be existences or thinkables. But it is quite possible for two things to be completely the same in kind, and yet still to differ, *if* they differ only in the degree to which they possess the same characteristics. And, as we have seen, it is also possible—a point not noticed by Kant—for two things to differ superficially in kind, while still being exactly alike in their underlying make-up or constitution.

Hence a single all-embracing continuum in nature need not exclude all differences. It allows for differences in degree and for superficial differences in kind. It excludes only radical differences in kind; for, if such exist, there is an underlying discontinuity in nature. Nor does a hierarchy of forms in nature (involving, as it does, radical differences in kind) totally exclude continuity.

This last point requires explanation, first, as to the meaning of "hierarchy," and second, on the relation of hierarchy to continuity. A hierarchy is a discontinuous and finite series of kinds, ordered in grades of perfection from lowest to highest—in which no two kinds are equal in grade, but each is higher or lower than another. For example, on the hypothesis that plants, brute animals, and men are radically different in kind, these three kinds constitute a hierarchy of living things.

If the order of nature—or the world of living things—is a hierarchy of kinds in the sense defined, then nature cannot also be conceived as a single all-embracing continuum. Continuity and hierarchy are incompatible when both are made co-extensive throughout nature. This is the contradiction that we have already observed in Leibniz and Locke.

Aristotle avoids this contradiction by conceiving nature as a hierarchy of radically distinct kinds, but also seeing a continuum of degrees within each grade of the hierarchy; for example, lower and higher degrees of plant life; lower and higher degrees of brute animal life; lower and higher degrees of human life. In the *Metaphysics*, Aristotle says that the order of species is like the series of integral numbers (each one higher or lower than the next, with no intermediates). [27] This statement appears to be inconsistent with the following statement in the *History of Animals*: "Nature proceeds little by little from things lifeless to animal life in such a way that it is impossible to determine the exact line of demarcation, nor on which side thereof an intermediate form should lie." But if we read a little further in the same chapter, the meaning becomes clear: "There is observed in plants a continuous scale of ascent towards the animal. . . . And so throughout the entire animal scale there is a graduated differentiation in amount of vitality and in capacity for motion." [28]

To see how the hierarchy of nature envisaged in the *Metaphysics* can be reconciled with the continuity of nature as described in the *History of Animals*, we need only add to each whole number the discontinuous series of fractions that approach but never reach the whole number next above it. Thus, 1 plus the series of fractions approaches but does not ever reach 2; 2 plus the series of fractions approaches but does not reach 3. The basic discontinuity between 1 and 2 is not abrogated by the continuous series of fractions which almost but does not completely fill the gap between 1 and 2. In short, the principle of hierarchy excludes a single all-embracing continuum, but it allows for a plurality of continua that permit a lower kind to approach the next higher kind by a scale of degrees.

Continuity and hierarchy are incompatible only when both are made co-extensive throughout nature. This is the contradiction that we have already observed in the thinking of Locke and Leibniz. Aristotle and, following him, Aquinas avoid this contradiction by conceiving nature as a hierarchy of radically distinct kinds (inorganic beings, plants, brute animals, and men), and they fill in the picture by seeing a continuum of degrees *within* each of the grades of the hierarchy; for example, lower and higher degrees of vegetative life, lower and higher degrees of animal life, lower and higher degrees of human life. [29] In contrast, Leibniz and Locke try to do the impossible. They try to combine the hierarchy of living things—vegetative, sensitive, and rational—with one complete continuum of degrees that leaves no gaps or breaks between the lowest and the highest. This amounts to combining the assertion of the unbroken continuity of nature with the assertion that in nature there are radical differences in kind. Since the latter introduces discontinuities into nature, the two assertions are in irreconcilable contradiction to each other.

(6)

I can now summarize my answer to the question that I asked at the opening of Section 5: *What are the philosophically tenable alternatives?* They are: (1) the principle of continuity understood as allowing for differences in degree and for superficial differences in kind, but excluding radical differences in kind; (2) the principle of hierarchy understood as asserting radical differences in kind and allowing for a plurality of partial continua within the sphere of each of the distinct kinds, but denying the existence of a single all-embracing continuum in nature.

These two principles are at first glance inconsistent. Both cannot be true. Where this analysis differs most fundamentally from the one advanced by Kant is in its assertion that, of the two alternatives, one can be true and the other can be false. Since I think it is clear that basic continuity and basic discontinuity in nature are not only exclusive but also exhaustive, I would go further and assert that these two principles are not merely inconsistent but contradictory—one must be true, and the other false.

This philosophical clarification of the issue about the order of nature controls the treatment of the question about man—not only as a purely philosophical question, but also as a mixed question. The introduction of scientific evidence bearing on that question does not and cannot alter the picture so far as the relevant principles are concerned, precisely because they are principles. Any determination of how man differs, whether in the light of common experience alone or in the light of all the scientific evidence that is now available or that ever will be available, must be in accord with one or the other of the two opposed principles.

So much for the philosophical issue about continuity and discontinuity in nature. Now what about the question concerning man's difference, treated *as if* it raised a purely philosophical issue?

Here, at first blush, it would seem that the position that asserts man's radical difference in kind had the edge of the argument over the position of the classical materialists who assert that man differs only in degree. For two reasons: first, because the common experience of mankind falsifies the view that man differs only in degree from other things, or the view that, throughout the whole of nature, there are only differences in degree of material complexity; second, because the classical doctrine of atomistic or mechanistic materialism, quite apart from questions about the order of nature and about the difference of man, is also falsified by our common experience. To accept this doctrine, we must dismiss our common experience as illusory. If our common experience is not to be dismissed as illusory, we must reject the doctrine.

But, as we saw in Section 4, the dialectical materialism of the Marxists is able to affirm manifest differences in kind and also to maintain the principle of continuity in nature. It is able to do this by positing critical thresholds in an underlying continuum of degrees. These explain the manifest differences in kind and, in so doing, render them superficial rather than radical. Dialectical materialism's affirmation of the continuity of nature, is, therefore, not falsified by common experience, for it allows for the reality of all the differences in kind that we find in our common experience. In addition, not only dialectical materialism but also mechanistic materialism, as that has become more sophisticated and subtle in the twentieth century, regard themselves as able to maintain their doctrine without treating common experience as illusory in any respect.

These things being so, the affirmative position loses the advantage it appeared to have at first blush. The issue, treated *as if* it were purely philosophical, appears to be irresolvable; neither side can persuade the other by philosophical arguments alone. On the one hand, scientific evidence is needed to establish, as a matter of fact, the critical thresholds *posited* by the dialectical materialists, without which observed differences in kind cannot be reconciled with the underlying continuity of nature. On the other hand, even if the position that men and other animals differ radically, not superficially, in kind, has additional philosophical arguments to support its view of man (I think it has such arguments, and I will deal with them in Chapter 12), these arguments cannot settle the matter without submitting to empirical tests—not just by reference to the facts of common experience, but also by reference to the special data obtained by scientific investigation.

CHAPTER 5

Why Darwin Answered the Question As He Did

(1)

A NUMBER of eighteenth-century naturalists and speculators constitute a transition from the purely philosophical to the mixed treatment of the question about how man differs. While Buffon, Bonnet, Robinet, and Jenyns are not scientific investigators in the full sense of that term, as it is applicable to Darwin and his contemporaries, they do take account of evidences that lie outside the common experience of mankind. To the extent that they do, they represent the entrance of science into the picture; perhaps it would be more accurate to say the entrance of modern science, for Aristotle, in addition to being a philosopher, was a biological scientist—an observer and investigator whose extensive array of data on the characteristics and habits of animals established a zoological classification so detailed and, in many respects, so accurate, that it persisted to the time of Linnaeus, and then, with slight Linnaean revisions, right down to the time of Darwin.

Aristotle's double role—as an empirical philosopher and as a scientific investigator—may account for the way in which he combined a conception of nature as consisting in a hierarchy of radically distinct grades of being (plants, brute animals, and men) with the recognition that within the domain or kingdom constituted by each of these grades of being (e.g., the plant kingdom or the animal kingdom), there was a continuous ascent by degrees from lower to higher forms of life. His recognition of these diverse continuities did not prevent him from maintaining that animals differed from plants, and men from animals, by a difference in kind, not just a difference in degree; nor was his insistence on this point inconsistent with his recognition of the continuous scale of degrees by which forms of plant or animal, or even human, life vary from lower to higher.

The eighteenth-century writers with whom we shall now be briefly concerned were so impressed by the appearance that nature gave of a continuous ascent through a scale of degrees from lower to higher forms of life that they converted Aristotle's several and separate continua into a single all-embracing continuum of nature. It might be thought that, in doing so, they had merely adopted the view held by Leibniz and Locke, that nature consists in a single continuum of forms, varying by degrees from lower to higher. But it must be recalled that Leibniz and Locke also retained a version of the Aristotelian hierarchy of grades of being which required them to assert, quite inconsistently, differences in kind as well as differences in degree. Not so Buffon, Bonnet, Robinet, and Jenyns; they—or at least the most consistent of them, Robinet—carried the principle of an unbroken continuity in nature to its inevitable conclusion. He saw that the principle allows only for differences in degree, which carries with it the equally inevitable corollary that species are nonexistent and that distinctions in kind are illusory or at best only apparent. [1]

In his *Histoire Naturelle*, published in 1749, Buffon discarded the notion of species as artificial and misleading. "In reality," he declares, "individuals alone exist in nature." Hence, if they differ, they differ in degree; or if they appear to differ in kind, that is appearance only, never the real state of affairs. [2] Buffon later repudiated this extreme position, but it was espoused by Bonnet in his *Contemplation de la Nature* in 1764–65. However, Bonnet qualified it somewhat by dividing the continuous scale of natural things, differing only in degree, into four general classes—inert bodies, plants, animals, and men. [3] He was criticized in 1768 for this qualification of the principle of continuity by J. B. Robinet who argued that the principle of continuity, correctly understood, requires us to reject the reality of all species, kinds, or class distinctions, and to see the whole of nature as one continuous scale of differences in degree. [4]

Robinet, of course, does not hesitate to treat man as differing only in degree from higher animals; and even Bonnet, in spite of assigning men and brutes to distinct classes, minimizes the differences between man and ape. He may have been influenced in this by the views of Lord Monboddo who, in 1770, declared that man and the higher apes, especially the chimpanzee and the orangutan, are of the same species. [5]

Even earlier, in 1754, Rousseau, as had Locke before him, expressed the view that the line between man and brute was a shadowy one. (We must, for the moment, ignore the fact that both Locke and Rousseau also espoused the opposite view that the line is a sharp one—drawn by Locke in terms of man's exclusive possession of abstract ideas and by Rousseau in terms of man's exclusive possession of free will.) Locke in several places suggests that if you compare the lower degrees of humankind with the higher degrees of animal life (a feeble-minded man, for example, with a baboon or drill), you will find that they overlap. [6] Rousseau thinks that the same ideational powers belong to men and animals, especially the man-like apes, and that the apparent difference in kind between them can be explained by man's *accidental* development of language. [7]

Still another example of the same kind of thinking is to be found in Soame Jenyns; but where Locke aligns the baboon with the idiot, Jenyns aligns the chimpanzee with the Hottentot. Though some men are superior in degree to some animals, the lowest degree of humankind is about on the same plane with the highest degree of animal life. [8]

I have briefly reviewed this line of thought, not because it represents a clear handling of the problem of continuity and species, or of the question about man's difference, but because it sets the stage for Darwin—for his theory of evolution, as set forth in *The Origin of Species* (1859); and for his application of that theory to man in *The Descent of Man* (1871). I will deal, first, with the theory of evolution quite apart from man—beginning with Darwin and coming down to the present day. After that I will deal with the question about man in the context of evolutionary theory and research—as handled by Darwin without the benefit of paleontological evidence, and as treated in our day in the light of fossil remains.

(2)

The theory of biological evolution, as formulated by Darwin, can be summarized by saying that it converts Leibniz' principle of continuity into a temporal law—a law of development. [9] All the diverse forms of life, including forms now extinct and forms now extant, are connected developmentally. In the succession of countless generations, in each of which the offspring vary slightly from their ancestors and from each other, differences multiply; but at the point in time and space at which they first occur, they are slight, almost insensible, differences in degree.

Borrowing the expression to which Leibniz first gave currency, Darwin emphatically declares: *Natura non facit saltum* ("Nature does not make jumps.") [10] *If* by "a jump" is meant the crossing of the gap that is made by a real difference in kind—a difference constituted by one thing's having a characteristic totally lacking in another—*then* "nature does not make jumps" means that evolutionary development (by descent with modification from ancestral forms) excludes the reality of kinds. To this extent Darwin would appear to be in agreement with those of his immediate predecessors—especially J. B. Robinet—who espoused the principle of continuity in its extreme form.

If Darwin had done only that, he might have had a theory of evolution (a temporalized, developmental version of the principle of continuity in nature), but he would not have had a theory of speciation (a theory of the origin of species). Varieties or races of one and the same species, like individual members of a species, may differ from one another in degree; but if the diverse species of a single genus are to be distinguished from the diverse varieties or races of a single species, the difference between distinct species must at least *appear* to be one of kind.

Darwin expresses many doubts about the possibility of distinguishing varieties or races from species. He often says that species are nothing but well-marked varieties. There is no problem here, of course, if the naturalist's taxonomic scheme is something he imposes upon nature for his own convenience—if the kinds or groupings that he sets up are artificial. But if his class distinctions are supposed to represent "natural kinds"—natural groupings that differ in kind, not just in degree—then he is confronted with the problem of reconciling natural kinds with his evolutionary principle of developmental or phylogenetic continuity. For if evolution is a continuous development of living forms from living forms—without jumps, by insensible gradations or differences in degree—how is it possible for new species to come into being at any point in the developmental continuum? Or, to put the same question in a different way: Must not the taxonomist's classification of the living organisms now extant into a large number of distinct species, be artificial—something imposed on nature rather than a representation of divisions actually existing in nature itself?

It would look as if Darwin's answer to this question should have been in accord with the one given by Robinet—that species have no reality. But if he had given that answer he could not have developed a theory of the origin of species. The answer he gives agrees with Robinet and conforms to the principle of continuity in one respect—it denies that the difference between species is a *real* difference in kind, i.e., it denies that species are kinds between which intermediates are impossible. But in another respect his answer departs from Robinet. Even though species are not really different in kind, species are nevertheless naturally existing groups that *appear* to differ in kind because the intermediates that might have connected them by a continuous series of gradations in degree are *absent* or *missing*. The absent intermediates—often called the "missing links" in the chain—create the *appearance* of a difference in *kind* between species. Between the varieties or races of a single species there are no missing links or absent intermediates. That is why they are only varieties or races, not species.

The metaphor "missing links" is unfortunate because a chain does not convey the image of a continuous series. I prefer to speak of "gaps" or "breaks" in the continuum—like the interference bands or interruptions in the spectrum of light. An *apparent* difference in kind exists where intermediates, though *possible*, are *absent*, and so a gap or break occurs in the continuum of degrees. [11]

By treating species as naturally existing groups or organisms that are only *apparently* different in kind—separated islands in an interrupted continuum—Darwin developed a theory of speciation that did not violate his evolutionary principle of developmental continuity. Species originate, according to his theory, by a process of natural selection that operates to perpetuate certain varieties and to cause the extinction of other varieties—thus giving rise to gaps or interruptions in the continuum, without which there would be no species.

Viewed *developmentally*, this means that the organisms we distinguish at a given time as different species of the same genus were represented at an earlier time by ancestors that were distinguished as races or varieties of the same species. At the earlier time there were also intermediate races or varieties; but through the process of natural selection these gradually became extinct. With the extinction of the intermediate varieties, the extreme varieties tended to separate genetically through various barriers to interbreeding; and thus they became the distinct species of a single genus, where earlier their ancestors were merely different varieties of the same species.

Viewed *taxonomically*, this means that co-existing species at any given time are distinct kinds only by virtue of the absence of intermediate forms or varieties that have become extinct. *If* the geological record of fossil forms were complete instead of imperfect, and *if* fossil remains enabled us to reconstruct all previously existing organisms, we could repair the broken or interrupted continuum by filling in the gaps; and we could thus re-establish at one time the continuity of nature, with no differences in kind at all, not even apparent, but only differences in degree. [12]

(3)

Let me now try to summarize briefly the main import of Darwin's theory before turning to post-Darwinian modifications in the theory of evolution and of speciation.

Darwin's theory of developmental continuity excludes the possibility of there being any radical differences in kind among the species of living things; for, if there were, it would be impossible for them to be connected in a phylogenetic series constituted by slight variations in degree; nor could they have originated by the extinction of intermediate varieties through the operation of natural selection.

It is difficult to say whether Darwin's theory also excludes the possibility of superficial differences in kind. The fact that intermediates are impossible in this case as well as in the case of radically distinct kinds would seem to suggest that such differences in kind should also be excluded, since Darwin's theory requires the *possibility of absent intermediates.* On the other hand, superficial differences in kind, involving as they do an underlying continuum of degrees with a critical threshold, do not violate the evolutionary principle of phylogenetic continuity. As we shall see, post-Darwinian theories of speciation differ from Darwin's in admitting the possibility of superficial—real, not merely apparent—differences in kind.

The Origin of Species does not mention man, except in a single sentence in the concluding pages, where Darwin says: "Light will be thrown on the origin of man and his history." (In later editions, this was changed to "much light.") In those same concluding pages, however, Darwin does consider the question whether the origin of life is monophyletic or polyphyletic. He answers this question by saying: "I believe that animals are descended from at most only four or five progenitors, and plants from an equal or lesser number." He goes on to say: "Analogy would lead me one step further, namely, to the belief that all animals and plants are descended from some one prototype. But analogy may be a deceitful guide." [13] He did not have to rely on analogy; for strict adherence to his own principle of phylogenetic continuity should have led Darwin to postulate, as did J. B. Robinet, a single prototype or progenitor for all living organisms—both plants and animals.

If there were as many as two original progenitors—one for all forms of animal life and one for all forms of plant life—it would mean that the plant and animal kingdoms are separated by a real (and maybe even radical) difference in kind, not by an apparent difference in kind that masks a continuum of degrees in which gaps have occurred. A polyphyletic origin of life is incompatible with the principle of phylogenetic continuity.

(4)

The most important change in post-Darwinian theory involves a shift from natural selection and the extinction of intermediate varieties as the explanation of the gaps in the continuum that are indispensable for the origin of species. Where Darwin used the extinction of intermediate varieties by natural selection of the fittest to explain the genetic isolation of the remaining extreme varieties, the post-Darwinian theorists—with greatly improved genetics and much more paleontological evidence—use geographic barriers as the explanation of the genetic isolation responsible for the formation of new species. It is now generally accepted that most speciation is allopatric—the result of geographical separations that bar interbreeding between varieties of the same species, with the result that the gene pools of the spatially separated varieties become isolated from each other. In the exceptional cases of sympatric speciation—the origin of new species in the same locality—the explanation given is polyploidy, an explosive genetic change unknown, and probably unimaginable, to Darwin. [14]

Though post-Darwinian theory has distinguished three or four different types of speciation and has given us a different explanation of the factors productive of it, the central point remains the same: namely, that distinct species are genetically isolated populations between which interbreeding is impossible, arising (except in the case of polyploidy) from varieties between which interbreeding was not impossible, but between which it was prevented. Modern theorists, with more assurance than Darwin could manage, treat distinct species as natural kinds, not as man-made class distinctions. Ernst Mayr and Julian Huxley even go so far as to regard speciation as introducing "discontinuity" into nature. Since they subordinate this "discontinuity of species" to the basic phylogenetic continuity of the evolutionary process, it is clear that they do not mean "discontinuity" in the sense that excludes the possibility of intermediates in the underlying continuum of degrees that explains superficial differences in kind. [15]

Another important change in post-Darwinian theory is the departure, in a number of exceptional cases, from strict adherence to the rule that nature makes no jumps. George Gaylord Simpson and Theodosius Dobzhansky speak of quantum jumps in evolution —what, in effect, is saltatory speciation. This involves something like breaks in the developmental continuity of evolution, just as ordinary speciation introduces manifest gaps in the continuum of coexisting populations. Quantum evolution—or "breaks in the evolutionary continuity"—occur, according to Dobzhansky, "when the differences between the ancestors and the descendants increase so rapidly that they are perceived as differences in kind." [16]

What are these differences in kind that are produced by any of the diverse types of speciation recognized by modern theory? Are they all only apparent? Or may they also include some that are real differences in kind?

In the first place, it is necessary to reiterate that the post-Darwinian theory of evolution and speciation excludes radical differences in kind as emphatically as does Darwin's theory; for such differences are plainly incompatible with developmental continuity which, even when it involves breaks or quantum jumps, cannot be equated with the basic discontinuity called for by radical differences in kind.

In the second place, leading contemporary theorists—Dobzhansky, Mayr, and Julian Huxley—agree that there would be no species at all if interbreeding were totally unrestricted and all the possible genetic combinations or genotypes were simultaneously realized in co-existing or extant phenotypes. Such genetic swamping would result in an array of individual differences. [17]

Dobzhansky asks us to consider "an imaginary situation, a living world in which all possible gene combinations are represented by equal numbers of individuals. Under such conditions no discrete groups of forms . . . could occur. . . . The variability would become a perfect continuum." He goes on to say of the actual world: ". . . if the representatives of different groups interbred at random, all the gene combinations that are now rare or absent, would be produced, given a sufficient number of individuals, within a few generations from the start of random breeding. That would mean a breakdown of the separation of groups, and an emergence of continuous variation over a part of the field. If all the organisms were to interbreed freely, a perfect continuum postulated above would result." [18]

Does this lead to the conclusion that the manifest differences in kind that exist in the actual world, the world in which we know that completely random interbreeding between groups does not occur, are only *apparent*, not real, differences in kind; and that, in reality, the situation is as Robinet and Darwin supposed it to be; namely, one in which, except for the accident of absent intermediates or missing links, there would only be differences in degree? I do not think so. Genetic swamping would, of course, result in an abolition of species or group differences, replacing it with an array of individual differences. But it does not follow that all individual differences are necessarily differences in degree. If we bear in mind the distinction between a superficial and a radical difference in kind, we can see that there is no difficulty about there being superficial differences in kind between the individuals that have been produced by genetic swamping, for such differences do not preclude genetic continuity in the process by which they have been produced.

Without the critical insight provided by the distinction between superficial and radical differences in kind, biologists might be tempted to follow Darwin in thinking that all differences in kind must be apparent, not real. In the absence of that distinction, it would be natural—almost unavoidable—to suppose that unrestricted or random interbreeding, with consequent genetic swamping, would not only replace specific groupings by an array of individual differences, but would also make the only real differences in nature differences in degree. Dobzhansky might appear to be adopting this view when he refers to a "perfect continuum," for a perfect continuum without any breaks whatsoever, even of the sort that are produced by manifest and merely superficial differences in kind, would exclude all differences except differences in degree. But, as we shall see in the following chapter, he, along with Ernst Mayr, Julian Huxley, and most of the other leading evolutionists who deal with the origin of man, affirm a real difference in kind between the *Hominidae* and the *Pongidae* and *Hylobatidae*, though, of course, they regard it as a superficial, not a radical, difference in kind. Their theories of saltatory speciation or quantum jumps in evolution indicate that they recognize superficial differences in kind at many other points in the phylogenetic continuum. It would be plainly inconsistent with such views on their part for them also to hold that completely random interbreeding and genetic swamping would abolish all differences in kind, replacing manifest differences in kind that are merely apparent with differences in degree.

(5)

Let us now return to the question about man. Bringing the foregoing discussion to bear on that question, we are confronted with the following alternatives. (1) *If* the view of Darwin is adopted, then the human species differs from other closely related species by no more than an apparent difference in kind, a difference that is really a difference in degree, which is masked or concealed by the absence of intermediate forms—the missing links. (2) *If*, on the contrary, the view of most post-Darwinian evolutionists, and especially the paleoanthropologists among them, is adopted, then even within the framework of evolutionary development and without violating the principle of phylogenetic continuity, the difference between man and other animals may be a real difference in kind—superficial, of course, not radical.

We need not let the matter stand with such iffy alternatives unresolved. The immense array of data that has accumulated since Darwin's day and the significant advances in the theory of evolution that have been made since his time lead us to embrace the second answer. It is, nevertheless, useful to try to understand why Darwin gave the answer that he did. Light is thrown on this by the state of evolutionary facts and theories at the time, within the context of which he developed his views of man.

Darwin addressed himself to the question about man hesitantly, almost reluctantly; *The Descent of Man* was published in 1871, twelve years after *The Origin of Species.* In his Introduction to *The Descent of Man*, he acknowledges that other evolutionists had applied evolutionary theory to the origin and nature of man. He mentions Lamarck, who antedated him by many years—more than sixty, in fact. He also mentions among his more immediate contemporaries, the writings of Wallace, T. H. Huxley, Lyell, and Haeckel; and expresses special indebtedness to Haeckel's discussion of the genealogy of man in a book published in 1868. [19]

The relation of Darwin to three of these contemporaries deserves a brief further comment. Lyell, in the closing chapter of

The Antiquity of Man (1863), demurs "to the assumption that the hypothesis of variation and natural selection obliges us to assume that there was an absolutely insensible passage from the highest intelligence of the inferior animals to the improvable reason of man." That, says Lyell, may have been accomplished by a leap: nature "may have cleared at one bound the space which separated" the highest stage of the unprogressive intelligence of the inferior animals from the first and lowest form of improvable reason manifested by Man." [20] Referring to the foregoing statement by Lyell, Darwin remarked, "it makes me groan"—and well it might, for it denied his principle that nature makes no jumps. [21]

Wallace, first in a paper published in 1864, and more emphatically in a paper published in 1869, denied that the theory of speciation by natural selection and by the extinction of intermediate varieties could explain the origin of man. He did not think there was sufficient time for this to take place, and he was puzzled by the absence of the fossil evidences that would be needed to support Darwin's theory. This led to a serious rift between Darwin and his closest colleague in the development of the theory of evolution. [22]

On the other hand, Darwin could draw support from the views of another of his associates—T. H. Huxley, who in 1863 published a book of essays on *Man's Place in Nature*. Huxley took the position, later to be taken by Darwin, that man, in all his mental faculties, differs only in degree from the anthropoid apes and other higher mammals; though he also concedes, somewhat inconsistently, that man "*alone possesses* the marvellous endowment of intelligible and rational speech." [23] Huxley also devotes one of his essays to the fossil remains of early man, and discusses the Engis and Neanderthal skulls; whereas Darwin, in his handling of the subject, makes no reference at all to these fossil evidences that were available to him as well as to Huxley.

Lacking the rich and varied fossil finds of later paleoanthropology, and obviously regarding the two early human skulls discussed by Huxley as insufficient to support his thesis about man's origin from a remote ancestor common to the one living human species and the several extant species of apes, Darwin argued entirely from a comparison of the behavior of living man with the behavior of the living apes and other extant species of animals, especially the higher mammals. His argument had to take the form of establishing the proposition that the behavioral differences between man and other animals indicate that the difference in their mental powers is only one of degree. In the light of all the comparative evidences that he is able to marshall, he thinks he is justified in concluding that "the difference in mind between man and the higher animals, great as it is, is certainly one of degree, not of kind." [24] To which he later adds the remark: "A difference in degree, however great, does not justify us in placing man in a distinct kingdom." [25]

Like Huxley, he concedes that rational speech is peculiar to man; but he qualifies this in many ways by pointing out incipient and rudimentary forms of expression and communication in other animals; [26] and, in addition, he explicitly disagrees with Max Müller that man's use of language implies the power of forming general concepts and with Müller's further view that, since no animals possess this power, there is a real and, perhaps, radical difference in kind between men and animals. He says: "With respect to animals, I have already endeavored to show that they have this power, at least in a rude and incipient degree." [27]

Though in one place he attributes man's development of articulate speech to his intellectual powers, he explains man's intellectual superiority, as manifested in his linguistic performance, by reference to the superiority of his brain in size and complexity —a difference in degree from that of other animals. [28] I mention this because, even if one were to say to Darwin that man's exclusive possession of articulate speech made his difference from all other animals a real difference in kind, we can imagine a philosophically instructed Darwin countering this by saying that, if it is real, it is at most superficial, based on a critical threshold in the continuum of degrees in brain size and complexity.

The reason why Darwin had to argue in this way should be perfectly plain. If he had conceded the possibility that man might really differ in kind, and could not show—as at his time he could not—that this was only a superficial difference in kind, he could not support his thesis that the human species originated in the same way that all other animal species have: by descent with modification from a common ancestor, accompanied by the extinction of intermediate varieties. The only view of man's difference compatible with this theory of his origin is a difference in degree or, at most, an apparent difference in kind—where that apparent difference in kind arises solely from the absence of intermediates, the missing links responsible for a gap in the continuum of degrees. Hence Darwin argued in the light of all the comparative evidence he could cite that the mental powers of man differ only in degree from those of other animals. But, because of the absence of fossil remains, he also had to hypothecate, without sufficient evidence, the earlier existence of forms intermediate between man and the apes. The fact that these are now extinct explains the breaks or gaps in the continuum that should connect man and the apes. [29] These gaps or breaks do not alter Darwin's view that man and the apes have evolved from a common ancestral form by a continuous process of descent—without jumps or gaps. [30]

(6)

Before I turn in the next chapter to the fossil evidences of modern paleoanthropology, I would like to close this discussion of Darwin with three comments on his position and on his mode of argument.

(1) The principle of phylogenetic continuity, central to the theory of evolution and supported by a vast array of data, controls Darwin's reasoning. If comparative evidence with respect to human and animal behavior had shown that man really differed in kind from other animals, Darwin would not have concluded that the principle of continuity was false or that it did not apply to the origin of all other animal species. He would have concluded instead that man was the one or rare exception, and that the origin of the human species could not be explained in the same way as the origin of all other species. However, thinking as he did that the comparative evidence showed only differences in degree, Darwin felt justified in applying the principle of phylogenetic continuity and his theory of speciation to the origin of man.

(2) It is of the utmost importance to observe the direction of Darwin's reasoning here. It is *not* from a hypothesis about man's origin (based on fossil evidences) to a conclusion about man's nature or man's difference. On the contrary, Darwin's line of

reasoning is from a conclusion about man's nature and his difference, based on comparative evidence of human and animal behavior, to the support of, though not the indubitable proof of, a hypothesis about man's origin: namely, that his speciation is like that of all other animals.

(3) The effect of Darwin's *Descent of Man* is best summarized by the remark of William Graham in 1881: "That man is an animal," he wrote, "is the great and special discovery of natural science in our generation." [31] Read one way, this is a very strange remark, indeed. With the possible exception of Descartes, who ever denied that man was an animal? With that one exception, every philosopher—from the Greeks to Kant and Hegel—who held that man differs radically in kind from other animals also asserted that man is an animal—a *rational* animal, but an *animal* nonetheless.

What then is the meaning of William Graham's remark? It is simply that man is a *brute* animal; or that there is no radical difference in kind among animals between those that are rational and those that, being not rational, are therefore brutes. What Graham is saying, in short, is that Darwin overthrew the prevailing view that the world of living things is divided into three kingdoms—plants, brute animals, and rational animals or men. Animals share with plants the common characteristics of all living things, but we do not say, therefore, that animals are plants. Hence, the fact that men share with brutes the common characteristics of animal life should not lead us to say that men are brutes unless we mean to deny, as Graham obviously thought Darwin had, the existence of a radical difference in kind between men and other animals.

CHAPTER 6

The Line Drawn by the Fossils

(1)

THE discovery of fossil types of man or manlike organisms (other than the two skulls known at Darwin's time)—the australopithecine fossils from South Africa, in the early Pleistocene strata of 1,000,000 or more years ago; the fossil remains of various types of *Pithecanthropus erectus*, now classified as *Homo erectus*, from Java, from Peking, and from Heidelberg, in the middle Pleistocene strata of about 500,000 years ago; the Swanscombe skull found near London, dating back to about 250,000 years ago; the Neanderthal fossils from Germany and elsewhere in Europe, and the somewhat later but related finds in Palestine, in Java, and in Rhodesia, all dating back to between 40,000 and 100,000 years ago; the Cro-Magnon and many similar fossils that, dating back to about 35,000 years ago, represent the immediate ancestors of neolithic and historic man—all these discoveries would seem to confirm Darwin's hypothesis of man's evolutionary descent and also to support his conjecture that the missing types in the developmental picture would be found and would fill the gaps in the continuum. [1]

What I have just said is the usual interpretation of the post-Darwinian findings in paleoanthropology. But, in fact, a closer examination of the matter shows, on the contrary, that modern paleoanthropology departs from Darwin's views on man in certain striking respects.

Let me say at once that all contemporary anthropologists in good standing agree with Darwin about the evolutionary descent of man and about the origin of the human species by exactly the same processes that are responsible for the speciation of all other forms of life. But as we observed in the preceding chapter, Darwin, in the absence of fossil remains, was forced to argue in support of his theory of man's origin by trying to establish the proposition that man and other animals differ only in degree. In sharp contrast, contemporary anthropologists regard their rich array of fossil finds as sufficient confirmation of man's phylogenetic continuity with earlier forms of animal life, so that they need not support that theory of man's origin by trying to show that man differs only in degree from other animals. On the contrary, having the various fossil specimens to interpret and explain, contemporary anthropologists must perforce try to show that all members of the family *Hominidae*—fossil as well as living types of man—really differ in kind from the other two most closely related family groups in the primate order—the *Hylobatidae* (i.e., the gibbon) and the *Pongidae* (i.e., the orangutan, the chimpanzee, and the gorilla).

If the contemporary anthropologists were to follow Darwin in thinking that man differs only in degree from non-man, they could not classify the fossil specimens into those that belong to the hominid family and those that belong to the pongid family—the fossil and living species of apes. In order for them to point a finger at the time and place where human life begins, they must be able to draw a sharp line between human and non-human; and, in order to draw that line, they have to view man as really differing in kind from non-man, not just in degree.

This is nicely confirmed by the fact that Darwin, in the light of his own insistence upon difference only in degree, writes: "In a series of forms graduating insensibly [i.e., by slight differences in degree] from some ape-like creature to man as he now exists, it would be impossible to fix on any definite point when the term 'man' ought to be used." [2] To which he adds: "But this is a matter of very little importance."

It may have been of very little importance for him, but it is of the greatest importance—it is crucial—for contemporary paleoanthropologists who try to order and classify the fossil specimens into those that represent extinct species in the genus *Homo*, or at least in the family *Hominidae*, as contrasted with those that represent extinct species belonging to the family *Pongidae* or the family *Hylobatidae*.

(2)

Having stated wherein they agree with Darwin and having pointed out how they depart from his central proposition about man, let me try briefly to summarize the views of such leading scientists today as Julian Huxley, Dobzhansky, Mayr, Simpson, Leakey, Rensch, Eiseley, von Koenigswald, Oakley, Washburn, and Le Gros Clark who, either as paleoanthropologists or as evolutionists in general, deal with the problem of man's origin and difference.

In one set of terms or another, they all assert the *uniqueness* of man as an animal, by which they mean: first, that man possesses certain characteristics (forms of behavior springing from certain powers or abilities on his part) that are not possessed to any degree by non-human animals; and hence, second, that man really differs in kind from non-human animals, not just in degree. In addition, there are several unique human traits that are not behavioral: man's erect or bipedal posture, his flexible hand with thumb opposed to forefinger, and the dominance of his cerebral cortex by either the left or the right hemisphere. [3]

The behavioral characteristics of fossil species are partly inferred from physique, especially the size of the brainpan and the structure of the jaw, but mainly from fossil artifacts that indicate such things as the making—the *making*, not just the *using*—of tools (e.g., the hand ax), the use of fire, hunting, cannibalism, burial rites, permanent dwelling places, the adornment of the body or of tools, the decoration of cave walls by representative or symbolic drawings, the making of statues, etc. [4]

Fossil forms of the *Hominidae* are differentiated from other fossil forms in the primate order (such as the *Pongidae* and the *Hylobatidae*, both of which are *Hominoidea*) by morphological characteristics and by distinctive behavioral traits. The latter are either indicated by the fossil artifacts associated with their skeletal remains or inferred from anatomical properties, such as cranial capacity or dentition. The paleoanthropologists are in agreement that the behavioral trait that distinguishes all hominid forms from the other fossil primates is toolmaking, and many of them associate this with what, in the earliest forms going back to 1,000,000 years ago or more, must be described as capacities for linguistic communication and for social organization. The basic disagreement among the anthropologists—with Raymond Dart, Robert Broom, and L. S. B. Leakey, on one side, and with most of the others against them in various degrees of doubt or indecision—concerns certain South African fossils that date between 1,000,000 and 500,000 years ago.

Both sides agree that these fossils were definitely hominids. The moot question is whether they belong to the genus *Homo* or to the genus *Australopithecus*—the two main divisions of the hominid family. Leakey claims that his fossils represent an early species in the genus *Homo*, a species that he has named *Homo habilis*. His opponents claim that these early hominid fossils do not belong to the genus *Homo*, but to the genus *Australopithecus*. The difference of opinion about the classification of these South African hominid fossils occurs within the context of agreement about the behavioral characteristics that differentiate the two hominid genera—the genus *Homo*, on the one hand, and the genus *Australopithecus*, on the other. Only sporadic or *ad hoc* toolmaking can be attributed to the earlier hominids of the genus *Australopithecus*; in contrast, to the later hominids of the genus *Homo* can be attributed sustained and systematic toolmaking, along with the use of fire and co-operative social behavior.

The South African anthropologists argue that the association of their fossil skulls with fossil artifacts that indicate the making of tools, the hunting of animals, and the use of fire, is conclusive evidence that their finds represent not only hominids, but also members of the genus *Homo*, belonging to the earliest of its species, *Homo habilis*. Their opponents doubt this interpretation of the fossil artifacts; they fortify that doubt by reference to the small brain size of these fossil forms; and, while conceding that they are, indeed, early representatives of the hominid family, regard them as belonging to the genus *Australopithecus*, not to the genus *Homo*. [5]

This difference of opinion concerns only the antiquity of the genus *Homo*, not the antiquity of the hominid family; and it in no way affects the agreement that prevails concerning the differentiation of the *Hominidae* from the *Pongidae* or, within the hominid family, the differentiation of the genus *Homo* from the genus *Australopithecus*. These agreements are the significant points for us, for we are here concerned with *how* the anthropologists draw the line between human and non-human forms of life, as these are represented by fossil remains and living species, *not where* they draw the line in time and space, *nor how* they trace the line or lines of phylogenetic development along which living man descended from ancestral hominid forms.

Whether or not certain fossil hominids, dating back to 1,000,000 years ago or more, are classified as belonging to the genus *Homo*; and whether that genus consists of three distinct species (*Homo habilis*, represented by the fossil forms just mentioned; *Homo erectus*, represented by the fossil forms found in Europe, Java, and China, dating back to about 500,000 years ago; and *Homo sapiens*, including the Neanderthal and Cro-Magnon fossils dating from about 120,000 to about 35,000 years ago) or the genus *Homo* includes only two species, *Homo erectus* and *Homo sapiens*, the line that divides hominids from non-hominids and the characteristics that differentiate the genus *Homo* remain the same. The evidences of industry (toolmaking, use of fire) and the evidences of culture (stable forms of association, linguistic communication) become more marked as we move, within that genus, from the species *Homo erectus* to the species *Homo sapiens*, less clearly in the case of Neanderthal man, more clearly in the case of Cro-Magnon man. Here the evidences of culture include such things as burial rites and other ceremonialisms, decorative art, painting, and sculpture. Oral speech, which precedes written speech, leaves no fossil remains, but the anthropologists infer that Cro-Magnon man and living man are of the same species from the evidences of Cro-Magnon modes of life and behavior to be found in the fossil artifacts associated with Cro-Magnon man.

The argument runs somewhat as follows. If Cro-Magnon man had sufficient intelligence or brain capacity for symbolic or representative works of art, he also had enough intelligence or brain capacity for articulate speech. The many rapid changes in technology and in culture that took place in Cro-Magnon times, it is further argued, indicate that Cro-Magnon man not only had a capacity for articulate speech, but also used it to develop a propositional language such as ours. He could not have done what he did without it.

Some anthropologists—for example, Oakley, Le Gros Clark, Leakey, and Dart—go even further. They argue that one piece of evidence may be decisive; namely, toolmaking. Toolmaking, Oakley maintains, indicates the power of conceptual, as opposed to perceptual, thought. But the power of conceptual thought is all that is needed for the development of all the other aspects of distinctively human culture, including symbolic art and articulate speech. Hence, even though we can find no fossil traces of them, articulate speech as well as the use of fire and symbolic art may have been present in the life of whatever fossil species is associated with fossil artifacts that are indisputable evidence of toolmaking. [6]

By this line of reasoning, the existence of men in all generic respects like living men may be carried as far back as 500,000 or 1,000,000 years ago, and the existence of hominids that have a family resemblance with living men may go back even further—to almost 2,000,000 years ago. The significance for us of this reasoning does not lie in the precise ascertainment of man's first appearance on earth, as represented by the antiquity of the genus *Homo* or the antiquity of the family *Hominidae*, but rather in the fact that what the anthropologists are asserting in effect is that the power of conceptual thought, possessed by man and not possessed to any degree by non-toolmaking animals, constitutes a clear difference in kind between man and these other animals.

The argument would have the same significance if some other human characteristic, such as propositional speech, were used as toolmaking is here used; namely, as the sign that man possesses the power of conceptual thought, a power totally lacked by animals that do not develop propositional speech to any degree whatsoever. The choice of tools or of fire as the sign of conceptual thought on the part of fossil man merely reflects the fact that these products of human behavior leave fossil remains; speech, at least *oral* speech, leaves none.

(3)

The foregoing summary indicates that the leading contemporary students of human evolution maintain that man really differs in kind from other animals. They themselves epitomize their own position strikingly, in one of two ways. Simpson and Mayr declare themselves against the view that man is "nothing but an animal," by which they mean, I take it, "nothing but a brute." Julian Huxley and Dobzhansky flatly deny that man is "just a superior ape." It will be profitable, I think, to cast an eye on a few capital texts from the writings of these scientists, and then to examine passsages in the writings of others that confirm or concur in these opinions.

In *The Meaning of Evolution*, George Gaylord Simpson, Professor Emeritus of Vertebrate Paleontology at Harvard University, writes:

> To say that man is nothing but an animal is to deny, by implication, that he has essential attributes other than those of all animals. [7]
>
> As applied to man the "nothing but" fallacy [for naming which Simpson gives credit to Huxley] is more thoroughgoing than in application to any other sort of animal, because man is an entirely new kind of animal in ways altogether fundamental for understanding his nature. It is important to realize that man is an animal, but it is even more important to realize that the essence of his unique nature lies precisely in those characteristics that are not shared with any other animal. [8]

Simpson then makes what would at first appear to be the paradoxical statement that man is both "unique in degree" and also "unique in kind." [9] I say "paradoxical" because a strict meaning of the word "unique" entails the possession, by one of two things being compared, of characteristics not possessed at all by the other, neither specifically nor generically, whereas a difference in degree entails that the two things being compared both possess the same trait, one more of it and the other less. Hence, it would seem as if "uniqueness in degree" were a contradiction in terms. Since not only Simpson, but many other scientists also refer to man's uniqueness as, in part at least, a uniqueness in degree, it is important to understand what they mean by this mode of speech.

The meaning is as follows. The statement that only man has

a brain large or complex enough to function linguistically asserts the *unique degree* of man's brain capacity as compared with that in other animals. The statement that only man is a maker of sentences, or that only man is a maker of tools, asserts uniqueness in kind, as contrasted with uniqueness in degree; for it points to something that man does which no other animal does at all—in any degree.

Simpson mentions four things that exist in man to a much higher degree than in other animals (intelligence, flexibility, individualization, and socialization). In each of these respects, Simpson considers man unique in the degree of his capacities or attainments. [10] But though he thinks man is clearly the highest animal in all these respects (highest in degree), he also maintains that "it is still false to conclude that man is nothing but the highest animal." His reason is that there are other respects in which man is unique in kind (e.g., speech, moral sense, cumulative cultural development, self-awareness). [11]

In *Animal Species and Evolution*, Ernst Mayr, Professor of Zoology at Harvard University, expresses similar views. Considering the evidences of man's evolution, he speaks of "the gradual emergence of man's being 'not merely an animal.'" [12] A page earlier he writes: "No more tragic mistake could be made than to consider man 'merely an animal.' Man is unique. . . ." What Mayr means is plainly "unique in kind," for he refers to the distinctive properties of man (i.e., possessed by man alone) that, he says, have been pointed out by "Huxley, Haldane, Simpson, Dobzhansky, and other recent writers." [13] The properties he mentions are such things as speech, toolmaking, cultural traditions, [14] to which he adds one property that is not directly observable, "the ability of abstract thinking." [15]

In *Mankind Evolving* and in *Evolution, Genetics, and Man*, Theodosius Dobzhansky, of Rockefeller University, writes in the same vein.

> Man is not simply a very clever ape. On the contrary, he possesses some faculties that occur in other animals only as rudiments, if at all. [16]
>
> Human intellectual abilities seem to be not only quantitatively but also qualitatively different from those of animals other than men. [17]

Man, in other words, is not just superior in the degree to which he possesses the same abilities (i.e., he is not just unique in degree), but he is also unique in kind because he possesses traits not possessed at all by other animals. As examples of these, Dobzhansky cites man's "symbolic language," [18] man's toolmaking, [19] and man's cumulative transmission of culture. [20]

In three books—*The Uniqueness of Man, Evolution in Action*, and *Evolution, The Modern Synthesis*—Julian Huxley says, again and again, that "man . . . is in many respects unique among animals." [21] That he means unique in kind is plain from such passages as the following:

> The first and most obviously unique characteristic of man is his capacity for conceptual thought; if you prefer objective terms, you will say his employment of true speech, but that is only another way of saying the same thing. . . .
>
> This basic human property has had many consequences. The most important was the development of cumulative tradition. The beginnings of tradition, by which experience is transmitted from one generation to the next, are to be seen in many higher animals. But in no case is the tradition cumulative. . . .
>
> The existence of a cumulative tradition has as its chief consequence—or, if you prefer, its chief objective manifestation—the progressive improvement of human tools and machinery. . . .
>
> Speech, tradition, and tools have led to many other unique properties of man. . . . [22]

In man's mental organization, according to Huxley, the two crucial novelties are speech and the creation of a common pool of organized experience for the group. Though he adds other unique human traits, such as toolmaking and "a sense of right and wrong in the abstract," he regards these two as "man's major uniqueness." [23] That Huxley thinks of man as unique both in degree and also in kind is seen in the following passage: "The last step yet taken in evolutionary progress . . . is the *degree* of intelligence which involves true speech and conceptual thought: and it is found *exclusively* in man." [24] (Italics added.)

Other evolutionists and paleoanthropologists concur, in whole or part, with slightly different emphases. For example, the German zoologist Bernhard Rensch, in *Evolution Above the Species Level*, says that "man has reached a unique evolutionary position in the realm of organisms," which he attributes to man's acquirement of "a fundamentally new evolutionary faculty"—rational speech. [25] Others—Washburn, Oakley, Le Gros Clark, Dart—stress not just speech, but the conjunction in man both of sentence-making and toolmaking; and among these authors, Washburn and Oakley explicitly express the view that these two distinctive properties of man imply his exclusive possession of the power of abstract or conceptual thought. [26]

This last point is confirmed by two observers of the behavior of apes. In *The Year of the Gorilla*, George Schaller not only distinguishes between man's tool*making* and the tool-*using* of gorillas (as do Oakley, Dart, Leakey, and others), but also asserts that the absence of language on the part of gorillas implies the absence of concepts on their part, with the consequences that they make no reference to past or future. [27] The eminent Gestalt psychologist Wolfgang Köhler, in the second edition of *The Mentality of Apes*, makes a similar point about chimpanzees; he associates the narrow limits of time within which they live (largely the immediate present) with their lack of speech. "Besides lack of speech," he writes, "it is in the extremely narrow limits in this direction that the chief difference is to be found between anthropoids and even the most primitive human beings"—and it is this limitation "that prevents the chimpanzee from attaining even the smallest beginnings of cultural development." [28]

(4)

Let me now summarize—from the literature that we are engaged in reviewing—the various things that are said to be distinctive of human behavior and are made the basis for saying that man differs in kind from other animals. *With the one exception of language* (sentence-making behavior), there are minority dissents on all these indications of man's uniqueness in kind—dissents that treat these indications as signifying only superiority or uniqueness in degree.

In the sphere of what is plainly overt and observable behavior:

1. Only man employs a propositional language, only man uses verbal symbols, only man makes sentences; i.e., only man is a discursive animal. [29]
2. Only man makes tools, builds fires, erects shelters, fabricates clothing; i.e., only man is a technological animal. [30]
3. Only man enacts laws or sets up his own rules of behavior and thereby constitutes his social life, organizing his association with his fellows in a variety of different ways; i.e., only man is a political, not just a gregarious, animal. [31]
4. Only man has developed, in the course of generations, a cumulative cultural tradition, the transmission of which constitutes human history; i.e., only man is a historical animal. [32]

In the sphere of interpreted behavior, involving an admixture of inference with observation:

5. Only man engages in magical and ritualistic practices; i.e., only man is a religious animal. [33]
6. Only man has a moral conscience, a sense of right and wrong, and of values; i.e., only man is an ethical animal. [34]
7. Only man decorates or adorns himself or his artifacts, and makes pictures or statues for the non-utilitarian purpose of enjoyment; i.e., only man is an aesthetic animal. [35]

These wholly or partly overt forms of behavior, said by the majority of the scientists in this group to be distinctive of the human species or genus are often interpreted by them as implying the presence in man of psychological processes or abilities that are not present in other animals. Distinguishing between what they call perceptual and conceptual thought, or between generalization on the sensory level and the formation of abstract concepts, they attribute conceptual processes or the ability to form abstract concepts to man and man alone. [36] They ground this attribution—this inference to unobserved processes or abilities—on the fact that propositional speech, toolmaking, and cumulative cultural transmission all involve a transcendence of or emancipation from the immediate environment as that is momentarily present to the senses; and so, in their view, these distinctively human performances must have their basis in psychological processes or abilities that go beyond sense perception and even beyond sensory residues, such as images. [37]

But while such authors as Dobzhansky, Huxley, Mayr, Oakley, Rensch, Carrington, and others, place this psychological interpretation on what they regard as distinctively human performances in the sphere of overt behavior, they also say things that are either inconsistent with this interpretation or qualify it considerably. Thus, for example, Huxley asserts that conceptual thought is to be found only in man, but he also says that the lack of true speech on the part of apes indicates "an inadequate faculty of forming concepts." [38] He goes further in this direction: "Chimpanzees can construct some sort of concepts; but conceptual thought only became efficient and productive with the aid of proper tools, in the shape of verbal symbols." [39]

To say that conceptual thought is found only in man is to assert a difference in kind; but to say that conceptual thought is more developed or more efficient in man than in chimpanzees is to assert a difference in degree. The two assertions cannot both be true. What Huxley may intend, though it is certainly not entirely clear, is that man differs in kind from apes with respect to the use of verbal symbols and propositional speech, and that this difference gives man superiority in degree with respect to concept-formation. We shall return to this point later.

Similarly, while Dobzhansky says that the power of "abstract thinking" on man's part is the source of his use of verbal symbols —his ability to bestow meanings on meaningless sounds or marks [40]—he also says that animals can form non-verbal concepts. [41] Unless Dobzhansky carefully distinguishes between perceptual generalizations and conceptual abstractions (which it is not clear that he does), the two statements would appear to be inconsistent; for one seems to say that only man has verbal symbols because only man has concepts, while the other seems to say that animals have concepts, too, though these are non-verbal.

Again, Oakley, while attributing man's language and tool-making to his "capacity for conceptual thinking, in contrast to the mainly perceptual thinking of apes and other primates," [42] admits, in another place, "the possibility of gradation between these two extremes, perceptual thought in apes, conceptual thought in man." [43] In spite of this, Oakley does insist that we must not underestimate the gap (in *kind* or *degree?*) that separates man's invention and construction of tools for relatively remote future use and the ape's improvisation of tools for immediate employment in the present situation.

Rensch best exemplifies the way in which some of these authors qualify their correlation of human language with abstract thought on man's part. His contention is that man's possession of speech, itself directly the result of his enlarged brain capacity, is in turn the source of all the rest of man's distinctive performances or abilities: his abstract or verbal concepts, his reasoning, his political institutions, his cumulative cultural inheritance, etc. [44] He says that all animals capable of learning have the power of abstraction (without the aid of language), and so he attributes non-verbal concepts, non-verbal judgments, and non-verbal reasoning to animals other than man. [45] What this comes to, in short, is that man differs in kind from other animals, or is unique, only in his possession of language, not in the possession of psychological processes or abilities. With respect to the latter, he differs in degree from other animals, and this difference in degree is, in part at least, a function of his having language. At the opposite extreme from Rensch is Carrington, who makes the power of abstract or conceptual thought man's "unique distinguishing feature"—the source of his distinctive properties, such as language, toolmaking, and cumulative cultural transmission. [46]

In view of the foregoing recitation of dissents, inconsistencies, and qualifications, how can we formulate the minimum clear concurrence of the group of scientists that we have been considering? I think it can be done as follows.

In the first place, it is necessary to separate statements about observable behavior from theoretical interpretations of them, especially those that posit psychological powers or processes of a given sort in order to explain the observed behavior. When we do this, we can say that the leading paleoanthropologists agree without dissent or qualification that only man makes sentences or has the power of propositional speech, that only man makes tools, fire, clothing, etc., that only man makes his own laws of behavior and thereby constitutes his social life, that only man has a cumulative cultural tradition. We shall find dissent from all but one of these statements, both by comparative psychologists and by ethologists, and will consider such dissent in the chapter to follow. The *one exception* is the statement that only man makes sentences and has the power of propositional speech. Yet if that one statement alone is agreed upon by all as unimpeachable fact, at least as far as evidence at present available goes, that by itself would suffice to warrant the assertion that man differs in kind from other animals and that this difference is real, not apparent; for between the ability to make sentences and the lack of that ability, no intermediates are possible.

In the second place, when they come to interpreting the fact that man and man alone has a propositional language, some, like Rensch at one extreme, make man's brain capacity the direct source of his linguistic ability, and his possession of language, in turn, the source of his verbal or abstract concepts; whereas some, like Carrington at the other extreme, make man's brain capacity the direct source of his power of abstract or conceptual thought and that, in turn, the source of his having a propositional language. Most of the others are indecisive on this question of causal sequence. But they tend to agree that man's possession of speech and whatever psychological powers are associated with it, either as cause or as effect, give rise to all his other distinctive achievements—his technological productions, his cumulative transmission of culture, his legally constituted forms of social organization, etc.

In the third place, while the paleoanthropologists are not clear on whether man's exclusive possession of propositional speech implies that man alone has the power of conceptual thought and the use of abstract symbols (as we have seen, they often take back in one place what they have asserted without qualification in another), they do appear to be clear on a matter that relates to the question whether man's difference in kind is superficial or radical. They never, of course, raise this question explicitly, for they do not seem to be aware of the distinction between a radical and a superficial difference in kind. Nevertheless, we can easily determine how they would answer the question if it were raised for them and if they understood it. They are almost unanimous in attributing man's difference in kind to the much greater magnitude of man's brain, as compared with the brains of living chimpanzees, gorillas, and orangutans; in their view, the same comparison holds for the brainpans of the fossil species that they classify as *Hominidae* or as *Pongidae*. They regard the phylogenetic series as involving a continuum of degrees of brain magnitudes and complexity, with a critical threshold above which the unique behavioral characteristics of man first make their appearance. [47] Hence, if asked the question, they would certainly say that man's difference in kind is only superficial, not radical.

(5)

Neither the position taken by Darwin (that men and other animals differ only in degree) nor the position taken by post-Darwinian paleoanthropologists (that man differs superficially in kind from other animals) is established by the evidence to which their proponents respectively point. The position taken in each case is taken in order to be consistent with the general theory of evolution and the particular theory of speciation held by the proponents of the position. In Darwin's theory of speciation, species differences are at most only apparent differences in kind, resulting from the absence of intermediate forms. In contemporary theories of speciation, the same holds for most species differences, but there may be some that are real differences in kind, i.e., those resulting from polyploidy or from quantum jumps or what is called "saltatory speciation." Having admitted real differences in kind, the post-Darwinian evolutionists, in order to be consistent with phylogenetic or developmental continuity in the origin of all species, must then regard these differences in kind as merely superficial, to be accounted for by a critical threshold in an underlying continuum of degrees of organic complexity.

The only position that is inconsistent with, and therefore excluded by, the theory of evolution (and with it, the principle of phylogenetic continuity) is the position that man differs radically in kind from other animals. But inconsistency with the theory of evolution does not eliminate that position as false, any more than consistency with the theory of evolution establishes as true the alternative positions—that man differs only in degree or at most only superficially in kind. The truth of evolutionary theory in general, even if it were as firmly established as it could be by research, may or may not apply to the origin of man. To assume that it does apply, and then to use that assumption as a basis for saying that man's observed difference in kind from other animals is either only an apparent or at most a real but superficial difference in kind, is to beg the question.

To avoid begging the question, we must resolutely follow Darwin's line of reasoning even if he did not always follow it himself. We must proceed from the comparative evidences of human and animal behavior to a conclusion concerning how man differs from other animals; and from that conclusion to the support or rejection of the evolutionary hypothesis as applied to the origin of man—*support*, if our conclusion is that man differs only in degree or at most only superficially in kind; *rejection*, if our conclusion is that man differs radically in kind from other animals.

Let me digress for a moment to comment briefly on the logic of confirming and infirming scientific principles. The evolutionary principle of phylogenetic continuity and the more general scientific principle of the continuity of nature are regarded by scientists as amply confirmed by empirical data of all sorts, and as not yet infirmed or falsified by a single piece of decisively negative evidence. In this appraisal of the situation, the scientists are correct, at least so far, but this should not lead anyone acquainted with the logic of empirical confirmation of general principles to conclude that the special and the more general principle of continuity are established beyond the shadow of a doubt as certain and incorrigible truths. That is not the case. Furthermore, until the last shred of relevant evidence is in, such principles as these are subject to the infirmative force of evidence having a contrary tenor and they are open to being falsified by decisively negative evidence.

If the principle of phylogenetic continuity were established as finally true, instead of merely having its relative truth highly confirmed by all the evidence so far amassed, the truth of that principle would eliminate as false the proposition that man differs radically in kind from other animals; for radical difference in kind is incompatible with phylogenetic continuity. Whatever evidence tends to show that man differs in degree or only superficially in kind tends to confirm the truth of the principle of phylogenetic continuity. But, by the same token, whatever evidence tends to show that man differs radically in kind from other animals is infirmative in its effect and may even, if it becomes decisive, render the principle of phylogenetic continuity inapplicable to man while leaving it applicable to the rest of living things.

(6)

The paleoanthropologists do not have in all their fossil skeletons and artifacts the kind of evidence that is needed to decide whether the manifest difference in kind (which they assert) between man and other animals is only superficial or is radical. The series of brain weights for the various fossil specimens, inferred from the size of their brainpans, is by itself not decisive; for it is necessary to discover whether in that series there is a critical threshold functionally related to the absence and presence of such observed behavioral characteristics as propositional speech, toolmaking, cumulative cultural transmission, rule-making, and variable forms of association, etc.

The inadequacy of the paleontological evidence is not relative to the present stage of research, to be remedied by further fossil finds. Nor is its inadequacy a matter of the tenuous interpretations and inferences that the paleoanthropologists are forced to make from the kind of data they handle. Its inadequacy is absolute and irremediable for the simple reason that no amount of fossil data, no matter how carefully and soundly interpreted, can establish the existence of a critical threshold in the continuum of degrees of brain size and complexity. Without that being shown, it is impossible to tell whether a difference in kind that certainly looks like a real difference in kind, and is thought to be so by the paleoanthropologists, is superficial rather than radical.

How, then, can this matter be settled? *In the first place*, only by behavioral comparisons made with respect to living species—comparisons of human behavior with the behavior of other animals—whether based on laboratory data obtained by experimental psychologists or on data gathered by ethologists working in the field with animals in their natural habitats. The latter type of evidence has been greatly improved in precision and objectivity since the time of the naturalists on whose accounts, too often in the form of anecdotes about animal behavior, Darwin had to rely because he had no other evidence to go on.

Nevertheless, Darwin's procedure—that of comparing the behavior of men and of other animals—is the only sound procedure, and it must still be employed today even though we now have fossil remains lacking to Darwin. The fossil evidences are at best data from which we can infer the behavior of species not now living; and it is in terms of the inferred behavior that we classify the fossil species as human or non-human.

In the second place, if comparative behavioral data do establish an observed or manifest difference in kind, then in order to determine whether that difference in kind is superficial or radical, we need other types of evidence. Behavioral comparisons by themselves cannot make this determination. We need evidence in support of one or another psychological interpretation of the observed behavioral differences. We need neurological evidence, especially data gained from the comparative study of the neurological correlates of behavior. In addition, as we shall see, we may need evidence of the sort that can only be obtained by computer technology and by experiments with artificial intelligence, i.e., with machines devised to simulate human behavior.

CHAPTER 7

The Laboratory Findings and Their Interpretation

(1)

THE disagreement that we noted in the preceding chapter, between Darwin and the post-Darwinian evolutionists, especially such leading paleoanthropologists as Julian Huxley, Dobzhansky, Simpson, Mayr, Oakley, von Koenigswald, Washburn, and Leakey we shall find repeated here. The position taken by Darwin, that man differs only in degree from other animals, is here taken, with one exception to be noted, by the experimental comparative psychologists, but on the basis of a quite different type of evidence than that available to Darwin. There was no laboratory study of human or animal behavior in his day. For his knowledge of animal behavior, Darwin relied mainly on reports from naturalists in the field; and for conceptions of the human mind and its abilities, he had to turn to the pre-experimental literature of psychology. It is, therefore, quite striking that the experimentalists whose work we shall consider in this chapter should align themselves with Darwin by interpreting their laboratory data as definitely showing, or at least tending to show, that man has no behavioral traits or abilities that animals do not also have to some degree.

In confining our attention in this chapter to the experimentalists who are for the most part American scientists, I have not overlooked the contributions made by the leading European ethologists, such as N. Tinbergen of Oxford, Konrad Lorenz of the Max Planck Institut of Munich, and W. H. Thorpe of Cambridge. As Tinbergen points out in his introduction to *The Study of Instinct*, the American behaviorists have concentrated their attention on all forms of learned behavior. "The result," he writes, "has been a certain neglect of innate behavior, which has led in some instances to entirely unwarranted generalizations." [1] I will in subsequent chapters deal with the distinction between innate and acquired behavior, particularly insofar as it has a critical bearing on the question of man's difference. For the present, let it suffice to say that Tinbergen's position on that question is unclear, that Lorenz quite clearly regards man's difference as one of kind, and that Thorpe tends to agree with the American behaviorists who maintain that man differs only in degree, though when we examine his views on the subject more closely we shall find—surprisingly, in view of Tinbergen's comment—that he could not have reached this conclusion if he had taken due account of the distinction between innate and acquired behavior. [2]

We observed in the preceding chapter that the disagreement between Darwin and the leading paleoanthropologists today arises, in part at least, from the kind of evidence being examined and the problem to be solved, which affects the way the evidence is interpreted. The same observation holds for the disagreement between the paleoanthropologists and the comparative psychologists. The paleoanthropologists, comparing both living and fossil species, pay almost exclusive attention to human products, the products of technology and culture, as differentiating man from other animals; they infer distinctive human powers from the distinctive works of man. The comparative psychologists, making laboratory studies of human and animal behavior, pay almost exclusive attention to the processes of learning, problem-solving, perception, memory, and generalization that can be studied objectively and experimentally by observing the behavior of men and animals under controlled laboratory conditions.

Not only are the data being examined by the two groups of scientists quite different, but so also are the problems that each is trying to solve. The paleoanthropologists, as we have seen, focus their attention on the problem of placing and dating the advent of man on earth; they must, therefore, attempt to draw the line that separates human from non-human fossil remains, and so they interpret their data accordingly. The comparative psychologists, like Darwin, by whom they are greatly influenced, think—wrongly, as we shall see—that they have to establish the similarity of human and animal behavior in order to uphold the evolutionary kinship of men with other animals; with that controlling aim they, too, interpret their data accordingly.

Having summarized the position of the paleoanthropologists in the preceding chapter by reviewing the evidence to which they appeal and their interpretation of it, I will now do the same for the comparative psychologists. This should put us in a better position to assess their disagreement and to come, finally, to a critical examination of the one point on which there is universal agreement; namely, that man and man alone has true language—propositional or syntactical speech. It is with respect to this one agreed-upon, observed fact that sharply diverging interpretations lead some scientists to assert, in spite of it, that men differ only in degree, while others maintain, because of it, that men really differ in kind.

(2)

The comparative study of human and animal behavior owes its rise and development to the influence of the theory of evolution and especially to Darwin's *Descent of Man*. That book, as Professor Ernest R. Hilgard of Stanford University points out, is itself "essentially a comparative psychology." [3] In the decades following *The Descent of Man*, two opposite tendencies manifested themselves. The writings of G. J. Romanes (*Animal Intelligence*, 1882; *Mental Evolution in Animals*, 1883; and *Mental Evolution in Man*, 1888) followed Darwin in arguing for the continuity of animal and human intelligence along a scale of degrees, but tended to exaggerate the powers of animals by collecting anecdotes about their remarkable performances. The work of Lloyd Morgan (*Introduction to Comparative Psychology*, 1894, and *Animal Behavior*, 1900), based on empirical investigations rather than on anecdotes, tended in the opposite direction. Where Romanes, in trying to close the gap between men and animals, raised animals up almost to the human level, Lloyd Morgan lowered man almost to the animal level. In doing so, Morgan applied the basic methodological principle that he had laid down for theorizing about the observed data. "In no case," he declared, "may we interpret an action as the outcome of the exercise of a higher psychical faculty, if it can be interpreted as the outcome of the exercise of one which stands lower in the psychological scale." [4]

Morgan's principles, methods, and conclusions greatly influenced the next generation of American investigators, notably Edward L. Thorndike (*Animal Intelligence*, 1898), and John B. Watson (*Behavior, An Introduction to Comparative Psychology*, 1914, and *Psychology from the Standpoint of a Behaviorist*, 1919). Animal experimentation was begun at Harvard at the beginning of the century by Thorndike and Yerkes; and animal laboratories quickly multiplied in other institutions. The names of Hobhouse, Small, Jennings, and Hunter should also be mentioned among the early experimentalists in the field of animal behavior. [5] Nevertheless, most of the critical work in this field has been done in the last forty years, and the best of it—work done with painstaking laboratory controls—has been done in the last twenty, by investigators too numerous to name. I will, in what follows, name only the scientists whose books are the sources of my summary of the findings and conclusions in this field of research.

If we go to the authors who, in recent years, not only have reviewed the vast literature of comparative psychology, both books and periodical articles, but who have also tried to assess or interpret the findings and formulate the conclusions that can be drawn from the experimental data, we cannot help noting three assumptions that are widely shared.

One is the assumption of materialism, not as a metaphysical truth, but as a working hypothesis—a procedural decision to avoid theories that employ references to mind or mental processes as something distinct from neurological processes and from observable or inferable elements of bodily behavior. Thus, for example, Donald Hebb, Professor of Psychology at McGill University, writes:

> Mind and mental refer to processes inside the head that determine the higher levels of organization in behavior. . . . In this book, we shall assume that mind is an activity of the brain, and that our knowledge of it is chiefly theoretical,

inferred from behavior rather than obtained directly from self-observation (i.e., from introspection).

He goes on to say that one theory of mind is animistic, the view that "the body is inhabited by an entity . . . having nothing in common with bodily processes." The other theory is physiological or mechanistic. "It assumes that mind is a bodily process. . . . Modern psychology works with this latter theory only." To which Hebb adds: "There is certainly no decisive means available of proving one [theory] to be right, the other wrong." [6]

Similarly, Professor Charles E. Osgood of the University of Illinois tells us that psychologists must follow J. B. Watson in eliminating mentalistic constructs—such as thoughts, ideas, images—from psychological science; or, if we admit them, we must at least deny that "they partake of something other than the material world. Otherwise we should be unable to investigate them at all with scientific methods." [7] Again it is clear that the materialistic assumption is made for methodological reasons. This is further confirmed by a remark of T. C. Schneirla, Curator of Animal Behavior at the Museum of Natural History in New York. He points out that attempts to conceive such processes as thinking, reasoning, conceiving, anticipating, etc. as "constituting a single non-corporeal agency, distinct at all times from 'body,' have failed dismally as a basis for prediction in science." [8]

A second assumption that follows closely on the first is also clearly procedural. It stipulates that scientific method in the comparative study of human and animal behavior must treat human and animal subjects in the same way and under the same kind of laboratory conditions. In both cases, the data of research must be objective, i.e., observable items of behavior, including the treatment of protocol statements made by human subjects as observable units of behavior.

The third assumption is the principle of continuity. This lies at the foundation of comparative psychology—its legacy from the theory of evolution, in the context of which comparative psychology arose and developed. Implicit everywhere in contemporary psychology and behavioral science, it is sometimes explicitly stated as a controlling or regulative principle of psychological investigation and interpretation.

In an essay on "The Evolution of Learning," Professor Harry

F. Harlow of the University of Wisconsin writes: "If we are to explain learning in terms of evolutionary theory, there should be continuity from the simplest to the most complex forms of learning. The appearance of a radically new kind of learning at any evolutionary point or period, including that during which man developed, is not in keeping with modern gene theory. . . ." Harlow then criticizes Dobzhansky for saying that "man is not simply a very clever ape, but a possessor of mental abilities which occur in other animals only in most rudimentary forms, if at all." [9]

A less careful writer, C. Judson Herrick, formerly Professor of Neurology at the University of Chicago, declares the continuity of nature to be an established fact, though he also immediately concedes that that is not quite so. He first tells us that "the continuity of the series of changes in both overt action and internal structure as we pass from the inorganic through the ranks of the animal kingdom up to and including mankind may be regarded as established." Then, in the very next sentence, he admits that it is not yet established: "The apparent interruptions of this continuity are successively closed as our knowledge of the facts is enlarged." [10] Schneirla more frankly admits that "a scientifically developed evolutionary conception of man as a higher animal" must, in line with the principle of continuity, regard man as merely superior in degree, never as different in kind. [11]

In general, it can be said that the comparative psychologists and behavioral scientists acknowledge that the complete and unbroken continuity of nature is not yet fully established. They admit that the supporting evidence is still far from complete, but they also believe that all the evidence so far amassed is confirmative: no experimental findings, they claim, tend to invalidate this assumption, or even to cast doubt upon it. They therefore feel that they are justified in using it as a working assumption in carrying out further experimental work in the comparative study of human and animal behavior.

(3)

Let me now attempt a brief summary of the state of scientific opinion in this field of research. On each point on which there is clearly a majority or a prevailing opinion, I will indicate the dissents that exist and have a bearing on the question of man's difference.

With one exception to be noted, the prevailing opinion among comparative psychologists is that man differs from other animals only in degree, and that his marked superiority in certain respects —his uniqueness in degree in these respects—can be accounted for without positing any psychological factors or processes that would make him unique in kind. This position is taken by such representative authors as Harlow, Hebb, Osgood, Nissen, Schneirla, Maier, Heron, Scott, Leeper. [12]

The reversal in position of C. Judson Herrick is worth noting. When, in 1926, he wrote *The Brains of Rats and Men*, Herrick declared that "symbolic thinking is a new kind of function," that first appears in man. With regard to the forms of behavior to which this gives rise, he further maintained that "we have not the slightest evidence that these . . . are possessed in any degree by any of the lower mammals." [13] Thirty years later, writing *The Evolution of Human Nature*, he takes account of the more recent experimental work done by Harlow, Maier, Yerkes, Hebb, Schneirla, and others, and in consequence he reverses himself. In his recent book, Herrick adopts the now prevailing view that symbolic functions, conceptual learning, abstraction, reasoning, and insight are all found in animals. The fact that man uses verbal symbols and animals employ non-verbal symbols in learning and thinking may account for man's superiority in degree, but it does not establish a difference in kind. He explicitly rejects "the claim that 'man uses symbols; no other creature does' and that 'there are no intermediate stages' " between the lower animals and man in symbolic function. Such claims, he says, are "obviously contrary to fact." [14]

The one clear exception to the prevailing view that I have been able to find is a paper on "The Evolution of Intelligence" by Professor M. E. Bitterman of Bryn Mawr, an experimental comparative psychologist. [15] He observes the fact that from the early experimental work of Thorndike on, "learning was thought to involve qualitatively similar processes throughout the evolutionary hierarchy," [16] and it was generally supposed that "differences from species to species are only differences of degree." [17] He claims that experimental work done in his laboratory on habit reversal and probability learning suggest that "as we ascend the evolutionary scale we do not find a pattern of intellectual continuity but one of discontinuity"—differences in kind, not just degree. [18] That Bitterman regards these differences in kind as superficial, not radical, is indicated by his statement that the "brain structures evolved by higher animals do not serve merely to replicate old functions and modes of intellectual adjustment, but to mediate new ones." [19]

This one exception hardly changes the picture, but it does raise an interesting question. Bitterman, like most of the paleoanthropologists and students of human evolution that we have examined, sees no conflict between the general evolutionary principle of phylogenetic continuity and the recognition of differences in kind, as long as these are merely superficial (i.e., based on differences in degree of complexity in the central nervous system). Why, then, do the rest of the comparative psychologists appear to think that the principle of phylogenetic continuity must exclude all differences in kind and require the showing—by experimental data—that there are only differences of degree in the scale of behavior from the lower orders through the higher and up to man?

One answer could be that they mistakenly identify all differences in kind with radical difference in kind. The latter does violate the principle of continuity. Failing to recognize superficial differences in kind as an alternative to differences in degree, they insist that all differences must be differences in degree. A more likely answer, however, is that their experimental work and their theoretical interpretations of it are dominated by Lloyd Morgan's canon—the methodological rule which says that we should not interpret an action as the outcome of a higher psychical faculty if it can be interpreted as the outcome of a lower one. The consequences of adopting this rule are manifest in the conclusions about which there is a general agreement among comparative psychologists.

There is general agreement that the same psychological factors or processes are present—in varying degrees—on all levels of animal behavior, including the behavior of the human animal. Experimental findings are said to show that at different levels in the scale of animal behavior there are only differences in degree with respect to: (1) the capacity for delayed response; (2) the capacity for mental set, i.e., preparation for response prior to overt behavior; (3) the capacity for solving detour problems; (4) the capacity for solving problems by trial and error; (5) the capacity for being guided by cues; (6) the capacity for solving problems by insight; (7) the capacity for reasoning, i.e., for combining different parts of past experience; (8) the capacity for discrimination, generalization, abstraction, and concept-formation. [20]

Harlow, in "The Evolution of Learning," summarizes these results by saying that all the phenomena of learning and thinking (without any sharp distinction between learning and thinking), from habituation in the lower animals to abstract thought in the higher, can be ordered in a single system in which all differences can be explained in quantitative terms (i.e., as differences in degree). [21] He states his conclusion as follows:

> The existing scientific data indicate a great degree of intellectual communality among the primates, and probably a greater communality among all animals, than has been commonly recognized. There is no scientific evidence of a break in learning capabilities between primate and nonprimate forms. [22]

In addition, Harlow and his students have done experimental work on monkeys which, in their judgment, shows that learning —or problem-solving—for its own sake is not an exclusively human trait. [23]

Though there are conflicting data and conflicting interpretations of the data derived from experimental work on animal problem-solving by trial and error and by insight, on animal discrimination, generalization, and abstraction, and on animal reasoning, there is no difference of opinion among the leading scientists in this field that the psychological factors and processes involved in animal behavior are identical with the psychological factors and processes operative in human behavior. Stated negatively, the prevalent opinion is that *no new* psychological factors or processes are to be found in human behavior; and that *no additional* factors or processes need be posited to explain human behavior.

This last point is emphasized by the widely shared opinion that non-verbal symbols and concepts function in animal behavior as verbal symbols and concepts function in human behavior. Abstraction, generalization, and concept-formation are not exclusively human abilities; nor is the use of symbols, if we distinguish between verbal and non-verbal symbols. [24]

Two statements by H. W. Nissen epitomize the point being made.

> A major dimension of difference among animals is the sheer number of percepts and concepts available to the organism. . . . Incidentally, just where perceptions leave off and concepts begin is impossible to say; these terms represent quantitative differences on a continuum, to the extremes of which we apply different names. [25]
>
> In all attempts to characterize the uniqueness of human intelligence, the factor of language, propositional language, is emphasized. . . . Language, or verbal mediating responses, represent an instance of extremely efficient central integration. . . . But language does not seem to introduce any really new psychological process. [26]

To which should be added the following statement by Hebb:

> Animal studies have already shown us that thinking need not depend on language (since animals do not have language but do have fairly complex mediating processes). Human studies allow us to go further; not only do important steps of thought occur without language, they cannot be put into language after they have occurred. [27]

Finally, we must note that the most important theoretical development in recent years has been the rejection of the oversimplified stimulus-response mechanisms employed by Thorndike, Hunter, Watson, and other early behaviorists to explain animal behavior. [28] It is necessary, in the opinion of the leading theorists today, to complicate the explanatory schema by introducing what are called "mediating factors" or "mediating processes" between stimulus and response. These mediating factors or processes represent the functioning of the central nervous system as something more than a pathway of connections between the sensory receptors on the stimulus side and the motor effectors on the response side. The difference in degree between human and animal behavior—in learning, problem-solving, thinking, concept-formation, the use of symbols, etc.—is to be explained by the presence in man of more numerous and more complicated mediating factors or processes. Thus, for example, Hebb explains man's unique possession of propositional language and its verbal symbols by "man's capacity for having several sets of mediating processes at once, relatively independent of each other." [29]

I have omitted from the foregoing summary the agreement of the experimental psychologists among themselves as well as with the paleoanthropologists and other scientists—the agreement that man and man alone uses verbal symbols and has a propositional language. It is always risky to use the word "unanimous" in reporting the state of opinion in any field of research. Nevertheless, in this case I would like to use the word as short for the statement that I have found concurrence on this one point throughout the scientific literature that I have examined. The only exception I have found turns out, on closer examination, not to stand up. I will deal with this solitary exception in the next chapter and there show why it does not require the retraction of the word "unanimous."

Even those scientists who think that there is rudimentary toolmaking in other primates (or that there is a shadowy line between tool-using and tool-improvising, on the one hand, and toolmaking, on the other) concede that sentence-making is confined to man. The same can be said for those scientists who think that a shadowy line also divides cumulative from noncumulative cultural transmission; or who think that the difference between human and non-human forms of association is one of degree rather than of kind. Of the seven distinctively human performances mentioned in the preceding chapter (see p. 91) as constituting manifest differences in kind between human and animal behavior, all except the first have been doubted, challenged, or explicitly dissented from. The one exception is the observed fact that man and man alone is a maker of sentences.

This fact may be explained in various ways, but no matter how it is explained it cannot be explained away. Any observed performance that belongs exclusively to one species of animal and to no others constitutes a manifest difference in kind. If no intermediates are possible between the presence and absence of that performance, as is the case with sentence-making, the manifest difference in kind is real, not just apparent—not a masking of what is really a difference in degree. But whether that real difference in kind is radical or only superficial depends on how it is explained by reference to underlying processes or factors, psychological or neurological. It is only this last point that is affected by the way in which we explain the observed difference between men and other animals with respect to the possession of a propositional language.

The problem of interpreting the uniqueness of human language is of such critical importance to the question of how man differs that I shall devote the next three chapters to it, in the first of which I will try to explain why the experimental psychologists, while conceding the fact that man and man alone has a propositional language, persist in clinging to a view that is patently inconsistent with that fact; namely, that men and other animals differ only in degree. But before I turn to these matters, I would like to conclude the present chapter with one comment on the findings and theories in the field of comparative psychology that have here been reviewed. Do they, apart from the fact that only man has propositional language, establish the proposition that human and animal behavior differ only in degree? Do they tend to confirm the assumption of a complete and unbroken continuity in nature?

My answer to both questions is negative. The methodological postulates that govern both the experimental research and the theoretical interpretation of the data could lead to no other results than those obtained. Lloyd Morgan's canon has been interpreted by the researchers as an injunction to find only differences in degree and as an admonition always to employ exactly the same theoretical constructs in explaining the observed facts of both human and animal behavior. (I will attempt to show in Chapter 9 that this is a grievous misinterpretation of Lloyd Morgan's rule which, correctly understood, will be seen as a special application of the principle of parsimony in explaining observed facts. Occam's razor is double-edged and cuts two ways, not one.)

In addition to misinterpreting Morgan's rule, the researchers operated under the restrictive postulates of metaphysical, not just methodological, behaviorism, and were constrained by the general framework of their evolutionary views to look for evidences of the kinship between men and animals. One could, therefore, have predicted in advance that scientists, operating under these conditions, would find data in support of differences in degree; or that whatever data they did find would be interpreted by them as betokening differences in degree and as being consistent with the principle of phylogenetic continuity. Hence, the results can hardly be taken as confirming the continuity of nature or as providing us with a decisive scientific solution of the question of how man differs from other animals.

CHAPTER 8

The Pivotal Fact: Human Speech

(1)

LET ME repeat: among scientists who consider the matter, there is unanimous agreement that man and man alone uses verbal symbols and has a propositional language and syntactically structured speech. Included here are not only the biologists and paleoanthropologists who are concerned with the evolution of man, but also comparative psychologists, ethologists, and behavioral scientists generally (sociologists, cultural anthropologists); and, in addition, experimental neurologists.

We must not let our concentration on the state of scientific opinion lead us to forget that common experience also provides evidence of this fact, evidence so clear that common-sense opinion, without awaiting confirmation by the special data of investigative science, has long held speech to be probably the most distinctive mark of man. And if we remember the etymology of the words "logical" and "rational," and observe that both of these words have a linguistic as well as an ideational connotation, we will recognize that the philosophers who, on the basis of common experience alone, regarded man as the only logical or rational animal were, in effect, saying no more than that man is the only talking, the only naming, declaring or questioning, affirming or denying, the only arguing, agreeing or disagreeing, the only discursive, animal.

These are all matters of common observation. We are here merely describing human behavior, not explaining it by reference to unobserved psychological or neurological factors or processes. When we come to explanation, we shall see that disagreements cut every which way; they set philosophers against scientists as well as philosophers against philosophers and scientists against scientists. Leaving aside for the moment the problem of explaining the observed fact of difference, I want to comment on the remark made above that scientific investigation so far has done nothing more than confirm what common-sense opinion has long known in the light of common experience. This should not be interpreted to mean that scientific efforts in this field are supererogatory. On the contrary: since the matter under consideration is one that is capable of investigation, it should be investigated. We should never rest content with common experience about matters where investigation can add special experience that may be either confirmative or infirmative.

The fact that up to this date the scientific study of animal communication has not turned up infirmative evidence by discovering sentence-making animals by no means precludes the possibility that science in the future, perhaps even the very near future, may do so. At least we must face with a completely open mind work now going on with the bottle-nosed dolphin, and also with chimpanzees and dogs—work that may show either that other mammals have a propositional language of their own or that they are capable of learning and using ours. On the other hand, having an open mind about future possibilities should not be equated, as unfortunately it sometimes is, with having an undecided mind about present actualities; for we are obliged, at any time, to judge in the light of the evidence that is then available. At this moment, there are no scientific data infirmative of the proposition that only man has a propositional language.

(2)

What in detail is the substance of the prevailing agreement on this proposition? As I see it, it involves five points, which I will now enumerate and comment on where comment may be necessary or illuminating.

(1) It is agreed that, while other animals communicate and employ expressive cries or gestures, some of which function as signals that convey desires or demands, and in addition respond to signals that are behavioral cues, they do not use symbols that are parts of speech (i.e., which function as nouns, verbs, adjectives, adverbs or as their morphological equivalents) and that can be combined syntactically in a wide variety of ways to form declarative and interrogative sentences.

At the beginning of Western thought, Aristotle wrote:

> Man is the only animal whom [nature] has endowed with the gift of speech. And whereas mere voice is but an indication of pleasure and pain, and is therefore found in other animals (for their nature attains to the perception of pleasure and pain and the intimation of them to one another and no further), the power of speech is intended to set forth the expedient and the inexpedient, and therefore likewise the just and the unjust. [1]

The context being a treatise on politics, Aristotle here chose human declarations of the sort that have political significance. If we turn to his treatise on logic, we will find him there dealing more generally with every type of utterance that can be true or false; i.e., declarative sentences, distinguishing these from supplications, injunctions, or requests. [2] The outcries of animals or their signals resemble utterances of the latter sort, not the former. In short, animals never "say" anything that is either true or false. With less precision, Julian Huxley observes that "true speech involves the use of verbal signs for objects, not merely for feelings. Plenty of animals can express the fact that they are hungry, but none except man can ask for an egg or a banana." [3]

(2) It is agreed that, while the so-called "dance-language of the honey bees" definitely does give the appearance of involving declarative statements—utterances that may turn out to be true or false—this fascinating process of communication on the part of these insects is a purely instinctive performance on their part and does not represent, *even in the slightest degree*, the same kind of highly variable, acquired or learned, and deliberately or in-

tentionally exercised linguistic performance that is to be found in human speech. [4]

Apart from the dance language of the bees, no form of animal communication, instinctive or learned, appears to involve declarative statements. In all other cases, animal communication takes the form either of expressive outcries and gestures, or of making and responding to signals; there is no naming or stating. And by far the greater part of animal communication—outside of laboratories and apart from human tutelage—is instinctive rather than learned. Konrad Lorenz stresses this point.

> Animals do not possess a language in the true sense of the word. In the higher vertebrates, as also in the insects, particularly in the socially living species of both great groups, every individual has a certain number of innate movements and sounds for expressing feelings. It has also innate ways of reacting to these signals whenever it sees or hears them in a fellow-member of the species. The highly social species of birds such as the jackdaw or the greylag goose, have a complicated code of such signals which are uttered and understood by every bird without any previous experience. The perfect coordination of social behavior which is brought about by these actions conveys to the human observer the impression that the birds are talking and understanding a language of their own. Of course, this purely innate signal code of an animal species differs fundamentally from human language, every word of which must be learned laboriously by the human child. Moreover, being a genetically fixed character of the species—just as much as any bodily character—this so-called language is, for every individual animal species, ubiquitous in its distribution. [5]

Lest there be any quibbling about the words "innate" and "instinct," concerning the meaning of which American behavioristic psychologists do not see eye to eye with such European ethologists as Tinbergen, Thorpe, or Lorenz, let us adopt as the minimum meaning that can be agreed to by all parties, the formula proposed by Donald Hebb: namely, that a pattern of behavior can be called innate or instinctive insofar and only insofar as it is "species-predictable," which is to say, in Lorenz' words, "ubiquitous in its distribution" among *all* members of the species *without exception.* [6] One or a few negative instances that cannot be accounted for by observed pathological factors would constitute infirmative evidence that the behavior was not innate or instinctive. By this strict criterion, it is extremely doubtful that, apart from a few simple reflexes and emotions or desires, there is any human behavior that can properly be called instinctive. Negative instances abound with respect to every pattern of human behavior that appears to be widely manifested by members of the species, though this statement may not hold for the so-called "instinctual drives" that have been attributed to man in common with other animals in the vertebrate group.

I will return to this point later, especially to consider its significance for the difference it makes that man differs in kind from other vertebrates with which he may also share certain common instinctual motivations that certainly would have an effect on his behavior. For the present, I will only reiterate what everyone knows—that no human form of utterance is species-predictable or ubiquitous. By the commonly accepted meaning of the term, human language is not instinctive, nor are any of the other performances that the paleoanthropologists cite as distinctive of man—the making of tools, the building of shelters, or the fabrication of clothing; the organization of social groups and the formulation of rules of social behavior; the decoration of objects or the making of pictures or statues for an aesthetic rather than an exclusively utilitarian purpose. None of these human performances is species-predictable as a definite pattern of behavior or as always productive of a result that is uniformly the same or ubiquitous throughout the species.

It is for this reason that the bower-birds of Australia do not constitute an exception to the statement that only man is an aesthetic animal that produces a wide variety of works of art for the pleasure that beholding them affords him. Of the bower-birds of Australia, Professor Thorpe tells us that some species "paint the walls of the bower with fruit pulp, with charcoal or with dried grass; and at least one [species] manufactures a painting tool out of a small wad of spongy bark." [7] The word "manufactures" is, of course, misused in the foregoing description. Quite apart from that, if, as appears to be the case, the "interior decoration" of the bower-birds, like the "operatic warbling" of other species of birds, is species-predictable and instinctive, then the activities in question, though they may look like interior decoration or like the making of music, are not at all comparable to the human performances they resemble, any more than the instinctive dance-language of the honey bees is comparable to human speech. [8]

The critical principle here is of such great importance that it needs to be stated explicitly and with precision. Failing to abide by its stricture leads to all sorts of errors about the similarity or difference between men and other animals, not only errors made by naive human beings who have a fondness for animals and wish to glorify them by romanticizing about their anthropomorphic qualities, but also mistakes made by scientists whose training should make them more critical and who, therefore, should know better than to compare instinctive with learned behavior. The principle, stated in a way that most directly bears on the difference of man, is as follows: *With respect to any statement about some performance that man and man alone exhibits—and which some men may, in fact, engage in and others not—an apparently similar performance by another species of animal does not constitute an infirmative negative instance if the latter is instinctive or species-predictable, while the human performance is acquired or learned and voluntarily or intentionally exercised, as evidenced by its nonubiquitous distribution and by its wide range of variability within the human species.*

The foregoing discussion of the incomparability of instinctive and non-instinctive behavior, as bearing on the question of how man differs from other animals, has immediate relevance to the pivotal fact of human language, concerning which I have said that there is unanimous agreement on the part of scientists. I explained that by "unanimous" I simply meant that I could find no dissenting voice in the literature, and added that the one exception I could find did not, on close examination, stand up. That one exception is Professor Thorpe. For example, and this is only one of many instances of the same error on his part, he tells us that it "used to be argued that animal language is emotive only, whilst human language is supposed to be emotive *and* propositional." This distinction, which would, of course, constitute a difference in kind, Professor Thorpe then goes on to say, "has been abolished by the dance-language of the honey-bee. The dances are truly propositional in that they transmit precise information about the direction and distance of a food source. . . . So this distinction falls to the ground." [9]

It does not fall to the ground at all, in view of the wholly instinctive character of the honey-bee performance: it is not the distinction, but Professor Thorpe's comment about it, that fails to stand up. Nor will his concluding comment on the subject pass muster. He writes:

> Perhaps the most reasonable assumption at present is that however great the gulf which divides animal communication systems from human language, there is no single characteristic which can be used as an infallible criterion for distinguishing between birds and men in this respect. Human speech is unique only in the way in which it combines and extends attributes which, in themselves, are not peculiar to man, but are found also in other groups of animals. . . . I think we can sum up this matter by saying that although no animal appears to have a language which is propositional, syntactic, and at the same time clearly expressive of intention, yet all these features can be found separately (to at least some degree) in the animal kingdom. Consequently, the distinction between man and the animals, on the ground that only the former possesses true language, seems far less satisfactory and logically defensible than it once did. [10]

What is logically indefensible is not the distinction, but Professor Thorpe's statement that other animals have a language that is propositional and syntactic, the only evidence for which he can offer—the dance-language of the honey bee—is totally irrelevant to the point, because it is wholly instinctive behavior. Even *if* Thorpe were correct in his statement that other species use signals that are "clearly expressive of intention" on their part, a statement with which Lorenz sharply disagrees, it would not follow that the distinguishing feature of human language—its propositional character and its syntactical structure—has been found in other species of animals *to any degree whatsoever*, once the instinctive performance of the honey bee is dismissed as incomparable and, therefore, irrelevant. [11]

(3) It is agreed that the lack of speech by other primates does not result from the lack of the vocal apparatus requisite for speech. [12] It is further agreed that when in other animals, especially in such birds as the myna bird or the grey parrot, the vocal apparatus is used to imitate human speech sounds perfectly and to utter human sentences, the fact that such performances are obviously learned rather than innate must not mislead anyone into thinking that the birds are engaging in true speech behavior. As Konrad Lorenz observes:

> Not even the cleverest "talking" birds which, as we have seen, are certainly capable of connecting their sound-expressions with particular occurrences, learn to make practical use of their powers, to achieve purposefully the simplest object. Professor Koehler, who can boast of the greatest successes in the science of training animals and who succeeded in teaching pigeons to count up to six, tried to teach [his] talented grey parrot "Geier" to say "food" when he was hungry, and "water" when he was dry. This attempt did not succeed, nor, so far, has it been achieved by anybody. [13]

As for Professor Koehler's success in teaching pigeons to count, on the basis of which he attributes to them "unnamed number concepts," I think it can be shown that his theory of "unnamed concepts" in animals is untenable. I will try to do this in the next chapter where I deal with the whole question of whether conceptual thought can be attributed to animals. Even Professor Thorpe, who thinks it can be, says of Koehler's work that, though it brings "the counting achievements of birds a step nearer that of man, . . . it is still not true counting in the fully human sense." [14]

(4) It is agreed that while animals can learn to respond to verbal cues, they do not initiate or use verbal cues to elicit behavioral responses on the part of other animals or men; nor can they be taught to do so. [15]

(5) Finally, it is agreed that man's exclusive possession of a propositional language is correlated with and, to some extent, depends on the size, structure, and complexity of his cerebral

cortex, including its dominance by one hemisphere or the other; in all of which respects except the last man is vastly superior in degree to other primates and to all other animals, with the possible exception of the bottle-nosed dolphin. In this last respect —the asymmetrical functioning of the human brain, with dominance by either the left or the right hemisphere of the cortex (as in right- and left-handed individuals)—man is unique; and this unique characteristic of his brain definitely appears to be connected with his exclusive possession of a propositional language. [16]

(3)

I have called man's exclusive possession of a propositional language the pivotal fact in this consideration of how men and other animals differ. It is the only one with regard to which a thorough search of the literature can discover no tenable demurers. That it may stand alone in eliciting such unanimous assent does not in any way minimize its logical effect in establishing the proposition that man and other animals differ in kind. That proposition being thus established, we must, of course, inquire why certain scientists, mainly psychologists, who concede that only man has a propositional language still persist in denying the truth of the proposition and asserting the opposite; namely, that man differs only in degree. And we must pursue a much more germane and more important inquiry concerning the character of this manifest difference in kind—to try to discover, when we come to explanations of man's exclusive possession of propositional speech, whether this difference is superficial or radical.

In treating as pivotal the fact that man alone names things and utters sentences, I do not mean to dismiss as unimportant or insignificant other evidences of man's difference in kind, of which two are almost as unanimously agreed upon as the fact of language. One is man's invention and fabrication of tools for use at some future time; the other is man's having a sequentially developed historical tradition that results from the cumulative transmission of cultural products from one generation not just to the next, but to remote generations, sometimes through intervening ones and sometimes jumping over them.

The few dissenting opinions with respect to the uniqueness of man's toolmaking appear to arise from a failure to distinguish between the invention and production of implements, such as the hand ax, for future use and the merely implemental use of natural objects at hand for immediate application in the present situation. Even when the latter appears to involve some improvisation of a tool by combining or adapting natural objects for the purpose, it is quite distinct from the fashioning, out of natural materials, of an implement designed to be used at a distant time and on objects not now perceptually present.

Similarly, the few dissenting opinions with respect to the uniqueness of human history appear to arise from a failure to distinguish between the cumulative transmission of technology, institutions, practices, and beliefs, on the one hand, and the non-cumulative transmission to one filial generation of behavior learned by its *proximate ancestors.*

With these distinctions acknowledged and understood, the uniqueness of man as the only toolmaking and the only history-making animal is not only as well established by the evidence, but it could also be as unanimously agreed upon as the fact that man is the only sentence-making animal. However, as I have just remarked and think it useful to repeat, it would make no difference if that were not so; for one type of behavior performed by man and not performed in any degree by other animals is quite sufficient to establish the proposition that man differs in kind, not just in degree. The addition of other unique human performances—such as toolmaking and history-making—does not, in strict logic, render "truer" the proposition that man differs in kind. The only logical effect of the additional items is to provide more things that would have to be refuted by evidence in order for the proposition to be empirically falsified.

Quite apart from the logic of proof and falsification, the additional items may, of course, make a significant contribution; for by seeing what is common to sentence-making, toolmaking, and history-making, we may be able to understand better what *underlies* the difference in kind that is manifested by these three forms of observable human behavior. For this reason, in what follows, I will, at times, refer to all three marks of man's difference in kind, though I will for the present concentrate on the significance of human language.

In saying that we were entitled to conclude that men and other animals differ in kind (even if that rests only on the pivotal fact of human language), I have always added "tentatively." Since the conclusion does follow from that fact, why is it *tentative?* The answer is that the present state of the evidence does not preclude the future discovery of contrary evidence. Evidence may be forthcoming, for example, that the bottle-nosed dolphin can make sentences. However, the fact that the conclusion about man's difference in kind is tentative in this sense, and only in this sense, does not distinguish it in any way from the best established of scientific opinions. All are tentative in the sense that they can be falsified by new data. If the possibility of contrary future evidence were to disbar us from drawing conclusions from the evidence now available, we could never draw any conclusions whatsoever from the data of scientific investigation.

(4)

The fact of man's difference in kind being established, only one question remains to be answered: *Is that difference in kind superficial or radical?* This question gives rise to two issues; for there is, first, a disagreement about whether the psychological explanation of man's linguistic performance renders it superficial; and, second, a disagreement about whether the neurological explanation of it has that effect. Of these two, the first is the pivotal issue in this inquiry, with which we shall deal at some length in the next chapter.

Before that, however, I would like to answer a question raised earlier in this chapter. Why do a considerable number of scientists, especially comparative psychologists and other behavioral scientists, still persist in saying that man differs *only in degree* when they do not dissent from the proposition that man and man alone has a propositional language, and when they neither offer any evidence to the contrary nor try to impugn the evidence that is available on this point? Since man's unique linguistic performance is quite sufficient to establish man's difference in kind, why do these scientists so flatly contradict themselves by admitting this and still asserting that man differs only in degree?

The contradiction is so patent that we can suppose they are

unaware of it only by supposing that they do not understand the distinction between difference in kind and difference in degree, or that they do not realize that one characteristic possessed exclusively by man, such as propositional speech, is sufficient to establish his difference in kind from other animals. That may be the case, but it seems so unlikely that I have another conjecture to propose. It involves a number of points.

In the first place, the scientists whom we are considering all affirm without question the evolutionary principle of phylogenetic continuity. If this principle is true without exception, then, in the realm of living things, including man, there can be no radical differences in kind, for such differences would introduce unbridgeable discontinuities into the picture.

In the second place, these scientists appear to be unacquainted with the distinction between a radical and a superficial difference in kind, and so they regard all differences in kind as if they were radical and, therefore, as creating discontinuities, which they look upon with abhorrence. Unaware that superficial differences in kind do not violate their evolutionary principles, they necessarily think that only differences in degree are compatible with the principles of continuity in nature and of phylogenetic continuity. Hence they find themselves obliged to assert that man differs only in degree even though they also admit the contrary fact of man's unique linguistic performance.

In the third place, and this is the most important point, they regard themselves as "explaining away" that contrary fact by showing—in their opinion, successfully—that the psychological processes and factors that underlie man's linguistic performance are fundamentally the same as those operative in non-linguistic animals, although they exist to a much higher degree in man than in these other animals. In their opinion, it is this difference in degree which *not only explains, but also explains away* the uniqueness of man's linguistic performance as a difference in kind. Explained in this way, it becomes a superficial difference in kind; but when it is not only explained, but also *explained away*, as these scientists appear to think, the manifest difference in kind is, in effect, eradicated and replaced by the underlying difference in degree. Hence they feel justified in saying that, in spite of his unique linguistic performance, man differs only in degree.

This mode of thinking involves a highly questionable assumption on their part. It is the notion that to explain something that is accurately described is to explain it away or to challenge the accuracy of the description. Even if man's unique linguistic performance were to be explained in terms of a higher degree of the same psychological processes and factors that are operative in non-linguistic animals, that would not in any way detract from the accuracy of the purely descriptive statement that linguistic and non-linguistic animals differ in kind, just as viviparous and oviparous animals differ in kind, or just as vertebrate and invertebrate animals differ in kind.

In addition, their attention must be called to the fact that their way of explaining the difference in kind between linguistic and non-linguistic animals would, if sound, only have the effect of rendering it a superficial and not a radical difference in kind. Were they to realize this and to understand its significance, they could then withdraw their assertion that men and other animals differ only in degree without in any way withdrawing or qualifying their adherence to the principle of phylogenetic continuity.

This last point is confirmed by the position taken by another group of scientists, mainly the evolutionary biologists and paleoanthropologists, who do not hesitate to affirm that man differs in kind, by virtue of his unique linguistic performance, or such other unique performances as toolmaking and history-making, while at the same time explaining this difference in kind in terms of differences in degree in brain size and complexity. Although these scientists do not seem to be acquainted, any more than their colleagues are, with the distinction between a superficial and a radical difference in kind, they nevertheless do see that their explanation of the difference in kind by reference to an underlying continuum of degrees render the difference in kind compatible with the principle of phylogenetic continuity—a principle that they espouse no less firmly than their colleagues in comparative psychology.

CHAPTER 9

The Pivotal Issue: Language and Thought

(1)

I SAID in the preceding chapter that the observed fact of man's unique linguistic performance was pivotal in the discussion, not only because it is the one fact that everyone accepts, but also because it falsifies the view that man differs from other animals only in degree, and supports the contrary view that he differs in kind as well as in degree. As the evidence stands at present, we need not further consider the question whether man differs only in kind or also in degree. That question is now closed. But another question remains quite open—whether the difference in kind is superficial or radical; and this question, as I pointed out, gives rise to two issues with which we shall concern ourselves in the remaining chapters of Part Two.

The first of these issues is constituted by the disagreement between (a) those who maintain that the underlying psychological factors or processes are exactly of the same kind in both linguistic and non-linguistic animals, and (b) those who deny this, maintaining on the contrary that man has the power of propositional speech because he has the power of conceptual thought, whereas the non-human animals lack the power of propositional speech because they lack the power of conceptual thought.

The second issue is constituted by the disagreement between

(a) those who, first of all, affirm that man alone has the power of conceptual thought, and then maintain that this intellectual power on man's part can be adequately explained by reference to neurological mechanisms and processes, and (b) those who deny this, maintaining on the contrary that conceptual thought requires for its explanation some factor in addition to the action of the brain.

Both disagreements relate to the question whether the difference in kind between linguistic and non-linguistic animals is superficial or radical. If, in the first case, the proponents of the view that exactly the same kind of psychological processes or factors are operative in linguistic and non-linguistic animals, though not to the same degree in both, are then able to show that it is the higher degree of these same factors or processes that accounts for man's unique linguistic performances, they have taken a long step toward showing that the difference in kind between linguistic and non-linguistic animals is only superficial. It only remains for them to show that there is a critical threshold in the continuum of degrees, above which linguistic behavior is possible, and below which it is not. Showing this does not preclude them from also maintaining that the critical threshold in the psychological continuum is paralleled by the critical threshold in the neurological continuum. Most proponents of the view here being considered do, in fact, appeal to differences in degree of brain magnitude and complexity in order to account for the difference in degree of the psychological factors and processes that are operative in both linguistic and non-linguistic animals. In other words, they regard the difference in kind between linguistic and non-linguistic animals as superficial in two respects: *first*, by reference to the underlying *psychological* continuum of degrees; and *second*, by reference to the even more fundamental *neurological* continuum of degrees.

Because of this, their opponents on the psychological level do not succeed in showing that the difference in kind is radical if they merely show that human language cannot be explained in terms of the same psychological processes or factors that are operative in non-linguistic animals. In order to establish a radical difference in kind, it is not enough to show that certain psychological processes or factors are present in man that are not present in non-linguistic animals. Should they succeed in showing only this, they do no more than remove one of the two grounds on which the difference in kind can be regarded as superficial; namely, the explanation of it by reference to a psychological continuum of degrees. The other ground remains untouched. Even if the power of conceptual thought, present in man and absent in non-linguistic animals, explains man's unique linguistic performance, the presence of conceptual thought in man and its absence in non-linguistic animals may itself be fully explained by the fact that man's brain is above a critical threshold in a continuum of degrees of neurological magnitude and complexity. If it can be so explained, then the difference in kind between linguistic and non-linguistic animals remains superficial, in spite of the fact that we have here not only a behavioral difference in kind but also a psychological difference in kind, i.e., a difference between the kind of psychological factors that must be posited to explain linguistic behavior and the kind of psychological factors needed to explain non-linguistic behavior.

It should now be clear why the first of the two disagreements constitutes the pivotal issue in this inquiry. Unless the first disagreement is resolved in favor of those who maintain that man and man alone has the power of conceptual thought, the second issue does not arise. If those who contend that different degrees of the same psychological processes or factors are operative in linguistic and non-linguistic animals are able to establish that contention, then they have also made it impossible to maintain that there is a radical difference in kind between man and other animals. No further consideration of the adequacy or inadequacy of the neurological explanation of human behavior is needed in order to answer the question whether man's difference in kind is radical or superficial. It *cannot be* radical. Only if it *can be* radical, must we go on to consider whether, in fact, it *is*. Since it *can be* radical only if it is *not* true that the same psychological processes or factors are operative in man and other animals, a negative resolution of the first issue is required before we turn our attention to the second.

Given that negative resolution of the first issue, we are then obligated to resolve the second before we can answer the crucial question about man's difference: Is it superficial or radical? To resolve the second issue, as we have seen, requires us to determine whether the neurological explanation of conceptual thought is or can be adequate or, in the very nature of the case, cannot be. If the second issue cannot be resolved, the crucial question about how man differs remains open; if it can be resolved in favor of *either* alternative, then the question is closed and an age-old dispute is settled with what, in my judgment, are serious practical and theoretical consequences.

(2)

I have now formulated the two issues that will be treated in subsequent chapters and shown why the first of these is pivotal. But I have not yet indicated the parties that confront one another in these disagreements. It may help the reader to keep track of what is going on if he knows the general character of the opponents and is acquainted with the names of the leading figures in each case—some at least, if not all. Some have already been mentioned and their views examined; others will now be named for the first time, and their views briefly documented.

In the first and pivotal issue, the comparative psychologists and other behavioral scientists are proponents of the view that the psychological explanation of man's exclusive possession of propositional speech renders his manifest difference in kind from nonlinguistic animals superficial, not radical. Leading contemporary figures in this group are the psychologists Harlow, Hebb, Osgood, Schneirla, Nissen, Leeper, Heron, Scott, and Razran. They are joined by such biologists as Rensch, Herrick, and Carlson; such ethologists as Thorpe; and such sociologists or anthropologists as Linton, Goldenweiser, and Hankins. [1]

On the other side of the first issue we have, among contemporary scientists, mainly the paleoanthropologists such as Julian Huxley, Mayr, Simpson, Dobzhansky, Oakley, Washburn, Teilhard de Chardin, and Carrington. They are joined by such neurologists as McCulloch, Crichtley, Lashley, Halstead, and Lord Brain; such comparative psychologists as Maier, Bitterman, Lilly, Craik, Bruner, Hunt, Klüver and, perhaps Köhler; such ethologists as Lorenz, Portmann, and Schaller; and by the sociologist Leslie White. [2]

In the second issue, almost all contemporary scientists—especially those in the fields of neurology, physiology, evolutionary biology, psychology, anthropology, and other social sciences—swell the ranks of those who maintain that an adequate neurological explanation can be given of the difference in kind between linguistic and non-linguistic animals. It includes scientists on both sides of the first issue; in short, almost every scientist who, by adherence to evolutionary principles, is committed to the view that if man differs in kind, the difference must be superficial, either on psychological or neurological grounds, because a radical difference in kind would be incompatible with man's phylogenetic continuity with the rest of animal life. Here there is some point in naming the few exceptions among twentieth-century scientists. They are mainly biologists, such as Sinnott, Dixon, and Jonas; or, what is even more striking, leading neurologists, such as Sherrington, Sperry, and Penfield. They express, in varying ways and degrees, quasi-philosophical doubts about the possibility of an adequate neurological explanation of man's distinctive behavior and its underlying psychological factors. To this extent, they can be regarded as adversaries of the prevailing scientific view that whatever is different about man amounts to no more than a superficial difference in kind. [3]

In the foregoing enumerations, I have omitted reference to two groups—the philosophers, on the one hand, and the computer technologists and experimenters with artificial intelligence, on the other. While the latter seldom speak directly to the first issue, they clearly align themselves with the prevailing scientific view on the second; more than that, it is a major aim of their experimental work to support that view. I will name them and discuss their views in Chapter 14.

As for the philosophers, who certainly play a significant part in the dispute of this mixed question, I have already indicated in Chapter 4 where the leading figures in Western thought stand. The materialists among them, either the atomistic and mechanical or the dialectical materialists, stand opposed to man's being radically different in kind from other things; and so, if the questions at issue were put to them, they would take the affirmative side on either the first or the second issue. Among the others, those who regard man as radically different in kind would, if confronted with the two issues in their current state, deny that the psychological processes or factors are the same, except for differences in degree, in men and other animals; and they would also deny that the action of man's brain can adequately account for the activities of his mind. When they conceive man as the only rational or logical animal, they are asserting more than his exclusive possession of a propositional language; they are affirming his exclusive possession of intellectual powers which are the underlying cause of his ability to name things and utter sentences that are true or false; and beyond this, most of them hold that man's power of understanding and his power of free choice involve an immaterial or non-physical factor that makes him radically distinct in kind from other living things.

There remains to mention the philosophers of our own century who approach the question in the light of the scientific evidence that is available and who are cognizant of the division of scientific opinion on the two issues with which we are concerned. On the first issue, I think it is fair to say that most of the leading figures in contemporary philosophical thought who speak to the question at issue are opposed to those scientists who maintain that, though markedly differing in degree, the same psychological processes or factors are operative in men and other animals. On the second issue, the balance shifts somewhat in the opposite direction; at least, that is my reading of the current literature that bears on the subject. Here there tends to be something more like an equal division of opinion—one group of philosophers espousing the prevailing scientific belief that man's behavior and psychological processes can be adequately explained in neurological terms; another group questioning, challenging, or arguing against that view.

I have refrained from enumerating the names of the aforementioned philosophers because I think it will be more appropriate to do so in later chapters where I shall report and discuss their theories. But here, in the concluding section of this chapter, I am going to cite the opinions of a number of twentieth-century writers in support of the position that man possesses intellectual powers not possessed to any degree by other animals. Most of these writers are philosophers; but some are scientists whose views have not yet been examined. This will complete a preliminary survey of the division of opinion on the first issue, and prepare for a resolution of that issue in the chapter to follow.

(3)

In contrast to the pre-Darwinian philosophers whose diverse views were examined in Chapter 4, the philosophers whom we shall now consider all carry on their thinking within the general context of evolutionary theory. They are, in varying degrees, acquainted with the relevant scientific data; some of them explicitly comment on recent experimental work and criticize the theories advanced to explain the phenomena described; others are concerned with reconciling traditional philosophical notions with current scientific ones. For them, the question about man is certainly a mixed one, involving both science and philosophy. They can hardly be dismissed as incompetent by reason of ignorance. In the brief survey of their views that follows, I am going to summarize their opinions on three critical points that bear on the pivotal issue; but first I would like to indicate their reasons for thinking that man differs in kind with respect to intellectual traits not manifested by other animals.

The group includes William James, Henri Bergson, John Dewey, and Ernst Cassirer of an earlier generation; and among those more recently at work, it includes H. H. Price, Jonathan Bennett, Peter Geach, and Wilfred Sellars (the first three Oxford and Cambridge men, the last a professor of philosophy at Yale University). With them, because of the affinity of their views on the three critical points mentioned above, I have associated an Austrian philosopher, Karl Popper, a British neurologist, Macdonald Crichtley, and an American sociologist, Leslie White. With the exception of Popper, all explicitly assert that man and other animals differ in kind; and some of them—James, Cassirer, Bennett, Sellars, Crichtley, and White—do so in the context of discussing or adverting to the distinction between a difference in kind and a difference in degree. [4] Again, with the exception of Popper, all concur in their description of two behavioral indices of the difference in kind between man and other animals. One is man's directly observable linguistic behavior. The other is man's transcendence of the immediate environment, his emancipation from the perceptual present, which is directly observable in the actions of men with regard to objects—past, future, or totally non-temporal—that do not exist in the perceptual field of the moment. They contrast this with the behavior of all other animals which, as most students of animal behavior concede and some, notably Schaller and Köhler, explicitly affirm, is confined to immediate or *slightly delayed* reactions to stimuli in the present perceptual field.

"With animals," Dewey writes, "an experience perishes as it happens, and each new doing or suffering stands alone." Man lives not, "like the beasts of the field, in a world of purely physical things but in a world of signs and symbols." It is this "which marks the difference between bestiality and humanity, between culture and merely physical nature." [5] According to Bergson, "man is the only animal whose actions are uncertain, who hesitates, gropes about and lays plans in the hope of success and the fear of failure. He is alone in realizing that he is subject to illness, alone in knowing that he must die. The rest of nature goes on its expanding course in absolute tranquility. Although plants and animals are the sport of chance, they rely on the passing hour as they would on eternity." [6]

Professor Price points out that the verbal thinking that is distinctive of man is "to a very considerable degree . . . independent of the perceived environment." [7] Expanding on this point, he writes:

> The autonomy of rational beings depends upon the use of symbols, and especially on the use of words. . . . This is what makes such beings independent in some degree of their physical and perceptually presented environments. . . . Such autonomy is beyond the reach of even the most accomplished sign-cognizant. And here, if anywhere, is the difference in kind between men and the lower animals. . . . Animal learning, with the responsiveness to signs which results from it, is a primitive form of induction, as Hume noticed. But the lower animals do not seem to rise to the independent or autonomous thinking which the use of symbols makes possible. Their thinking always remains "tied." And so, though we must not deny that they think, we hesitate to call them thinkers. [8]

The fact that men can make, and make quite separately, universal statements and also statements about past singular instances reveals, according to Jonathan Bennett, their transcendence of that which is both present and particular. He contrasts this with the pattern of present stimulus and present or slightly delayed response that characterizes the entire repertoire of animal behavior. And for him man's distinctive rationality, though it depends on his having a propositional language, consists in a power of judgment and inference that explains the way in which he uses language, but is not itself fully explained by the fact that he has the power of speech. [9]

Ernst Cassirer, while maintaining that, "in spite of all the efforts of modern irrationalism," the traditional "definition of man as an *animal rationale* has not lost its force," prefers "to define him as an *animal symbolicum*. By so doing," he writes, "we can designate his specific difference, and we can understand the new way open to man—the way to civilization." He goes on to say, "without symbolism, the life of man would be like that of the prisoners in the cave of Plato's famous simile. Man's life would be confined within the limits of his biological needs and his practical interests; it could find no access to the 'ideal world' which is opened to him from different sides by religion, art, philosophy, science." [10]

These writers then explain the observed phenomena—man's linguistic behavior and his behavior with respect to objects not perceptually present in his immediate environment—by reference to his possession of abilities that cannot be directly observed, but which, in their opinion, *must be inferred* in order to explain the behavior in question, and *need not be inferred* in the case of other animals precisely because they do not manifest such behavior. They attribute to man and to man alone an intellectual power that they variously name the power of "rational," "symbolic," "autonomous," or "conceptual" thought. (If I adopt the last of these adjectives to designate that which distinguishes human from animal thought, which, in contrast, can be called "perceptual," I also attach to it a meaning that includes whatever is included in the connotations of the other three adjectives. [11]) However it is named, it is the power that man exercises in naming things, in uttering sentences that can be true or false, in making judgments about their truth or falsity in the light of relevant evidence and arguments, in stating inferences and giving reasons, and in developing, as Cassirer points out, mathematics, art, science, history, philosophy, religion, the state, and all the other institutions of civilized life. [12]

While, in view of such opinions on their part, they concur in asserting an underlying psychological difference in kind between man and other animals, they do not all agree that this difference in kind is radical rather than superficial. Cassirer, Geach, and Bennett simply fail to discuss this point. In terms of his views on other subjects, James can be presumed to favor the position that the difference in kind is radical; as Bergson and Dewey, on the contrary, can be similarly presumed to regard it as superficial. And three of these authors—Sellars, Crichtley, and White—give us explicit indications that, in their view, man's difference in kind does not involve a basic discontinuity in nature or in phylogenetic development. [13]

On the critical side, these writers make three contributions to the contemporary consideration of the mixed question about man. *First* and foremost is their distinction between what might be called two modes of meaning or significance. This has, as we shall see presently, a direct critical impact on the equivocal use of the word "symbol" by the comparative psychologists—to cover, *without distinction*, both the elements of human speech and what they call "non-verbal symbols" in animal behavior.

James and White call attention to the fact that only men invent or institute signs or symbols by *convention*, whereas the signs that animals respond to or employ are *natural* elements in their experience or behavior. [14] White and Crichtley introduce a distinction between two types of *signifiers*—between what they call "signs" in animal behavior and what they call "symbols" in human behavior. [15] This distinction is much more clearly expressed and more fully developed by Cassirer, Price, and Popper.

Cassirer distinguishes between the *signals* that function *operatively* in animal behavior and the *symbols* that function as *designators, describers*, or *referents* in human behavior. Having pointed out that symbols "which have an objective reference or meaning" are totally absent from animal behavior, [16] Cassirer then goes on to say:

> Symbols—in the proper sense of the term—cannot be reduced to mere signals. Signals and symbols belong to different universes of discourse: a signal is a part of the physical

world of being; a symbol is a part of the human world of meaning. Signals are "operators"; symbols are "designators." [17]

Using the word "sign" where Cassirer uses the word "signal," Price makes the same distinction between the functional meaning of signs and the designative, descriptive, or referential meaning of symbols; [18] and he is at great pains fairly to state and yet incisively to criticize the efforts of the behavioristic psychologists and others to reduce symbols to signs or, what is in effect the same, to try to account for the significance of human words and for their significant use entirely in terms of what he calls the "sign theory" of meaning. [19]

Following proposals first made by Karl Bühler in 1918, Popper distinguishes four functions of language: "(1) the expressive or symptomatic function; (2) the stimulative or signal function; (3) the descriptive function; [and] (4) the argumentative function." While admitting that there may be still other functions, such as the prescriptive or the advisory, Popper then asserts "that these four functions mentioned constitute a hierarchy, in the sense that each of the higher ones *cannot* be present without all those which are lower, while the lower ones *may* be present without the higher ones." This leads him to his criticism of behaviorism, or what he calls a "causal physicalistic theory of linguistic behavior," with respect to which he enunciates two theses. One is that "any causal physicalistic theory of linguistic behavior can only be a theory of the two lower functions of language"; the other, that "any such theory is therefore bound either to ignore the difference between the higher and the lower functions, or to assert that the two higher functions are 'nothing but' special cases of the two lower functions." [20] The relevance of Popper's criticism to the question at issue will be seen in the light of the thesis, not enunciated by him, but by Cassirer, Price, Crichtley, White, and others that the two higher functions of language are manifested only in human linguistic behavior, and that animal communication—insofar as it is learned behavior and not instinctive—consists solely in performances that are comparable to the two lower functions of human language (i.e., expressive cries and stimulative signals).

The words "sign" and "symbol" are so variously used in the

literature—as well as so often misused—that I will, in what follows, employ other terms to express the critical distinction made by such philosophers as Cassirer and Price and by such scientists as Crichtley and White. I will use "signals" and "designators" for the two types of signifiers, each having a distinct mode of meaning or significance. The cry of an animal in danger operates as a warning signal to other members of the group, eliciting appropriate alertness on their part: the word "danger" used on a roadway sign operates in the same way for human beings; but human beings also use the word "danger" as a name to designate, describe, or refer to a whole class of threatening situations perilous to life and limb. That non-verbal signals are operative in animal behavior and that both verbal and non-verbal signals are operative in human behavior are facts beyond question. But there is no evidence whatsoever of the functioning of designators except in human linguistic behavior.

The *second* critical point made by these contemporary philosophers, and by such scientists as Crichtley and White, turns on their making a sharp distinction between perceptual and conceptual thought. This distinction is implicit in the observation that animal thinking is confined to the perceptual present, whereas human thinking transcends the immediate environment and extends not only to objects in the remote past and the remote future but also to objects that have no temporal locus whatsoever. Precisely because they are incapable of conceptual thought, animals, these writers contend, are not only (1) incapable of sentence-making that includes statements about the past and future, (2) unable to fabricate tools for remote future use, (3) devoid of a cumulative cultural inheritance that constitutes a long historical tradition, but they are also (4) incapable of any behavior that is not rooted in the perceptually apprehended present situation.

I have used the word "thought," as Price and many others do, with measured equivocation to cover both perceptual and conceptual thinking, in order to express the critical point here being considered. The question is not whether animals can think, any more than it is, as we shall see later, whether machines can think. Animals can certainly think, in the sense of learning from experience, generalizing, discriminating, and abstracting, solving problems by trial and error or by insight, and even, as Price, following Hume, points out, making inductive inferences from empirically learned cues or signals. The evidence is both plain and ample that they *can think in all these ways.* But it is equally plain from the observations of their behavior, in the laboratory or in the field, that they *cannot think in any of the following ways*: they cannot think about objects that are not perceptually present as well as about those that are; and with regard to objects of thought, present or absent, they cannot make judgments or engage in reasoning (i.e., think that such and such *is* or *is not* the case, or think that *if* such and such is the case, *then* so and so is not).

Among the authors whom we are here considering, William James is, of course, a most astute observer and analyst of the difference between perceptual and conceptual thought. [21] Two of the more recent writers—Geach and Bennett—not only sharpen the distinction, but also ably defend it with reference to experiments on generalization and perceptual abstraction in animals, and on problem-solving by trial and error and by insight.

Geach argues that the experiments that demonstrate an animal's capacity to recognize triangles or to discriminate between triangles and quadrangles (functioning as perceptible cues or stimuli) do not indicate that the laboratory animals have formed concepts of triangularity and quadrangularity. In his view, the laboratory data can be adequately explained without positing concept-formation in animals. To do so is to confuse perceptual abstraction on the part of animals with human concept-formation which, Geach convincingly shows, does not consist in a process of abstraction at all. [22]

Bennett argues that animal learning and problem-solving, whether by trial and error or by insight, does not involve any of the steps that constitute human reasoning from experience—the process whereby human beings either establish an empirical conclusion or refute one. Since that always involves the separate acknowledgment of a timeless universal, on the one hand, and of particular instances of past occurrence, on the other, animals, whose apprehensions are limited to the immediate perceptual present, cannot possibly engage in the kind of thinking that consists in giving reasons *pro* or *con.* And, Bennett further contends, behavior that involves giving or receiving reasons cannot be causally explained by reference to empirical sequences. In his view, there can be no behavioristic account of human rational behavior, as there can be of animal learning and problem-solving, in terms of causal connections between stimuli and responses or by reference to the causes at work in the formation of the conditioned responses or the imprintings that represent the modifications of animal behavior through repeated experience. [23]

The analyses offered by Geach and Bennett, together with the adverse appraisal that they make of the significance of the experimental data on animal behavior with which they are acquainted, amount to a refutation of the interpretation placed upon these data by a large number of comparative psychologists, especially those of behavioristic persuasion. Geach and Bennett are, in effect, saying that the data *can be adequately explained* without attributing either concept-formation or rational judgment to animals. Hence, to posit the presence in animals of non-verbal concepts, non-verbal judgments, and non-verbal processes of reasoning is to violate the very principle of parsimony on which the behavioristic psychologists are themselves so insistent. Not to attribute the power of concept-formation and of rational judgment to man is an equal and opposite violation of the other side of Occam's two-edged razor, since human linguistic behavior—naming things and uttering sentences that can be true or false—*cannot be adequately explained* without positing the power of conceptual or rational thought on the part of men.

The *third* critical point—again made most clearly by Geach and Bennett, though it is also adumbrated by Price's analysis of concepts and their manifestation—concerns the relation of language and thought. Is human language the cause of conceptual thought; conceptual thought, the cause of human language; or is each, in some reciprocal fashion, the cause of the other? The scientists who comment on the relation of human language and conceptual thought permit themselves to say either unclear or contradictory things about which is the cause and which the effect. Some regard language as prerequisite to conceptual thought; some regard conceptual thought as independent of and prerequisite to language; and some try to have it both ways, making each the cause of the other without explaining how this can be so. [24]

This matter cannot be clarified without carefully distinguishing between necessary and sufficient conditions, on the one hand, and between *causae cognoscendi* and *causae essendi*, on the other. To say that observable linguistic behavior on the part of man is a cause of our inferring or knowing *(causa cognoscendi)* that men have the unobserved and, in principle, unobservable power of conceptual thought is *not* to say that man's having a propositional language is the cause *(causa essendi)* of his having the power of conceptual thought. As both Geach and Price point out—one by reference to clinical data on aphasia and related speech disorders, the other by reference to the common experience of unverbalized thought that directs or seeks out linguistic expression [25]—conceptual thought is not inseparable from the private use of language in subvocal soliloquy, nor from its public use for the purpose of communication.

Viewed in terms of necessary and sufficient conditions, it can be said of man's propositional language and his power of conceptual thought that each is a necessary condition of the other, but that neither is the sufficient condition of the other. In other words, the fact that a man's concepts, viewed dispositionally, consist, in part at least, in his ability to use words significantly, and the fact that his ability to make up names and to frame sentences greatly enhances his conceptual thinking, do not, taken together, show that language and thought are inseparable; nor do they show that man's having the power of conceptual thought can be fully explained (sufficient condition) by his possession of a propositional language, or that man's having articulate speech can be fully explained (sufficient condition) by his possession of conceptual thought. What is reciprocal here in the relation of language and thought is only that each is a necessary—a *sine qua non*—condition of the development of the other: man could not exercise his power of articulate speech unless he had the power of conceptual thought; he could but barely exercise his power of conceptual thought did he not have the use of words and sentences. [26]

With respect to all three critical points, it is important to point out that they leave quite open the question of whether man's unique possession of conceptual thought—an indispensable prerequisite of his unique linguistic performance and his transcendence of the perceptually present environment—*can* or *cannot* be fully explained in terms of underlying neurological mechanisms and processes.

CHAPTER 10

Resolution of the Pivotal Issue (I): The Negative Argument

(1)

THUS FAR I have devoted my efforts to clarifying the mixed question, to clarifying the state of philosophical and scientific opinion by removing patent inconsistencies and irrelevant objections that stand in the way of an accurate appraisal of the state of the question at the present time, and to clarifying the issues by defining as precisely as possible the matters about which significant disagreement still remains. Thus far I have not taken sides. I do not regard the exposure of inconsistencies and irrelevancies as taking sides; that is a necessary part of the work of clarification. Nor do I regard my espousal of the proposition that men and other animals differ in kind, not degree, as taking sides on a question at issue. On that question, as we have seen, there is no other side to take; there can be no disagreement in the light of all the evidence now available, and once inconsistencies are resolved in favor of universally admitted and undisputed facts.

With regard to the question whether man's difference in kind is superficial or radical, I have not taken sides. As we saw in the preceding chapter, that question gives rise to two separate issues —one concerning psychological grounds for interpreting man's difference in kind as superficial, the other concerning neurological grounds for advancing such an interpretation. Of these, as we noted, the first is pivotal; the second does not arise unless the first is resolved in favor of the negative position, i.e., the denial that man's difference in kind is grounded on a critical threshold in a psychological continuum—lower and higher degrees of *exactly the same* psychological factors and processes.

In the preceding chapter, I indicated the character of the parties who take opposite sides on each of these issues, and I named leading or representative figures who, in virtue of the opinions they have expressed, can be construed as taking part in the dispute of these issues. In the course of so doing, I introduced a number of twentieth-century philosophers—and, with them, a few scientists. They, more than the others who take the negative side of the pivotal issue, propose distinctions and offer analyses that tend to support the negative answer. The preceding chapter, like earlier ones, still carried on the dialectical task of clarifying the present state of well-informed opinion on the question. It did not take sides.

Now I am going to take sides. And I am going to do so on one point only; for after I have done what I think must be done to resolve the pivotal issue, I am going to return to the dialectical role of clarifying the state of opinion on the remaining issue and constructing, so far as I can, the dispute of that issue—a dispute that is now quite active in contemporary thought.

(2)

The side I am going to take is the side taken by those contemporary philosophers and scientists who favor the position that the manifest difference in kind between linguistic and non-linguistic animals is to be *psychologically explained* by the operation in man, and in man *alone*, of an *unobserved* factor that henceforth, for brevity and constancy of reference, I will refer to as the power of conceptual thought. All the italicized words in the preceding statement are critical terms. The explanation of observed behavior always involves reference to unobserved factors, whether psychological or neurological. These are the theoretical constructs that scientists must have recourse to if they are going to explain the data of observation. If the theoretical constructs represent theories or conceptions of nervous mechanisms or processes, they are, of course, neurological constructs. If they represent theories or conceptions of abilities or activities of the organism as a whole (which may or may not be themselves fully explained in neurological terms), then they are psychological constructs.

Those who posit the power of conceptual thought and assert its exclusive possession by man are not the only ones who employ theoretical constructs in psychology in order to explain the observed behavior of linguistic animals. Those on the other side of this issue do the same thing. The comparative psychologists and others who hold that the behavior of linguistic and nonlinguistic animals can be explained in terms of the same set of psychological factors or processes (with attention, of course, to differences in degree in the two cases) necessarily have recourse to theoretical constructs, too. Whether they call them "ideational factors," "representative factors," "mediating processes," or "nonverbal as well as verbal abstractions or concepts," the unobserved items referred to are psychological constructs, not data of observation.

Which psychological explanation is correct? That is the nub of the question in this pivotal issue. The ultimate criterion of theoretical correctness, to which both sides do or certainly should appeal, is the principle of parsimony. The principle works two ways: on the one hand, it works *negatively* by imposing the stricture that no theoretical constructs should be resorted to that can be dispensed with in explaining the phenomena; on the other hand, it works *positively* by relaxing that stricture in the direction of justifying the employment of whatever theoretical constructs may be needed to explain the phenomena.

It is this double aspect of the principle of parsimony that I had in mind earlier when I said that Occam's razor is a two-edged instrument—one that works in opposite directions. It eliminates theoretical constructs that cannot be *shown* to be necessary for explanatory purposes; but it also justifies the retention of theoretical constructs the need for which can be *shown*. Here, again, the italicized word is critical. It is not enough for a theorist just to assert that such and such a theoretical construct is needed to explain certain phenomena; he must *demonstrate* it, so far as he is able. And since we are moving on the plane of explanation, not of observation, the demonstration must take the form of reasoning or argument. It cannot be accomplished by the introduction of additional data, for these, too, would stand in need of explanation.

While the position for which I am about to argue is no different from the position taken by those contemporary philosophers and scientists who think that the power of conceptual thought *must be posited* to explain the distinctive behavior of linguistic animals and *need not be posited* to explain the behavior of non-linguistic animals (or whatever behavior is common to both linguistic and non-linguistic animals), the arguments for that position which I will presently advance seem to me to go a little beyond what I can find in the literature of this dispute. My arguments certainly repeat or borrow distinctions that others have made. They lean on or adapt analyses that others have put forward. But they also pull together analytical or argumentative points that have not been previously collated; and they marshal these materials argumentatively and focus them within the framework of a somewhat clearer formulation of the mixed question about man than is currently available. It is in this last connection that the dialectical work of the preceding chapters signally contributes to the resolution of the pivotal issue.

I will try to achieve that resolution in two argumentative steps, one negative, the other positive. This procedure, the reader will recognize, accords with the negative and the positive fashion in which the principle of parsimony works—the two directions in which Occam's razor operates. In this chapter devoted to the negative phase of the argument, I will try to show, in the light of all the experimental or other data obtained by investigation, that the power of conceptual thought *is not needed* as a theoretical construct in psychology to explain the observed phenomena, i.e., the behavior of non-linguistic animals or whatever behavior is common to both linguistic and non-linguistic animals. In the next chapter, devoted to the positive phase of the argument, I will try to show, again in the light of scientific evidence but now also in the light of common experience, that the power of conceptual thought *is needed* as a theoretical construct to explain psychologically the distinctive behavior of linguistic animals.

For the sake of making sure that the reader fully appreciates the argumentative situation with as much clarity and precision as is possible, let me state the matter another way. In this chapter, the crucial question is: What theoretical constructs are needed—

and, therefore, justified by the principle of parsimony—in order to explain psychologically the behavior that is common to linguistic and non-linguistic animals; in other words, non-linguistic behavior? In the next chapter, the crucial question is: What theoretical constructs are needed and justified in order to explain psychologically the distinctive behavior of linguistic animals; and needed here, first of all, to explain linguistic behavior itself? I will argue, in both chapters, against the comparative psychologists and others who think that the answer to the two questions is exactly the same, except for differences in degree. But in this chapter the argument will attempt to show that it is only when the behavior being considered is non-linguistic or common to men and animals that the same theoretical constructs are needed to explain the behavior; whereas in the next chapter the argument will attempt to show that when the behavior being considered is linguistic or distinctive of man, an additional theoretical construct—namely, the power of conceptual thought—is needed to explain the behavior in question.

Before I proceed to examine the experimental observations of animal behavior which, I contend, can be explained without positing the power of conceptual thought, I must ask the reader to follow me in two preliminary sorties. The first is a critical examination of the methodology of comparative psychology and of the fashion in which this group of scientists employs or applies its technical terms. The second is an effort to correct the misuse of technical terms in this field by proposing clearer and more precise formulations of certain theoretical constructs—the ones on which the whole argument turns.

(3)

I pointed out, in Chapter 7, that Lloyd Morgan's procedural canon in comparative psychology is a special adaptation of Occam's razor, or the principle of parsimony. It appears to enjoin comparative psychologists against anthropomorphic interpretations of animal behavior. Do not posit, it cautions, the presence and operation of a higher (i.e., a human) psychological factor, if animal behavior can be explained in terms of a lower psychological factor (i.e., one common to men and other animals). But the comparative psychologists at work in this century have read Morgan's canon as if it *prescribed* the positing of the same psychological factors to explain both human and animal behavior, and *proscribed* the positing of any additional psychological factors to explain human behavior—*whether or not the behavior to be explained is common to men and animals or is clearly distinctive of man.*

That, in my judgment, is an egregious misreading of Morgan's methodological principle, and one that Morgan himself did not make. The misreading becomes apparent as soon as one understands, as one should, Morgan's principle as nothing but a special application of the more general principle of parsimony as regulative of all scientific—or, for that matter, even philosophical—theorizing. Then it will be correctly interpreted to enjoin the scientist (or philosopher) *not* to posit a theoretical construct *unless* it can be *shown* to be needed to explain the observed phenomena. Read this way, it permits him to posit—more than that, justifies him in positing—whatever theoretical constructs can be shown to be needed.

Misinterpreting Morgan's rule, and committed to the evolutionary principle of phylogenetic continuity, most comparative psychologists thought that, to follow the rule and to be faithful to their commitment, they had to find nothing but differences in degree between the observed behavior of men and other animals; or, failing that, at least to explain whatever differences in kind they did not find by positing the same psychological factors or processes in both, with a difference in the degree of these underlying psychological factors or processes to explain the manifest difference in kind at the level of observed behavior. Some of the early behaviorists thought they could explain animal behavior simply in S-R terms—stimulus, response, and the process of conditioning—without positing any "ideational" factors whatsoever; and so they excluded such factors from their explanation of human behavior, treating it entirely in S-R terms. Others of more recent date, while still behaviorists, have found it necessary or useful to posit what they call "ideational" or "representative" factors that function as "mediating" processes between stimulus and response in animal behavior. They then borrow from the psychological explanation of human behavior such traditional terms as "abstraction" and "concept" and identify them with the ideational, representative, or mediating factors that they have posited for explanatory purposes. With the qualification added that abstractions or concepts in animals are necessarily non-verbal, whereas they may be verbal or non-verbal in man, these comparative psychologists conclude by maintaining that the same theoretical constructs serve to explain human and animal behavior, both what is common thereto and also what is distinctive of man. Not only does this beg the question, but, in addition, it violates certain obvious rules of sound procedure.

First of all, it is necessary to separate the description of both animal and human behavior from the intrusion of explanatory theorizing. Then, with respect to the animal behavior described, the procedure should be to employ whatever theoretical constructs are necessary to explain the behavior, and no others, without regard to whether such theoretical constructs adequately explain human behavior or others in addition are needed. And in the case of human behavior, the procedure should be the same: employ whatever theoretical constructs may be necessary, without regard to whether they are or are not necessary to explain animal behavior. To lump human and animal behavior together on the *assumption* that both can be explained by the same theoretical constructs, and then to propose certain theoretical constructs that are *either* needed to explain animal behavior (and, therefore, it is claimed, also explain human behavior) *or* needed to explain human behavior (and, therefore, it is claimed, also explain animal behavior) is to beg the question. The very thing to be shown was assumed to begin with, and the assumption controlled the explanatory theorizing.

As time-honored and as basic as the principle of parsimony is the second rule of sound procedure that is violated by the comparative psychologists whose theories we are here considering. It consists in the simple maxim that technical terms—the terms that represent the theoretical constructs being employed in explanatory efforts and in theorizing about observed phenomena—should *always* be used with the same invariable and univocal meaning. If any departure from one and the same meaning is necessitated in order to express distinctions that a more refined theory finds it necessary to acknowledge, then the same term should be used with the requisite qualifications added; in which case the old term with the added specifying qualifications no longer represents a single theoretical construct. In its place we have the two new terms, each with a diverse qualification, and these represent two new theoretical constructs that replace the original one. These may have certain features in common, but they are not the same; and to treat them as the same by ignoring the effect of the added qualifications is to equivocate in the use of the original term that was subject to diverse specifying qualifications.

Equivocation may be desirable or indispensable in poetry; it may be unavoidable in ordinary conversation, but there it is relatively harmless and so is condonable: but it is noxious and hence inexcusable in scientific discourse. Yet the exposition of theory in comparative psychology abounds in equivocations, especially in the use of such critical terms as "concept" and "abstraction." These terms, along with "percept" or "perception," "memory," "image," and "idea," represent theoretical constructs in psychology. These terms are of a different order from "stimulus" and "response," both of which represent things *objectively* observable to the scientist who is trying to describe behavior; whereas whatever is referred to by "concept," "image," and "idea" are not. That is why the latter represent theoretical constructs. Whether or not whatever is referred to by "concept," "abstraction," and "idea," or even by "perception," "image," and "memory," are *subjectively* observable, is another question. Even if they were (which I, for one, have good reasons for thinking they are not), the terms that refer to them would still represent theoretical constructs in a psychology that remained thoroughly behavioristic in its methodology—*as it should in order to remain scientific.*

(4)

Further elaboration on two points just made are in order.

The first concerns the difference between such terms as "concept" and "abstraction" and terms like "stimulus" and "response." The scientist who uses the latter terms descriptively stays on the same level—or in the same universe of discourse—when, for explanatory purposes, he refers to *mediating factors or processes* in the central nervous system, or to such things as *inhibition* and *reinforcement.* [1] But when he substitutes percepts, images, memories, concepts, or ideas for what he has called the mediating factors that operate between stimulus and response, he moves to another level or into another universe of discourse and mixes two analytical vocabularies that should be kept distinct. Worse still, when he identifies whatever is referred to by such terms as "image," "concept," or "idea" with the mediating factors or processes that he conceives as operating between the stimulation of sense organs and the innervation of muscles or glands, he is assuming one of several possible answers to the difficult philosophical question about the relation of body to mind, or of nervous to mental processes.

The second comment I wish to make concerns methodological and metaphysical behaviorism. [2] Metaphysical behaviorism, as I pointed out earlier, is simply one form of materialism: it consists in denying the existence of anything immaterial, and in asserting that whatever exists or occurs is identical with, or at least inseparable from, the existence of bodies and the occurrence of their actions and interactions. In contrast, methodological behaviorism, understood most generally, applies to our knowledge of inert bodies and our knowledge of plants as well as to our knowledge of animals and of men. It is a general principle of method that governs inferences from objectively observed behavior in the form of actions or interactions to the existence of such unobserved properties as powers, habits, or dispositions, none of which can be objectively observed. Inferences of this sort are themselves controlled by the principle of parsimony: we are justified in positing a power, habit, or disposition only if it is needed to explain observed behavior. When what we are thus justified in positing is a general type of power, habit, or disposition, needed to explain the observed behavior not of this or that particular thing, but of this type of thing, whether inert or animate, then our notion of the power, habit, or disposition functions as an explanatory theoretical construct.

In the case of inert bodies, plants, and non-human animals, the procedures of methodological behaviorism have always been followed by natural scientists, ancient and modern, even though the principle of parsimony has not always been observed and though scientists of an earlier generation are usually regarded by more recent ones as having been fanciful or imprecise with regard to the powers or dispositions they attributed to inert or animate bodies. To say that the procedures of methodological behaviorism have always been followed in the scientific study of natural objects other than man is misleading if it allows anyone to think that some other procedure might have been used instead. That is not the case: no other procedure is possible if it is to be scientific in character, and not just an adventure in myth-making.

However, when we come to the case of man, the situation is different. During most of the Western tradition and even now in the twentieth century, the study of man has been and is carried on by introspective methods that are presumed to provide us with the direct observation of mental entities, occurrents, states, acts, or processes. If this presumption were true, which I think it is not, it would still be necessary to infer mental powers, habits, or dispositions from the observed data, and to posit them as theoretical constructs in psychology if they are needed for explanatory purposes.

Whether or not the presumption underlying the introspective method in the study of man is valid need not concern us here; for, as I pointed out earlier, the question about how man differs requires a comparative study of man and other animals; and, for that purpose, the evidence to be comparable must be obtained by the *same* method in the study of both. That being the case, the method must be behavioristic, not introspective, since only the former is applicable to both man and other animals. In attempting to resolve the pivotal issue in this inquiry, I will, therefore, not depart from the procedures of methodological behaviorism, either in this chapter or the next.

Though, as I pointed out above, the scientific study of natural objects has always followed the procedures of methodological behaviorism for the simple reason that no other procedures are possible in scientific work, the word "behaviorism" itself is new and dates from the time when students of man decided to forsake introspective methods and to substitute for them the same procedures that are employed in all the other natural sciences. The name is new and its newness is connected with a twentieth-century movement in psychology; but while the name was invented by the author of *Psychology from the Standpoint of a Behaviorist*, John B. Watson, then of Johns Hopkins University, and given currency fifty years ago by both his protagonists and his antagonists, the use of behavioristic procedures in psychology is as old as Aristotle. [3] What is new with Watson and all the varieties of behaviorism that have developed since his day is not only the name, but the supposition made by most psychologists and even by philosophers who call themselves behaviorists—the supposition, namely, that methodological behaviorism is inseparable from metaphysical behaviorism.

The question whether or not that supposition is true—*please note, not the question whether metaphysical behaviorism is true*—is, in effect, identical with the question whether the difference in kind between men and other animals, which we cannot investigate except by behavioristic methods, must, therefore, be resolved in favor of saying that the difference in kind is superficial. If methodological behaviorism entails or presupposes metaphysical behaviorism, and if the latter denies the existence of anything immaterial, then a radical difference in kind is precluded by the very fact that we must use the behavioristic method to engage in a comparative study of man and other animals. It seems very odd, to say the least, to have the adoption of a method to deal with a question predetermine the answer that must be given. If we allow that to happen, the question itself vanishes into thin air. It is no longer a question that we need to investigate, since the only way in which we can investigate it predetermines the only answer that can be given.

I will, therefore, proceed as if the aforementioned supposition is false; which is not to say that metaphysical behaviorism (i.e., materialism) is false, but only that one can be a methodological behaviorist, as I have tried and will try to be throughout this book, without being committed to the metaphysical doctrine of materialism, as I am not; and, let me add at once, without being committed to its opposite, either. However, it is necessary to recognize that certain leading psychologists today (e.g., Hebb, Harlow, and Osgood, among others) explicitly aver their commitment to metaphysical as well as to methodological behaviorism. They do not contend that they can demonstrate the truth of metaphysical materialism. They say only that they think it is necessary to assume its truth in order to carry on their psychological investigations in a scientific manner, i.e., by the procedures of methodological behaviorism. [4] This, of course, is tantamount to their making the supposition that methodological behaviorism either presupposes or entails metaphysical behaviorism.

In spite of this, these scientists do not confine themselves to the use of neurological constructs for explanatory purposes, nor even to such appropriately behavioristic terms as "mediating factors or processes that are operative between stimulus and response." They have recourse to such mentalistic terms as "abstraction," "concept," or "idea." They hasten to assure us, of course, that as materialists they regard such theoretical constructs as ultimately reducible to neurological mechanisms or processes, or at least to being their inseparable concomitants. Whether they are or not is a question to be considered later in this book. What is more germane to our present discussion concerns the equivocal use that is made of such mentalistic terms as "concept" and "abstraction." The equivocation occurs in one way when they are used without qualifiers to represent exactly the same theoretical constructs to explain the behavior of linguistic and non-linguistic animals. It occurs in an opposite fashion when they are used with such qualifiers as "verbal" and "non-verbal" to apply to linguistic and to non-linguistic behavior; and when, in spite of that, it is nevertheless supposed that the term "concept" or "abstraction" retains the same meaning and refers to exactly the same type of psychological factor or process in men and other animals.

(5)

To carry the negative argument forward, I am now going to propose a hypothesis contrary to the one that I am trying to disprove. Both mine and its opposite must meet the test of accounting for the same experimental data. My hypothesis is that, to such things as the conditioned response, inhibition, and reinforcement, nothing need be added beyond the power of perceptual thought in order to explain animal behavior, especially those forms of animal learning that comparative psychologists suppose involve concept-formation. According to the hypothesis I am proposing, nothing like concept-formation is needed to explain the behavior in question. To test this hypothesis, it is necessary to give precise meanings to such terms as "perceptual thought" and "concept-formation" and to other terms involved in getting these meanings clear.

Donald Hebb suggests that we attribute "thought processes" to animals only when their behavior is not "at a reflexive sense-dominated level"; and, he adds, "verbal behavior is not a necessary requirement." [5] Following Hebb's suggestion, I propose that the non-verbal thought processes of animals—processes that remove the animal, in one way or another, from the domination of the immediate sensory stimulus—consist in (a) perceptual traces or residues, and (b) perceptual attainments. By perceptual traces or residues I mean memory-images that function representatively, i.e., in place of sensory stimuli that are no longer themselves operative. By perceptual attainments I mean the products of perceptual generalization and discrimination. I will use the term "perceptual abstraction" to name such products. Since all these elements are perceptual—either the *consequences* or the *products of perceptual activity*—it seems fitting to identify the thought processes of animals with *perceptual* thought. This is in line with the proposed hypothesis that the power of perceptual thought, its processes and products, are the only theoretical constructs needed to explain animal behavior.

A word more must be said about the perceptual attainment that I have called a perceptual abstraction, resulting from perceptual generalizations and discriminations that are learned. By a perceptual abstraction in an animal I mean a disposition to perceive a number of sensible particulars (or, in laboratory parlance, stimuli) as the same in kind or as sufficiently similar to be reacted to as the same. For example, when an animal has acquired the disposition to discriminate between triangles and circles—in spite of differences in their size, shape, color, or position, and whether or not they are constituted by continuous lines or dots—that acquired disposition in the animal is the perceptual attainment I have called a perceptual abstraction. This disposition is only operative in the presence of an appropriate sensory stimulus, and never in its absence, i.e., the animal does not exercise its acquired disposition to recognize certain shapes as triangles or certain colors as red when a triangular shape or a red patch is not perceptually present and actually perceived.

Outside of the laboratory and in the field, ethologists have found that animals have the disposition to recognize other animals as members of their own species or as members of alien species, in spite of individual differences among the perceived instances.

Here again we have the operation of perceptual abstraction in animal behavior; but here the perceptual abstractions are, according to the ethologists, instinctive or innate. [6] They are not learned through experience by perceptual generalization and discrimination. Hence they are not perceptual *attainments*, but perceptual *endowments*. However, this difference does not affect their character or functioning as perceptual abstractions. While the innate disposition to discriminate between similar and dissimilar animals would appear to be a more complex perceptual abstraction than the acquired disposition to discriminate between triangles and circles, there is evidence that laboratory animals can learn to react in a discriminating manner to fairly complex types of objects. Degrees of animal intelligence are supposedly correlated with the degrees to which they possess the power of perceptual generalization and discrimination—the power to acquire perceptual abstractions. Degrees of this power, Professor Klüver has shown, can be experimentally measured by what he calls "the method of equivalent and non-equivalent stimuli." [7]

Perceptual abstractions are unobserved and unobservable factors in animal behavior, just as perceptual generalization and discrimination are unobserved and unobservable processes. They are theoretical constructs needed to explain certain types of observed animal behavior, just as the perceptual residue or memory-image is a theoretical construct needed to explain other types of observed animal behavior. Furthermore, conceiving the perceptual abstraction as a *disposition* accords with the principles of methodological behaviorism; for if the observed elements of behavior are actions or operations, the unobserved factors in behavior should be theoretically constructed as dispositions to act or operate in certain ways, without regard to whether the dispositions are innate powers or acquired habits.

(6)

Let me return to the hypothesis I have proposed, and let me repeat its central thesis: it maintains that such perceptual residues as memory-images and such perceptual attainments as perceptual abstractions are the *only psychological* constructs needed to explain the *learned* behavior of animals. I confine my attention to *learned* animal behavior because instinctive animal behavior, as I pointed out earlier, is not comparable with learned human behavior, and so is not relevant to the solution of the problem of man's difference. I also omit reference to conditioned responses and to the processes of conditioning, reinforcement, and inhibition, because while these factors or processes are needed to explain certain forms of *learned* behavior in animals, they are *neurological* constructs—constructs on the same level with stimulus and response. Calling memory-images and perceptual abstractions "mediating factors" is an attempt to put them on the level of stimulus and response by conceiving them as operating between the action of receptors and the action of effectors; but this attempt fails to alter their character as theoretical constructs. They are *psychological, not neurological.*

The thesis stated above can be tested against the same laboratory evidence that is offered by most comparative psychologists (with the possible exception of Klüver and Maier) to show that concept-formation must be attributed to animals in order to explain behavior observed in the laboratory. The thesis to be tested denies that this is so. It denies that the power of conceptual thought and its attainments are needed as theoretical constructs to explain the behavior in question. Before we examine the data by which the proposed hypothesis can be tested, it is necessary to expand the hypothesis to include a clear distinction between the perceptual attainment I have called a perceptual abstraction and the conceptual attainment I will now call a concept. (Both, by the way, are unobservable. Concepts are no more directly inspectable occurrents in experience than perceptual abstractions are. [8])

Clarity on this point is crucial. The comparative psychologists claim that unverbalized perceptual abstractions are non-verbal concepts; they claim that the process of perceptual generalization and discrimination that gives rise to perceptual abstraction is a process of concept-formation. The hypothesis I am proposing denies these claims. It maintains, on the contrary, that the process of concept-formation is beyond the power of perceptual thought, that concepts, non-verbal or verbal, are not the products of perceptual generalization and discrimination, and that perceptual abstractions cannot be identified with concepts, not even with non-verbal concepts. To do so is to use the term "concept" in a violently equivocal fashion.

Like the perceptual abstraction, the concept is an unobservable factor in behavior; it is, therefore, a psychological construct and should be defined in dispositional terms. If we restrict ourselves for the moment to concepts that relate to perceived or perceptible objects, a concept can be defined as an acquired disposition to recognize the kind of thing a perceived object is and to understand what that kind of thing is like. For example, to have the concept of dog is to have the disposition to recognize perceived animals as dogs and also to understand what dogs are like. In one respect a concept does what a perceptual abstraction also does. Since the concept enables us to recognize this sensible particular as being of a certain kind, it *ipso facto* enables us to recognize a number of sensible particulars as being of the same kind, and to discriminate between them and other sensible particulars that are not of the same kind. But the concept—of dog, for example—is first of all a disposition to understand what dogs are like; only secondarily is it a disposition to recognize this or that perceived particular as a dog; and it is only in the latter connection that it also functions as a perceptual abstraction does, to enable us to discriminate between sensible particulars that are and sensible particulars that are not the same in kind. In addition, the disposition to understand what dogs are like can be exercised when dogs are not actually being perceived as well as when they are; whereas perceptual abstractions, as dispositions to discriminate between sensible similars and dissimilars, function only when the sensible particulars are being perceived.

If animals had, through perceptual abstractions, the disposition to do more than discriminate between triangles and circles; if they had the disposition to recognize this perceived shape as a triangle and that perceived shape as a circle, together with the disposition to understand what triangles and circles are like; and if they could manifest by their observed behavior the latter disposition quite apart from perceiving any shapes whatsoever—then we would be justified in attributing concepts to them; for without this theoretical construct, their behavior could not be explained. However, as we shall see, no evidence is available to show that animals, over and above the disposition to discriminate between similars and dissimilars when presented with sensible particulars, also have the disposition to recognize this one sensible particular as being of a certain kind and to understand what kind of thing it is, i.e., to recognize this particular shape as a triangle and to understand what kind of shape a triangle is—in the absence of perceived triangles as well as in their presence.

A further point must be made, and it is of the greatest importance. All perceptual abstractions—in animals and in men—are dispositions that are operative only in the presence of perceived particulars. But human concepts, even when they relate to perceived particulars, are not operative only in the perceptible presence of those particulars; and *not all human concepts relate to perceived particulars*. In addition to concepts of such perceptible objects as dogs and roses, men attain, through the process of theorizing, concepts of such imperceptible objects as elementary physical particles and chemical valences. In philosophy they develop concepts of such imperceptible objects as truth and justice; and in psychological theorizing they employ concepts of such imperceptible objects as memory-images, perceptual abstractions, and concepts themselves.

Concepts of the latter type are the type that we have called theoretical constructs. They are formed (i.e., constructed) by relating other concepts—conjunctively, disjunctively, by negation, etc. Only concepts of the first type (i.e., concepts of perceptible objects) are formed on the basis of perceptual abstractions. Yet even these are not formed solely on that basis, but require, in addition, a process of construction in which concepts are related by conjunction, disjunction, negation, etc. In other words, *no concepts are derived solely from perceptual abstractions; none is simply an abstraction from perceptual experience; all are constructed, though some are constructed on the basis of perceptual abstractions and some are not; and it is only the latter that we call theoretical constructs.* [9]

To summarize: two points made above set up a sharp and clear distinction between perceptual abstractions and concepts. (1) As attained dispositions, perceptual abstractions are exercised only in the actual presence of perceived objects, whereas concepts are exercised even when the appropriate objects are not actually perceived, and even when they cannot be, because the objects are imperceptible. (2) Perceptual abstractions are attained solely by processes that involve the exercise of perceptual powers (i.e., perceptual generalization and discrimination), whereas concepts, even those that are concepts of perceptual objects, are never solely attained by the exercise of perceptual powers.

The fact that perceptual abstractions and concepts are functionally alike in one respect does not justify the comparative psychologists in saying that perceptual abstractions are rudimentary concepts. Though the concept of a perceptible object is a disposition to discriminate between similar and dissimilar particulars, it is never solely that, and it is that only in virtue of being a disposition to recognize each perceived particular as being of a certain kind and to understand what kind of thing it is. Furthermore, this disposition is operative when the perceptible objects are not actually being perceived as well as when they are. Hence a perceptible abstraction, which is a disposition *only* to perceive a number of sensible particulars as similar and to discriminate between them and other sensible particulars that are dissimilar, and is a disposition that functions *only* when the sensible particulars are being perceived, cannot be regarded even as a rudimentary concept of perceptible objects.

(7)

With my hypothesis sufficiently explicated and its constitutive distinctions made clear enough for the purpose at hand, we are now prepared to look at the relevant laboratory data, to see whether the experimental evidence supports the hypothesis proposed, or supports the contrary hypothesis advanced by most comparative psychologists. The evidence falls into two sets of findings, the first relevant to perceptual residues, the second relevant to perceptual attainments.

(1) The first set of findings consists of evidence derived from delayed-reaction and detour experiments. The data can be summarized as follows: (a) In delayed-reaction experiments, the animal, prevented from reacting immediately to a present stimulus, subsequently reacts, in the absence of that stimulus, in the way that it would have reacted to the stimulus at the time it was present, had it not been prevented from doing so. The inter-

val of the delayed reaction varies from extremely short intervals measured in seconds to a day or two at the most in a few exceptional cases. [10] (b) In detour experiments, the animal, blocked from a direct path of reaction to a present stimulus, takes a circuitous path that removes the stimulus for a time from the perceptual field. [11]

Can the behavior described be explained without the use of any psychological constructs whatsoever? Earlier experimenters with animals thought that it could be; but more recently, comparative psychologists (e.g., Hebb, Harlow, Osgood, and others) maintain that, to explain such behavior, it is necessary to posit mediating factors in the central nervous system—what Hebb calls "neural or humoral sets." These mediating factors (involving more than just connective action on the part of the CNS) explain, in the case of delayed-reaction experiments, the activation of the effectors at a time later than the activation of the receptors on the observed periphery of the animal's behavior; and, in the case of detour experiments, they similarly explain the animal's behavior during the time that the stimulus he is reacting to is not operative on his sense organs. [12]

The psychologists mentioned above and many others (especially those, such as Hunter, who made early use of the delayed-reaction experiment) are not content with this level of explanation. They wish to give a psychological as well as a neurological explanation of the observed behavior. To do this, they think it is necessary to introduce, on the psychological plane, something they call a "representative" or "ideational" factor as the psychological counterpart of the mediating factor in the central nervous system. Why? Because in the absence of the original stimulus (to stay on the psychological plane, they should say "with the cessation of the animal's perception of a certain object"), some psychological factor which takes the place of that perception must be operative to explain what the animal does after the elapse of a relatively short time or during the time that the animal is reacting to the object though it is not within his perceptual field. [13]

The scientists we are here considering call this factor "representative" because it takes the place of—it operates in place of —the perception that is no longer operative. But is it necessary to regard this representative factor as an idea or a concept? Only if ideas or concepts, which may be representative factors in certain types of human behavior that are quite unlike animal behavior in delayed-reaction and detour experiments, are the *only* representative factors that can be appealed to for explanatory purposes. As Maier and Schneirla point out, this simply is not the case. Conceptual attainments are not needed to explain the phenomena. Such perceptual residues as memory-images—either in immediate reverberating memory or in recall after longer intervals—suffice to explain the described behavior. No other theoretical constructs are needed except, perhaps, that of an emotional or appetitive drive that activates the memory in the case of the delayed reaction after an interval longer than seconds. Since, in the explanation of human behavior, memory-images are perceptual residues and ideas or concepts are not, it is a violation of Lloyd Morgan's rule to use ideas or concepts, as distinct from perceptual residues, when they are not necessary for the explanation of the behavior described. [14]

(2) The second set of findings consists of evidence derived from experiments on equivalent and non-equivalent stimuli, on generalization and transfer, on animal maze-learning, on cue-learning, on discrimination, and on solving multiple-choice problems. The data can be summarized as follows. The animal which, by learning or otherwise, reacts to a particular stimulus or cue in a particular way, transfers that same reaction to other stimuli or cues that are like it in type, though not like it in all particular respects. The amount of variation in the set of stimuli able to elicit the same response measures the degree of similarity required in order for the differing stimuli to function as equivalent. [15]

Can this behavior, as described, be explained without the use of any psychological constructs whatsoever? Yes, like the delayed reaction, it can be explained in neurological terms. That, at least, is the claim of McCulloch and Pitts, of Craik, and of others who have constructed electrical devices that simulate the action of the central nervous system in the perception of shapes and in pattern-recognition. However, these neurologists and computer technologists are not content to stay on that level of explanation, but insist upon introducing such terms as "concept" and "universal" into their treatment of the phenomena. [16] They are joined by the comparative psychologists who not only make these experimental findings the basis for attributing abstraction to animals, but also think that they have evidence here for concept-formation on the part of animals. [17]

They would be correct in their theory of the matter if they were content to employ a purely perceptual attainment, such as a perceptual abstraction, in order to explain a purely perceptual phenomenon; namely, discrimination between similars and dissimilars. But they do not stop there. As we have already noted, they make the same evidence that is the basis for inferring that animals abstract, generalize, and discriminate also the basis for inferring that animals form concepts. Of course, they have a right to use the word "concept" in this way—as referring to the same psychological factor that I have called a perceptual abstraction. But if they use the word "concept" in this way, then they do not have the right to use it also for a psychological factor that is operative in human behavior—a disposition to understand what a certain kind of object is like, whether or not it is actually being perceived and whether or not it is perceptible. To use the same word for psychological factors as different as these is to equivocate in a manner that renders a scientific theory almost worthless. [18]

The violence of the equivocation leads to the following patently fallacious piece of reasoning.

I. Concepts are
 (A) acquired dispositions
  (1) to recognize perceived objects as being of this kind or that kind and, at the same time,
  (2) to understand what this or that kind of object is like; and, in virtue of (1) and (2), also
  (3) to perceive a number of sensible particulars as being the same in kind and to discriminate between them and other sensible particulars that are different in kind; concepts are also
 (B) acquired dispositions to understand what certain kinds of objects are like
  (1) when the objects are not actually perceived, and
  (2) when they are not perceptible.

II. As experiments show, animals have, through the attainment of perceptual abstractions, acquired dispositions to perceive a number of sensible particulars as being the same in kind and to discriminate between them and other perceived particulars that are different in kind.

III. Therefore—because what is said in II above coincides with what is said in I, (A), (3) above—animals have concepts in some rudimentary form.

The conclusion may be true, but its truth is not established by the premises. What the premises do plainly show is that the experimentally observed behavior of animals can be adequately explained in terms of perceptual abstractions and the processes of perceptual generalization and discrimination that give rise to perceptual abstractions. These are the only theoretical constructs needed for explanatory purposes. Concepts (understood as quite distinct from perceptual abstractions) and concept-formation (understood as quite distinct from perceptual generalization and discrimination) are not needed and, therefore, they cannot be justified as theoretical constructs in the explanation of the observed behavior.

(8)

This concludes the negative phase of the argument. The hypothesis proposed, so far as it related to what theoretical constructs are and are not needed to explain the observed behavior of non-linguistic animals, has been checked against the relevant experimental evidence, and has found support therein. It remains to see whether the hypothesis, so far as it relates to what theoretical constructs are needed to explain human behavior, especially man's linguistic behavior, can be equally well supported. That belongs to the positive phrase of the argument and to the next chapter.

Two concluding comments may serve as a transition to the next chapter. *First*, I have said a number of times that the theoretical constructs that represent the processes or products of perceptual thought suffice to explain not only the behavior of non-linguistic animals but also whatever behavior is *common* to linguistic and non-linguistic animals. This may not be true for that part of human and animal behavior which involves perceptual abstractions. In the case of animals, perceptual abstractions are operative without benefit of the simultaneous operation of concepts. But if we assume for the moment that men have the power of conceptual thought, then it is unlikely that perceptual abstractions ever function in human behavior without the simultaneous operation of the concepts that provide an *understanding* in addition to a *recognition* of the perceived objects. It may rarely be the case (and then perhaps only under pathological conditions, such as those of agnosia) that perceptual abstractions are exercised blindly, i.e., the object is recognized but not understood. Only in such rare cases does the power of perceptual thought explain human behavior in the same way that it explains animal behavior. For the rest, it does not; because wherever in human behavior both concepts and perceptual abstractions are simultaneously operative with regard to the same perceived objects, that behavior cannot be equated with animal behavior. The only behavior that is common to linguistic and non-linguistic animals consists of performances (whether by men or by other animals) that do not involve concepts in any form or fashion. [19]

Second, it may be objected that all that has thus far been shown is that men *have* and animals *do not have* verbal concepts; and that when distinction is made between verbal and non-verbal concepts, perceptual abstractions can be identified with non-verbal concepts; in which case it would not be wrong, in the light of the evidence, to hold that animals do have concepts (i.e., non-verbal ones).

If by a verbal concept is meant a concept that is or can be expressed in words—not just in a name by itself, but in a sentence using that name—then it is at once clear that animals do not have verbal concepts, and equally clear that men do. If by a non-verbal concept is meant a concept that is not expressed in words, *but always can be*, then it seems to me just as plain that men have non-verbal concepts as well as verbal concepts, and that animals have neither.

However, the push of the objection may be in another direction. It may be to the effect that men have the type of concept that they do have *because they have words*, whereas animals have a different type of concept *because they are without words*. Thus understood, the objection contends that human concepts arise from or have their genesis in the use of language, and these are, therefore, properly called *verbal* concepts (i.e., concepts dependent on the use of words). In contrast, the objection may contend, animal concepts that do not arise from or have their genesis in the use of language are properly called *non-verbal* concepts (i.e., concepts not dependent on the use of words). Perceptual abstractions, which are no more than the disposition to recognize perceived objects as being of this or that kind, would then be the non-verbal concepts possessed by animals; whereas human concepts, which provide an understanding of what this or that kind of object is like (whether it is perceived, not perceived, or imperceptible), would then be verbal concepts in the sense above indicated.

The reply to the objection, thus understood, consists in challenging the sense in which the objection applies the terms *verbal* and *non-verbal* to concepts. (1) Are men able to form the type of concepts that they do form *because they have the words with which to form them*? (2) Or are men able to use the words that they do use significantly *because they have the concepts with which to use them*? Only if the answer to the first question is affirmative can the sense in which the objection uses *verbal* and *non-verbal* be sustained: for only then will all human concepts be verbal in type; and all non-human concepts, non-verbal in type. If, however, the reverse is the case and the answer to the second question is affirmative, no concepts are *verbal* in the sense in which the objection applies *verbal* and *non-verbal* to concepts; for then man's meaningful use of words depends on his having concepts, not the other way around. His having concepts and his use of them do not depend on his having and using words, though his use of language certainly helps to multiply and refine his concepts.

To attempt to show that concepts are the cause of man's meaningful use of words is all one with the effort to show the need (in order to explain the linguistic behavior of men) for theoretical constructs that represent the processes and products of conceptual thought—concept-formation and concepts. This is the task set for the next chapter and the positive phase of the argument. If it is successfully discharged, as I think it can be, the objection based on the distinction between *verbal* and *non-verbal* concepts will have been dismissed as without foundation.

CHAPTER 11

Resolution of the Pivotal Issue (II): The Positive Argument

(1)

EVEN though they admit that only man has a propositional language—that only man names things and makes sentences —the comparative psychologists nevertheless contend that the use of symbols is not confined to man. The behavior of other animals, they repeatedly assert, involves the use of symbols. Since the behavior of other animals is admittedly non-linguistic, they qualify this assertion by distinguishing between verbal and non-verbal symbols, just as they qualify their assertion that concepts function in the non-linguistic behavior of animals as well as in the linguistic behavior of men, by distinguishing between verbal and non-verbal concepts.

It was shown in the preceding chapter that the comparative psychologists equivocate in their use of the word "concept" when they use this word for a theoretical construct needed to explain the observed behavior of animals as well as men. When the difference between concepts and perceptual abstractions is clearly understood, it can be seen that all the experimental evidence advanced by the comparative psychologists can be explained without reference to concept-formation on the part of non-linguistic animals. The only theoretical constructs required for the explanation of non-linguistic behavior are perceptual residues (memories) and perceptual abstractions. The non-verbal mediating factors operative in the behavior of non-linguistic animals are memories and perceptual abstractions, not concepts. Hence, if there is any theoretical justification for dividing concepts into verbal and non-verbal, that must be derived from human behavior exclusively.

The same criticism applies to the use of the word "symbol" by the comparative psychologists. They use that word without distinction for two quite distinct types of signs—for *signals*, on the one hand, and for *designators*, on the other (i.e., on the one hand, for the type of sign that smoke is when it signifies fire, and, on the other hand, for the type of sign that the word "smoke" is when it signifies smoke). Once the distinction between these two types of signs or signifiers is clearly understood, it will be seen that the behavior of non-linguistic animals can be fully explained in terms of signals and without reference to designators. It can, furthermore, be shown that animals respond to verbal as well as non-verbal signals and that men use both verbal and non-verbal designators. Hence, it is not the distinction between verbal and non-verbal that differentiates human from animal behavior in the use of symbols, but rather the distinction between designators (verbal or non-verbal) and signals (verbal or non-verbal).

Because the word "symbol" has been used by so many writers in so many different senses, I propose to discard it entirely, and to replace it by the word "signifier" or, in shortened form, by the word "sign." [1] The latter is visibly present as the root of the words "signal" and "designator," which I will use for the two main types of signifiers. In these terms, it will be the task of this chapter to show that (1) the behavior of non-linguistic animals involves the use of signals, but never designators; (2) that human behavior involves both; (3) that the functioning of signals in the behavior of non-linguistic animals does not require concept-formation on their part; and (4) that the functioning of designators in human behavior cannot be explained without attributing the possession of concepts to man.

Of these four points, the last two are critical for the resolution of the pivotal issue concerning the difference between man and other animals. The establishment of the third point (that the functioning of signals in the behavior of non-linguistic animals does not require concept-formation on their part) will confirm the negative argument set forth in the preceding chapter. The establishment of the fourth point (that the functioning of designators in human behavior cannot be explained without attributing the possession of concepts to man) will constitute the positive argument that is needed to complete the resolution of the issue; for it is not enough to show, negatively, that the behavior of non-linguistic animals can be psychologically explained *without employing* concept-formation as a theoretical construct. It is also necessary to show, positively, that the psychological explanation of man's linguistic behavior *must employ* concept-formation as a theoretical construct.

When these two things have been shown, we shall be warranted in concluding that there is a psychological difference in kind between man and other animals—a difference in kind that turns on the use of concepts by man and not by other animals. That conclusion still leaves open the question whether the difference in kind is superficial or radical, as the opposite conclusion would not; for if the same psychological factors or processes, accompanied by differences in degree, could explain linguistic and non-linguistic behavior, we would know that the difference in kind between man and other animals, manifested by man's exclusive possession of a propositional language, was only a superficial, not a radical, difference in kind.

I propose to proceed in the following manner. I will first (in Sections 2 and 3 to follow) establish the distinction between signals and designators by showing how these two types of signifiers function in human behavior. I will next (in Section 4) examine the experimental data bearing on the role of signs in animal behavior, and show that the evidence points exclusively to the signal type of sign, not to designators; and in this connection I will argue that the functioning of signals in animal behavior *does not involve* concepts. Finally (in Sections 5 and 6), I will argue for the conclusion that the functioning of designators in human behavior *does involve* concepts.

The analysis of linguistic behavior that follows is by no means a complete or exhaustive account of human language or of all types of signifiers and all modes of signification. It is restricted to the one distinction that is needed for the present purpose—the distinction between signals and designators. And for this purpose, I will, furthermore, restrict the analysis to the simplest type of designators, exhibited in man's use of common nouns—the type of designators that a relatively young child employs in his first efforts to attach different names to the different types of objects that confront him. [2]

(2)

Let us examine some obvious examples of signals and signaling in human behavior. In terms of these examples, we will be better able to define this type of signifier and this mode of signifying. The examples fall into two groups.

(1) On the one hand, we have such things as clouds signifying rain, smoke signifying fire, or a darkened landscape in daytime, through signifying clouds, indirectly signifying rain. In each of these examples, we have one natural object perceived signifying another natural object that is, at the time, not perceived. Let us call these signs *natural* signals. Men learn their significance from experiences in which the thing signified (the rain or the fire) is related to the signifier in a temporal or causal sequence. These sequences are not invariable. The gathering of clouds is usually, not always, followed by rain; smoke is usually, but not always, produced by the lighting of fires. That is why Aristotle called such signs fallible, reserving the term "infallible sign" for the relatively rare instances in which the sign and the thing signified are natural objects that are invariably and necessarily connected as cause and effect, or antecedent and consequent. [3]

(2) On the other hand, we have such things as a railroad semaphore signifying an unseen train ahead; or a curved line on a highway plaque signifying an unseen curve in the road. In each of these examples, we have humanly invented or instituted signs functioning, when observed, to signify unperceived objects or conditions. Let us call these signs *conventional* signals, to indicate that the sign is not a natural object but man-made.

Natural and conventional signals differ in a number of respects. Whereas natural signals are usually fallible signs, conventional signals always are; there is no necessary and invariable connection between a conventional sign and the thing it signals. Furthermore, even when natural signals are fallible signs, their misleading character does not derive from intentional prevarication on the part of nature; i.e., when the perceived clouds lead us to expect rain and the rain does not occur, that is not because the clouds have lied to us, but because the natural sequence of rain following clouds is not invariable. Conventional signals, in contrast, can be used intentionally to deceive, as when prankish boys change a highway sign to mislead motorists. And while the meaning of natural signals is usually learned from experience and the meaning of conventional signals is usually learned by explicit verbal instruction, the reverse is also true. A motorist who had not studied the highway manual might learn solely from experience the meaning of the conventional signals posted along the road; so, too, children can be taught the meaning of natural signals by verbal instruction—that clouds mean rain, or that smoke means fire. None of the differences mentioned above affect in the least the mode of signifying that is common to natural and conventional signals. That remains the same whether the meaning of the signal is learned from experience or by verbal instruction, and whether the signal is a fallible or an infallible sign.

In addition to the natural and conventional signals illustrated in the foregoing examples, there are the signals that are elements of human behavior itself. Some of these are natural, some conventional. For example, an involuntary blush is a natural signal, signifying embarrassment; an involuntary scream or roar is a natural signal, signifying fear or anger. In contrast, we have elements of human behavior that are conventional signals, as when a contrived and voluntary gesture comes by custom to signify impatience or displeasure, assent or dissent; e.g., the waving of an arm or the nodding of the head. It will be noted that, in these examples, the thing signified is related to the signal as cause to effect, or antecedent to consequent; whereas in the earlier examples, the signal is the cause or antecedent and the signified the effect or consequent. This difference, as we shall see, does not affect the mode of signifying whereby signs function as signals. The underlying relation is the same whether the perceived signal is the cause or the effect, the temporal antecedent or the temporal consequent, of the thing it signifies.

Perceived signals of all sorts not only signify unperceived objects, happenings, or conditions, but they may also elicit actions with respect to the unperceived things that they signify. Thus, for example, the clouds that signal rain may elicit the action of carrying an umbrella; the railroad semaphore, the action of stopping the train; the roar of anger, the action of withdrawal; the gesture of impatience, the action of hurrying up. Contrary to the erroneous supposition that is central to the behavioristic account of the meaning of signs in human behavior, the actions thus elicited are *not* integral or constitutive parts of the meaning of the signal, but only adventitious consequences of the meaning. Clouds signify rain in the same way for those who do and do not carry umbrellas when they see clouds and read the signal as meaning rain. The same point can be made for all the other examples of signaling.

It is of the utmost importance to recognize that the action taken is something that *follows the interpretation of the signal*, and therefore falls outside that interpretation; it is, moreover, contingent—it may or may not happen. Whether or not it does, the interpretation of the signal remains the same; in other words, the meaning of the signal is in no way constituted by the action or inaction that follows. [4] The fact that we sometimes infer a person's interpretation of a signal from the action he performs when he has interpreted it does not alter what has just been said. We often make mistakes in such inferences precisely because a person's behavior is itself an unreliable signal of his interpretation or understanding of signals.

We are now ready for a definition of the mode of signification that relates signals to the things they signify. The relationship is that which obtains in ordinary if-then implications. Accordingly, to interpret clouds as signaling rain is to understand that clouds portend rain: *if* clouds, *then* rain. The same holds true for all the other examples given: if a dropped semaphore, then a train ahead; if an explosive roar, then anger in the person emitting the sound; if a nod of the head, then assent by the person nodding his head. For brevity of reference in what follows, I will speak of the mode of signification that signals possess as *implicative meaning*. To say that the perceived signal X signifies or means the unperceived object Y is equivalent to saying *X implies Y*, or *if X, then Y*; and the interpretation of signals is equivalent to making inferences of the sort that Hume described as being grounded in the frequent or customary conjunction of things in experience.

(3)

What is the mode of signification that relates designators to the things they designate, and how do this type of signifier and mode of signifying differ from signals and signaling? To answer these questions, let us consider some obvious examples of designation in human linguistic behavior.

I must begin by calling attention to the fact that the examples of designators to be given include no natural things, like clouds or smoke, the blush of embarrassment, or the roar of anger. *There are no natural designators; all are conventional*, i.e., man-made and somehow voluntarily contrived. The reason why this is so will not become clear until we understand how designators signify the things they designate.

The only examples that we need consider illustrate two different types of conventional designators. One type consists of words functioning as names, not as ejaculations, outcries, or commands. The other—the non-verbal type—consists of icons, such as the striped pole in front of the barber shop or the figure of a man on the door of a lavoratory reserved for men.

Consideration of these non-verbal designators helps us to see at once that designators can function in the same way that signals do—to elicit appropriate actions. The icon on the lavatory door not only designates the character of the room that lies behind the door, but it also usually elicits one sort of action from men and another from women. Though they act in opposite ways, men and women interpret the icon in exactly the same way; if they did not, they would not act in opposite ways. This is conclusive proof that here, as in the case of signals, the action elicited is not a constitutive part of the meaning, but only a contingent and variable consequence of it.

What is true of non-verbal designators holds as well for names, or verbal designators. Anyone who attentively observes the growth of a young child's vocabulary will find that the child is able to designate the objects in picture books, giving different types of objects different names, long before the child has had any direct experience with the objects pictured and long before he has developed characteristically different patterns of behavior appropriate to the different types of objects he is able to name.

He may later learn to respond in quite different ways to the things called boats and the things called airplanes, but since that is long after he is able to use the words "boat" and "plane" significantly, his non-verbal behavioral responses can be no part of the meaning that these verbal designators have for him at first.

When I distinguished a moment ago between words used as designators and words used as ejaculations or commands, I not only wanted to point out that words are not always used as designators, but also to point out that words can sometimes be used as signals. Thus the word "dinner" called out in a loud voice may sometimes function in the same way as the ringing of the dinner bell; and the word "danger" may function on a road sign as does the flashing red light. When they do function in this way, these words have implicative meaning; they function as signals do. But unlike the dinner bell and the flashing red light which never have any designative meaning, the words "dinner" and "danger" have a designative mode of signifying; that is their primary meaning, without which they could not ever serve as signals. If the word "danger" did not, in the first place, designate a certain type of situation, that word could not signal, like the flashing red light, the unperceived situation to which we usually but not always react by avoidance. In short, naming-words are primarily designators and only occasionally and secondarily do they serve as signals; and then only by virtue of their designative meaning.

These things being clear, I can now define the mode of signifying that relates designators to the things they designate. For this purpose I am going to consider only verbal designators, not icons; and among verbal designators, I am going to confine my attention to nouns used as common or general names—the very simplest case of naming.

Just as in the case of signals, where the logical relation of implication helped us to define the way in which a signal means the thing it signifies, so here the logical relations of denotation and connotation help us to define the way in which a designator means the thing it signifies. The denotation of a term is an object atended to—a thing, an event, or an action. But the object denoted by a common or general name is never denoted as an unclassified or unique individual, but always as a classified particular, i.e., a member of this or that class of objects. A description or definition of the class of objects to which the denoted particular belongs constitutes the connotation of the word that denotes the particulars in question. The familiar logical principle, that the denotation and the connotation of a term vary inversely, calls our attention to the fact that as more elements enter into the connotation of a word, the class of objects to which the word applies denotatively becomes more restricted. Thus, for example, the connotation of the word "dog" has more elements than the connotation of the word "mammal," and fewer than the connotation of the word "poodle"; inversely, the word "dog" denotes a more restricted class of objects than "mammal" and a less restricted class than "poodle."

I will subsequently show that this special linkage between the denotation and the connotation of words cannot be explained without reference to concepts and concept-formation. I will also show that the inseparability of denotation and connotation, which is based on the relation of concepts, explains the double use that men can make of common or general names: either (1) to designate a perceived particular as a member of a certain class of objects, or (2) to designate the class of objects itself when no particulars that are members of the class are at the moment being perceived. In the second alternative, it may even be the case that no particular instances of the class can ever be perceived, either because they are imperceptible or because they do not exist. [5]

For the present, however, let us confine our attention to the first and simplest case of designation—the one in which the thing designated is a perceived particular. A man's use of the word "clouds" or "rain" to designate these familiar objects when they are perceived will suffice to draw a sharp line between the denotative meaning of designators and the implicative meaning of signals. The *perceived and existent clouds* signal the *unperceived and as yet non-existent rain*. The perceived word "clouds" designates the *perceived clouds*, just as the perceived word "rain" designates the *perceived rain*. And if we were to extend our consideration to include the connotative as well as the denotative aspect of the meaning of words used as designators, we would go on to say that, whereas the perceived and existent clouds signal the unperceived and as yet non-existent rain, the word "clouds" or "rain" designates clouds or rain, *perceived* or *unperceived*, *existent* or *non-existent*. [6]

(4)

It was pointed out earlier in this chapter that comparative psychologists and other behavioral scientists claim that "non-verbal symbols" function in the behavior of non-linguistic animals. This claim is closely connected with another claim made by such writers as Osgood, Harlow, Hebb, Nissen, Heron, Herrick, and Otto Koehler; namely, that concept-formation and the use of concepts take place in non-linguistic animals. [7] The second claim would be substantiated if the functioning of the "non-verbal symbols" involved transcendence of the immediate perceptual environment, and so could not be explained except in terms of the use of concepts by the animal.

I now propose to examine these two claims and to show that the second is unsubstantiated. To do so, I must first expose the equivocation that is concealed in the phrase "non-verbal symbol." The psychologists whose position is here being criticized use the word "symbol" as if all "symbols" (i.e., signs or signifiers) were of the same type and had the same type of meaning or significance. As they use the word, a railroad semaphore signaling a train ahead and the word "dog" naming the animal lying in the path ahead are symbols in the same sense; for them the word "dinner" is a symbol in the same sense whether it names one of the three meals that we are accustomed to having each day, or signals, just as the dinner bell does, that a meal is ready to be eaten. Accordingly, it is possible for them to argue that since the non-verbal symbols that function in animal behavior are symbols in the same sense as the words that function in human behavior, it follows that whatever psychological factors or processes explain the operation of symbols must be present in the same way, though not to the same degree, in linguistic and non-linguistic animals.

The argument as stated is seen to be fallacious as soon as its equivocal use of the word "symbol" is pointed out. Once we make the distinction between two quite distinct types of "symbols"—or, in my terminology, between two types of signifiers or signs—the fundamental premise of the argument must be revised as follows. The assertion that the non-verbal symbols that function in animal behavior are symbols in the same sense as the words that function in human behavior must be replaced by the assertion that the signals (verbal or non-verbal) that function in animal behavior *appear* to be signals in the same sense as the signals (verbal or non-verbal) that function in human behavior. *Whether they are or not depends upon whether they function in precisely the same way in men and other animals.* In any case, the psychologists must concede that, in the behavior of non-linguistic animals, no signs occur that function as designators rather than as signals. Since human words sometimes do function as signals to elicit responses from animals, it cannot be said that words (i.e., verbal signals) do not occur as stimuli in the behavior of non-linguistic animals. But what can and must be said is that no signs having designative significance, whether words or icons, function in the behavior of non-linguistic animals.

The psychologists cannot deny this, for they admit that only man has a propositional language, which is tantamount to admitting that only man names things and makes sentences. But if only linguistic animals (i.e., animals with a propositional language) name things (i.e., use signifiers that have a designative mode of signification), then it would be self-contradictory to assert that the occurrence of signs in the behavior of non-linguistic animals includes the type of sign that is a designator as well as the type of sign that is a signal.

With the equivocation on the word "symbol" removed, we are left with the proposition that signals do appear to function in the behavior of non-linguistic animals. This is a matter of common observation. Anyone who has trained a domesticated animal knows that words of command or restraint elicit appropriate responses of a sort that makes the words look *as if* they were functioning as signals. Long before the era of laboratory research in the field of animal behavior, naturalists observed that perceptible changes in the environment—the darkening sky, the sound of distant thunder, the sudden outcries of other animals, certain smells carried by the breeze or sniffed upon the ground—appear to operate as signals insofar as they elicit responses appropriate to things that are, *at the moment*, not yet present or perceived. These observations have been confirmed by all the experimental work done on animals, especially the work on conditioned responses and on the learning of cues. What the experiments show is that animals can learn to respond to a given stimulus as if it represented or stood for something that, at the moment, is not perceptually present; e.g., the bell in Pavlov's conditioned-reflex experiment, eliciting anticipatory salivation, appears to function as a signal for the food that is not perceptually present; the shape or color that serves as a cue to the presence of food in one rather than another box appears to function similarly.

We can, for our present purpose, ignore the difference between learned and unlearned cues. For the most part, the field naturalists and the ethologists have studied the operation of unlearned cues—the smell that instinctively elicits the food-getting response, the noise that instinctively elicits the danger-avoiding response, the shape that instinctively elicits responses of approach and association. The laboratory psychologists have almost exclusively studied the operation of learned cues by means of experiments in which the learned cue is a stimulus that has been associated, either by contiguity or succession, with another stimulus that is capable of eliciting a certain characteristic response. Learned or unlearned, cues are stimuli that appear to function as signals—perceived objects that signify unperceived things or events to which the animal starts to react before they are perceived.

I have repeatedly said "appears to function as a signal" in order not to permit the question at issue to be begged. The critical question is whether the learned and unlearned cues that *appear* to function as signals in animal behavior *really* do function in the same way as the signals that operate in human behavior. In order to make the point quite clear, let us for the moment assume that they do.

When, in the human sphere, the dinner bell functions as a signal, the following obtains. The man who out-of-doors hears the dinner bell and who has learned its significance as a signal is made aware of an unperceived event or state of affairs: inside the house, a table has been laid and food is ready to be served. To say that the dinner bell, as signal, means this to him is to say that his interpretation of the dinner bell (i.e., his understanding of the signal's meaning) leads him to think of something he cannot at the moment perceive. He may or may not verbalize the inference that if the dinner bell has rung, then dinner is ready in the dining room. In addition, he may or may not react to the dinner bell by going in to dinner. If he is intensely occupied with other things, he may decide to forego the meal; if his hunger is intense enough to prevail, he may decide to stop what he is doing and go to dinner. But whether or not he verbalizes the inference and whichever way he reacts, the dinner bell has functioned as a signal if the perceived sound of a certain sort leads him to become aware of or to think of an unperceived state of affairs of a certain sort.

Behavioristic evidence that his perception of the signal has led him to think of the unperceived state of affairs will, of course, take the form of a verbalized statement made by him. That he is able to think of or be aware of an unperceived state of affairs points to the operation in him of some psychological factor that serves to represent that which is not perceptually present. What is this representative factor? (i) It may be a perceptual residue, an image; and this image may be abstract or generalized in the same way that perceptions themselves can be abstract or generalized. (ii) Or it may be a concept.

In the first alternative, the recognition of the particular sound as being of a certain kind (the sound of a dinner bell) involves a perceptual abstraction; and the awareness that a certain type of unperceived situation exists (that dinner is ready) involves the imaginal residue of another perceptual abstraction (the recognition of a certain state of affairs as being dinner). In the second alternative, the perceptual abstraction that enables the man to recognize a certain sound as a dinner bell may also call into operation the imaginal residue of another perceptual abstraction through which he can recognize a certain state of affairs as being dinner; but in this alternative, both may be accompanied by concepts (i.e., of dinner bell and of dinner) that enable him to understand what dinner bells and dinners are like even when no dinner bells are sounding and no dinners are laid before him to be eaten.

Can we tell which alternative is the correct description of the psychological factors in operation when the dinner bell functions as a signal in the human case? Yes, but only on the condition that we have recourse to statements by the man. If he makes statements in which such words as "dinner bell" and "dinner" are used with designative significance to name different types of objects, then, as I will attempt to show in the next section, we can be sure that concepts have entered into his interpretation of the dinner bell as a signal of dinner. But if the man were a totally non-linguistic animal (i.e., completely unable to use words designatively and unable to make sentences), we would have absolutely no grounds for asserting that concepts played a part in the functioning of the dinner bell as a signal. Hence, if we felt the need to posit the operation of a psychological factor that served to represent the unperceived dinner and to mediate between the perceived dinner bell and the overt response of going in to dinner, we would be justified in asserting no more than the presence of a certain type of perceptual residue (i.e., a generalized image of dinners). This would be justified because we know that an animal with perceptual powers can have such perceptual residues.

Now let us turn to a parallel case in the sphere of animal behavior. The bell in Pavlov's conditioning experiment *appears* to function for the laboratory dog as a signal of food, just the the dinner bell appears to function as a signal of dinner in the human case. Since the laboratory dog is a non-linguistic animal, he cannot verbalize for us the inference that if the bell has sounded, food will soon be forthcoming and so it is time for salivation to begin. To attribute such an inference to the animal, in the absence of verbalization, is an anthropomorphic interpretation of what is going on in the animal, an interpretation of the sort that Lloyd Morgan's canon was intended to prevent.

Without attributing to the animal an inference that would be expressed verbally in the sentence "If the bell sounds, then food will soon be forthcoming," can we still say that the sounding bell has the significance of a signal for the animal—that the bell *means* to the animal the imminence of food? To this question I think the answer must be *yes*, in one sense; *no*, in another. Let me explain. The animal's response to the bell in the form of salivation can be taken as an indication that the bell has functioned as a signal of the food to which, if it were perceptually present, the animal would have responded by salivation. But in the human case, as we have seen, the dinner bell functions as a signal of dinner whether the man who hears the dinner bell reacts by going in to dinner or refrains from doing so. In other words, the perceived sound in the human case functions as a signal whether the man's overt non-verbal behavior takes one form or another; whereas the perceived sound in the case of the dog can be said to function as a signal *only* if the dog overtly reacts to it in a certain way. Should the dog fail to salivate when the bell is sounded, we would have no grounds whatsoever for saying that the bell functioned for him as a signal.

Hence the perceived sound is not a signal in exactly the same sense for the laboratory dog and for the human being. We can regard the bell as a signal for the laboratory dog only when it elicits a certain type of reaction on his part, i.e., salivation. In the absence of that reaction, it is impossible to say that the bell has functioned as a signal. But in the human case, the meaning of the bell as a signal of dinner remains exactly the same whether the man goes in to dinner or refrains from doing so. In this case, the overt behavior—either of going in to dinner or of passing it up—is a *consequence* of the meaning that the signal has for the man, and is not *constitutive* of it. Signals have meaning for men, but they may function without meaning for other animals; hence the perceived sounds are not signals *in the same sense* for the man and for the dog, since to be signals in the same sense, they would have to have meaning *in the same way*, which is clearly not the case.

Nevertheless, we have conceded that signals do function in animal behavior, though in a non-human way. The way in which the sounding bell functions as a signal for Pavlov's laboratory dog can be taken as typical of all cues in animal behavior, learned or unlearned. What is required to explain the functioning of all such cues? Do we need to posit the possession of concepts by non-linguistic animals in order to explain their reactions to cues that involve behavior appropriate to objects which at the time are not being perceived? The answer to this question is, as we have seen, unqualifiedly negative. If, in the human case, we would not be justified in attributing concepts to a man who could not verbalize his interpretation of signals, we are in exactly the same position with respect to non-linguistic animals. Should there be a need to posit some psychological factor that serves to represent the unperceived object or situation to which the animal reacts under the stimulation of a signal or cue, the only thing we are justified in positing is a perceptual residue in the form of a generalized image of that which is at the moment unperceived. [8]

With this, the negative phase of the argument can be concluded. We saw in the preceding chapter that the experimental data on animal learning that involves delayed responses and detours or that involves perceptual abstraction and generalization can be explained without attributing concept-formation to non-linguistic animals. We now see that the functioning of learned or unlearned cues in animal behavior can also be explained without reference to concept-formation on the part of non-linguistic animals. If the cue is learned, the mechanism of the conditioned response together with the mechanisms of reinforcement and inhibition suffice to explain the animal's behavior in response to the cue as a signal, to which it responds without any apprehension of the signal's meaning. If the cue is unlearned, the mechanisms that underlie species-predictable behavior (i.e., instinctive patterns of response) suffice to explain the animal's behavior in response to the cue as a signal, again without any apprehension of the signal's meaning. In either case, if there is need to posit a psychological factor that is representative in function and that serves to mediate between stimulus and response, the need can be satisfied by a factor that falls within the range of the perceptual powers possessed by animals, i.e., by a perceptual residue in the form of a generalized image.

The psychologists who go beyond this to posit concepts and concept-formation in animals can do so only by ignoring a whole series of facts: *first*, that two kinds of signs operate in the behavior of linguistic animals (signals and designators), whereas only signals, verbal as well as non-verbal, appear to be present in the behavior of non-linguistic animals; *second*, that the signals which appear to be present in the behavior of non-linguistic animays are not signals in the same sense and do not have meaning in the same sense as the signals that function in human behavior; and *third*, that unless the meaning of the signal is or can be verbalized in the human case, the functioning of signals in human behavior does not require concept-formation for its explanation, and so *a fortiori* concept-formation is not required to explain the functioning of signals in the behavior of non-linguistic animals.

(5)

What remains to be seen is that concept-formation and concepts must be posited as theoretical constructs in psychology in order to explain the functioning of designators in human behavior.

Though designators may be either verbal or non-verbal (i.e., words or icons), we can for the purposes of the present argument confine our attention to verbal designators, and to the simplest type of these—such common or general names as "dog," "mammal," "poodle," etc.

Since the signs that function as designators are all conventional signs, they are all in the first instance *meaningless* marks or sounds that, as such, have no natural relation to the things that they come to designate. Clouds have a natural relation to rain, and smoke to fire; but the word "cloud" and the word "rain" have no natural relation to the phenomena they designate. The denotative and connotative meaning of a word is something that is acquired by a physical mark or sound when it is used as a name or designator. By acquiring designative significance, the originally meaningless mark or sound becomes a meaningful word. The physical mark or sound not only acquires or gets meaning; it may also undergo change in meaning, and even lose its meaning; moreover, the same physical mark or sound may be meaningful for some men and meaningless for others; and even for those for whom it has meaning, its meaning is seldom the same. All of this makes abundantly clear that the designative significance of a word is *separable* from its physical being as a mark or sound.

How, then, does a meaningless physical mark or sound acquire the denotative and connotative meaning whereby it becomes a meaningful word that is able to function as a name or designator? It may be thought that the physical mark or sound gets its meaning as a naming-word from the object that it is used to name. Thus, for example, by repeatedly attaching a certain sound to particular instances of a certain kind of object, or by repeatedly affixing a certain mark to pictures of instances of that kind of object, the child is taught to use this sound or this mark as the name or designator for that kind of object. According to this explanation, the sound or mark "dog" becomes a meaningful designator of a certain kind of quadruped by being imposed frequently enough either upon particular instances of that kind, or on pictures thereof.

Is this explanation correct? If the sound or mark "dog" were the only vocable or notation that could be imposed as a name on the objects that it designates, it might look as if that vocable or notation acquired the designative meaning of the word "dog" directly from the perceptible objects on which it had been imposed as a name with sufficient frequency to make the connection habitual. But we can and do use other vocables and notations for the very same objects, and these also become meaningful names. I have a whole series of meaningful words to name or designate the animal lying at my feet: "poodle," "dog," "quadruped," "mammal," and so forth. These meaningful words do not have the same meaning; they vary in connotation and denotation; but their connotation and denotation are such that each of these words words functions to designate or name this particular object that is now perceptually present to me; and, in addition, each would serve to designate or name an indefinite number of other perceptible instances of the same class. According as the denotative and connotative content of the meaning changes from word to word, the class of objects designated thereby also changes, and so also the perceived or perceptible instances to which the word can be significantly applied as a name.

These things being so, it would appear to follow that a meaningless mark or sound cannot get its meaning from the perceived or perceptible objects to which it is attached or on which it is imposed as a name. For if it could, why would not the words "poodle," "dog," and "quadruped" all have the same meaning, since all can be used to name the same perceived object, or other perceptible objects of the same kind? To which it may be answered that since the word "poodle" is used to name some dogs (i.e., dogs of a certain kind), but not all dogs, and since the word "dog" is used to name some quadrupeds (i.e., quadrupeds of a certain kind), but not all quadrupeds, they differ in meaning even when they designate one and the same object—the perceived quadruped lying at my feet. It may then be said that the denotative and connotative meaning which each of these words has when it functions in any particular case as a designator for a perceived object is not derived from that perceived object, but from the whole class of objects to particular instances of which it is applied as a name.

This shift in the explanation of how a given meaningless mark or sound gets the meaning that it has when it functions as a name or designator leaves something more to be explained. A class of objects is not itself an object of perception. As we saw in the preceding chapter, even when, through the attainment of perceptual abstractions, we acquire the disposition to recognize this or that perceived object as being of a certain kind, we do not thereby have the disposition to understand what that kind of object is like, both when the object is perceived and when it is unperceived, or even when it is imperceptible. We saw, furthermore, that, in contradistinction to a perceptual abstraction, a concept is a disposition to do more than recognize that a perceived object is of a certain kind; it is primarily a disposition to understand what that kind of object is like. From this distinction between what perceptual abstractions and concepts enable us to do, we are led to two conclusions concerning the ultimate source of the meaning that is possessed by our common or general names when they are used as designators.

The first conclusion is negative. We first saw that the meaning of the word "dog" cannot be derived from the perceived object to which this word is applied as a name, because the words "poodle" and "quadruped" can also be applied to the same object as names, and the three words, when so applied, each have a different meaning. We then saw that the differing denotative and connotative meaning of these three words is connected with the fact that each designates a different class or kind of object, the perceived or perceptible instances of which are not co-extensive. If this leads us to say that the meaning of the word "dog," as also the meaning of the word "poodle" or of the word "quadruped," is derived from a certain class of objects, we must also admit that a class of objects is not itself a perceptible object. All we can ever perceive is a particular instance of a class, but not the class itself. A perceptual abstraction, the highest attainment of our perceptual powers, enables us to recognize that a perceived particular is an instance of a certain class or kind, but no more than that. It does not enable us to understand, either in the presence or in the absence of perceived particulars, what that class or kind of object is like. Hence, we are forced to the negative conclusion that the designative meaning of our common or general names cannot be explained by reference to any psychological attainment within the reach of our perceptual powers.

The second or positive conclusion is simply that our having concepts can explain what our having perceptual abstractions fails to explain. Our concept of dog and our concepts of poodle and of quadruped enable us to understand what each of these three kinds or classes of objects is like, and it is that understanding itself which confers denotative and connotative meaning on the word "dog" and on the words "poodle" and "quadruped," when these words are used as designators. None of these concepts is simple. Each is formed by the conjunction, disjunction, and negation of a number of concepts; and one set of concepts thus related constitutes our conception of dog, another set our conception of poodle, and still another our conception of quadruped. [9]

Accordingly, we are not only able to understand what poodles are like, but also to understand why all dogs are not like poodles. It is through having such understanding that we are able to use the words "poodle" and "dog" with different connotative, and hence with different denotative, meaning, and so even when we use them as designators for the same perceived particular, we are saved from the mistake of supposing that the words have the same meaning by the fact that we also use them as designators for different classes of objects.

If the meaning of our common or general names were derived from the perceptual abstractions whereby we are able to recognize that a perceived particular is of a certain kind, we would never be able to use them, as we do, in the absence of any perceived instances of the class or kind, to designate the class or kind itself to which perceptible particulars belong. Nor would we have at our disposal, as we do have, the use of words to designate classes or kinds of objects that are intrinsically imperceptible, as are many of the theoretical entities posited in the natural sciences. That we are able to use common or general names as designators in all these ways is possible only because, over and above perceptual abstractions, we have concepts to confer meaning on them.

To be sure that what has just been said is clear, let me summarize it by returning to the simple case of the three words—"poodle," "dog," and "quadruped"—all used to designate the animal lying at my feet, yet each used with a different meaning, as is evident from the fact that "dog" can be used to designate objects that "poodle" cannot be used to name, and similarly "quadruped" can be used to designate objects that "dog" cannot be used to name. Since the animal lying at my feet is and can be perceived in only one way, it cannot be the object *as perceived* that confers meaning on the three words that I can use to designate it, for if that were the case, the three words would be identical in meaning. But the perceived object can be conceived in a wide variety of ways, and so it is the object *as conceived* in one way, another way, and in yet another, which confers different meanings on each of the three words that I use to designate it. In short, common or general names that function as designators of perceived objects, but have different connotative and denotative significance as designators, get their different meanings from the perceived objects *according as these objects are differently conceived*. If I could not conceive or understand the perceived object lying at my feet in different ways—as a poodle, as a dog, as a quadruped, as a mammal, as an animal, and so on—I could not use a whole set of different words to designate it, each with a different meaning, i.e., a different denotative and connotative significance.

This simple case of using different common or general names to designate a perceived object clearly establishes the proposition that designators derive their denotative and connotative significance from concepts, not from percepts, perceptual residues, or even such perceptual attainments as perceptual abstractions. But the proposition thus established covers more than the simple case with which we have been dealing. It covers the case in which we use words to designate a class of objects, no particular instance of which is at present being perceived; and it also covers the case in which we use words to designate a kind of object that is intrinsically imperceptible, such as the theoretical entities posited in the natural sciences, the objects of mathematical theory, certain objects of philosophical thought, and so on. In view of this, the proposition should be more comprehensively formulated in the following manner: *a word that is a common or general name can be used to designate anything that we are able to conceive, whether or not it is perceived and whether or not it is perceptible.*

(6)

The foregoing account of the source of the significance possessed by the words that function as designators in human language restates a traditional triadic analysis of the meaning of designators. The three elements are as follows: (1) the sign or signifier—the physical mark or sound that is originally meaningless and that is conventionally instituted to serve as a name or designator; (2) the object signified, which may or may not be perceived, and may or may not be perceptible; and (3) the significance or meaning itself, through which or whereby the sign designates the object signified. The first and originally meaningless element becomes meaningful and is able significantly to designate the second element, the object signified, *only through the mediation of the third element*—the significance or meaning. [10]

In other words, that which is itself meaningless and acquires a meaning gets its meaning from that which *is* itself a meaning. If it were to acquire its meaning from something else that had a meaning only through having acquired it, we would be involved in an endless regress that would make the acquirement of meaning inexplicable or unintelligible. The inescapable distinction underlying this last statement is the distinction between *having* a meaning and *being* a meaning: signs and signifiers of all types—both signals and designators—only *have* meaning. Meaning is adventitiously attached to them. They can *be without* meaning; they can *get* meaning and they can *lose* it, or the meaning that they have can *change*. One thing that *has* meaning may *get* its meaning from something else that also *has* meaning, as one word often gets its meaning from other words. But whence do these other words that *have* meaning get their meaning? There is no satisfactory answer to this question unless there are in the world some entities that simply *are* meanings—entities the very being of which is to mean, entities which, therefore, do not ever get, lose, or change their meaning.

If the reader has followed the analysis given above of the meaning possessed by the words that are used as designators in human speech, he will know that the source of all the meanings possessed by anything which has, gets, loses, and changes its meaning lies in concepts, for concepts *are* meanings. To say that concepts *are* meanings precludes saying that concepts *have* meaning, or that their meanings can be *altered*, *enlarged*, *contracted*, etc. In the process of concept-formation, we can change our concepts, form new ones, relate them differently, and so on; but when we do so, we change the meanings in our possession, not the meanings of our concepts. Since each concept that we have is a meaning that we possess, it is obviously improper to ask about the meaning of a concept, or to ask about its connotation or denotation. Such questions are properly asked only about signs that *have*, *get*, *lose*, or *change* their meaning, not about concepts that *are* meanings. [11]

It is precisely because concepts *are* meanings that they can confer connotative and denotative significance on the meaningless vocables or notations that, by acquiring meaning from concepts, come to have the significance they do have when they function in human speech as designators. This analysis applies to those words which function as signals, but derive their significance as signals from their primary significance as designators. Does it also apply to conventional signs, verbal or non-verbal, that do not function as designators and have only the significance of signals? And does it apply as well to such natural signs as clouds or smoke that cannot function as designators, yet do have meaning as signals?

The answers to these questions were anticipated earlier in this chapter where it was pointed out that under certain circumstances, men, like other animals, react to signals, natural or conventional, without being able to verbalize the implicative meaning that relates the signal to the object it signifies—without being able to say "If X, then Y." In such circumstances, the signal may function as it does in the case of non-linguistic animals: either (a) meaninglessly or (b) with a "meaning" that is nothing but the response elicited by the signal or cue. But when a signal has meaning prior to and quite apart from the reaction it elicits; when the meaning it has remains the same whether it elicits this response or that; when, therefore, the response elicited, whatever it is, is consequent upon the meaning of the signal, not constitutive of it; and when the meaning of the signal can be verbally expressed in a statement of the form "If X, then Y," then we cannot explain how the signal in question *has* such meaning for us except in terms of the concepts that confer such meaning upon it.

Two alternative possibilities just mentioned above with regard to the functioning of cues in the behavior of non-linguistic animals deserve a word of further comment. (a) One alternative is that they function meaninglessly and their functioning can be described and explained without reference to meaning; e.g., when a laboratory dog, having gone through a process of conditioning, salivates at the sound of the bell, the bell, functioning as a substitute stimulus for the salivary reflex, operates as a cue without signifying food. On this hypothesis, it would be illicit anthropomorphizing to attribute to the animal an interpretative act that amounts to its saying to itself "If the bell rings, then food will soon be forthcoming, and so I had better start salivating now." The bell elicits salivation *without meaning food*. (b) The other alternative is that, in the behavior of non-linguistic animals, signals or cues do have meaning, but only in that special sense of "meaning" in which the "meaning" of a signal is nothing but the response that the signal elicits; e.g., the meaning that attaches to the bell for the conditioned laboratory dog is identical with the salivary response that it makes. On this hypothesis, the bell has no meaning prior to and apart from a response by the animal. On neither hypothesis does the bell function as a signal for the animal as the dinner bell functions as a signal for the man who *first* interprets it as signifying or meaning food and *then* responds in one way or another.

The critical point here is that the word "signal" is being used equivocally when, on the one hand, it is applied to the cues that function in the behavior of non-linguistic animals either (a) meaninglessly or (b) with a meaning that is nothing but the response elicited (e.g., salivation); and when, on the other hand, it is applied to the signals that function meaningfully in human behavior and function meaningfully by signifying or meaning the object (e.g., food) to which one or another response is then made. In addition, the word "meaning" itself is being used equivocally when, on the one hand, with regard to the behavior of non-linguistic animals, it is said that such substitute stimuli or learned cues as the laboratory bell have meaning; and when, on the other hand, in the case of human behavior, it is said that such signals as the dinner bell or the fire bell have meaning.

(7)

At the end of Chapter 10 we reached the conclusion that the experimental and ethological evidence concerning the behavior of non-linguistic animals does not require us, for the purpose of explaining the manifestations of animal intelligence and learning, to attribute to non-linguistic animals concept-formation and concepts. The power of perceptual thought (including perceptual residues, such as images, and perceptual attainments, such as perceptual abstractions) suffices to explain the observed phenomena.

At the end of Section 4 of the present chapter we reached the conclusion that the power of perceptual thought also suffices to explain the functioning of signals, verbal or non-verbal, in the behavior of non-linguistic animals. Since non-linguistic animals do not use verbal designators, since they do not react to verbal designators as designators, but only as cues, and since the functioning of cues, verbal or non-verbal, can be adequately described in terms of the instinctive or learned responses that they elicit, *without reference to meaning*, their functioning can be satisfactorily explained without attributing concept-formation and concepts to non-linguistic animals.

To these two negative conclusions we must now add the positive conclusion that, in the behavior of man, the only linguistic animal, the functioning of signs—both verbal and non-verbal, and both signals and designators—cannot be explained without attributing concept-formation and concepts to human beings. By "the power of conceptual thought" we mean no more than the ability to form, have, and use concepts. A man's use of the concepts that he has formed and possesses is manifested in his verbalized interpretation of signals, in his use of words to name or designate objects (perceived, perceptible, or imperceptible), and in his making of sentences that explicate the meanings of their constituent words. Hence, to say the very least, we cannot explain man's observed linguistic behavior without positing the power of conceptual thought and attributing this power to man. [12]

We have now affirmatively answered the question: "Do linguistic and non-linguistic animals differ *psychologically* in kind?" The difference lies in the fact that man has and non-linguistic animals do not have the power of conceptual thought, which is just another way of saying that we can explain the behavior of non-lingustic animals without attributing the power of conceptual thought to them, but we cannot explain the linguistic behavior of men without doing so. [13]

Since the power of perceptual thought is present in both men and other animals, a number of interesting psychological corollaries follow from the fact that non-linguistic animals exercise their powers of perceptual thought without the contribution that would be made by the simultaneous exercise of the power of conceptual thought; whereas in man the power of perceptual thought is seldom exercised without the co-operative functioning of the power of conceptual thought. Since these corollaries, however interesting, have no direct bearing on the question at issue, and since they might divert us from the one point with which we are concerned, I will discuss them in an appended note rather than here. [14]

That man differs psychologically in kind from non-linguistic animals, by virtue of his exclusive possession of the power of conceptual thought, still leaves quite open the question whether man's difference in kind is radical or only superficial. It is to that question that we turn in the chapters to follow.

CHAPTER 12

The Efforts of the Philosophers to Resolve the One Issue That Remains

(1)

WHAT HAS been established so far in the light of all the evidence that is at present available? Two things. (1) On the level of *observable behavior*, no infirmative evidence as yet exists to falsify the proposition that man and man alone possesses a propositional language. The truth of this proposition carries with it the truth of the proposition that there is a manifest difference in kind between man and non-linguistic animals. (2) On the level of the *psychological explanation* of the observed behavior of both linguistic and non-linguistic animals, the application of the principle of parsimony produces two results. (a) The negative edge of Occam's razor cuts away the grounds for attributing to non-linguistic animals anything beyond the power of perceptual thought, in order to explain their behavior. (b) Its positive edge supplies the justification for attributing the power of conceptual thought to man and to man alone, since man's ability to name or designate objects and to make significant declarative sentences about them cannot be explained except in terms of man's having the ability to understand what different kinds of objects are like and his having the ability to make judgments about them in the light of such understanding. These two abilities together with the additional ability to draw inferences from the judgments made or to construct arguments out of them, constitute the power of conceptual thought, the root of which is the ability to form and employ concepts.

The two aforementioned results of applying the principle of parsimony to psychological explanations of linguistic and non-linguistic behavior establish the truth of another proposition concerning the difference of man; namely, that man differs in kind from other animals on the *level of inferred psychological factors or processes* as well as on the *level of observed behavior*. The establishment of this proposition resolves the pivotal issue in the controversy about man. Since this leaves quite open the question whether the manifest and psychological difference in kind between men and other animals is superficial or radical, one issue still remains.

The question at issue can be stated in a number of ways. One way of stating it is to ask whether, on the *level of the neurological explanation* of man's observed behavior and of the power of conceptual thought that must be posited in order to give a satisfactory *psychological explanation* of linguistic behavior, no factors or processes need be posited that are not employed in giving a neurological explanation of the behavior of non-linguistic animals. If this question can be answered by showing that the only neurological difference between men and other animals, needed to explain man's having and other animals' lacking a propositional language and the power of conceptual thought, consists in a difference in degree of brain magnitude and complexity, then the issue can be resolved in favor of the proposition that man's difference in kind is only superficial, not radical. The statement just made must be expanded by adding one critical point: it must be shown that, in the continuum of degrees of brain magnitude and complexity, there is a threshold above which propositional language and conceptual thought occur and below which they do not; and that the size and complexity of man's brain lies above this threshold, and the brains of all other animals fall below it.

Another way of stating the question at issue is to ask whether the power and action of the human brain are *not only a necessary, but also the sufficient, condition* of man's having and exercising the power of conceptual thought, without which he could not exercise the power of propositional speech. The power and action of the human brain constitute the *sufficient condition* of conceptual thought if conceptual thought can be *adequately explained* in terms of neurological mechanisms and processes. They constitute only a *necessary, but not the sufficient, condition* of conceptual thought, if conceptual thought *cannot be explained without reference* to neurological mechanisms and processes, but if it also *cannot be adequately explained by reference* to them. If, on the first alternative, we were to find that the brain is the sufficient condition of conceptual thought, then we would be justified in concluding that there is probably a critical threshold in the continuum of degrees of brain magnitude and complexity, below which conceptual thought does not occur, and above which it does. If, on the second alternative, we were to find that the brain is only a necessary, but not the sufficient, condition of conceptual thought, then, even though there might still be a critical threshold in the continuum of degrees of brain magnitude and complexity, this could not by itself explain man's possession of the power of conceptual thought that is totally lacked by non-linguistic animals. Hence, in the first alternative, man's difference in kind would turn out to be only superficial; in the second, it would be radical.

Still another way of stating the question is to ask whether the human brain, together with the entire sensory and motor apparatus that are its integral appendages, is the organ of conceptual thought in the same sense that it is the organ of perceptual thought (i.e., of sensations and sensory affects, of perceptions, perceptual residues such as sensitive memories and memory-images, and perceptual attainments such as perceptual abstractions), and of the initiation of all the bodily movements or reactions consequent thereon. One answer to this question claims that the brain is the organ of conceptual thought and of the linguistic behavior consequent thereon in exactly the same sense that it is the organ of perceptual thought and of the non-linquistic behavior that is thereby initiated. The opposite answer claims that, while the brain is an organ indispensable to conceptual thought and linguistic behavior, it is not the organ of conceptual thought in exactly the same sense that it is the organ of perceptual thought. The first answer leads to the conclusion that man's difference in kind from non-linguistic animals is only superficial; the second, to the conclusion that the difference is radical.

While these three ways of stating the question at issue are, in effect, equivalent, the third way makes explicit an assumption that is implicitly present in the other two. The opposite answers to the third question both accept the assumption that is made by the way the question is asked; namely, that the brain *is* the organ of perceptual thought and of the non-linguistic behavior consequent thereon. The two answers differ only with regard to whether the brain is *also the organ of conceptual thought in exactly the same sense*. The same assumption is implicit in the first two questions and is accepted by the opposite answers to them: thus, the first question assumes that a satisfactory neurological explanation can be given of perceptual thought and of non-linguistic behavior; and the second question assumes that the brain is the sufficient, not merely a necessary, condition of perceptual thought and non-linguistic behavior.

Another point of prime importance is common to all three ways of stating the question at issue. All three appeal to the principle of parsimony and appeal to it in the same way. In each case, what is being asked is whether there is any justification for positing a factor other than the power and action of the brain in order to explain conceptual thought and linguistic behavior. In each case, the negative answer maintains that conceptual thought and linguistic behavior can be adequately explained in neurological terms, and so, according to the principle of parsimony, there is no justification whatsoever for positing any non-neurological factor for explanatory purposes. And in each case, the affirmative answer maintains that conceptual thought and linguistic behavior cannot be adequately explained in neurological terms, and so the other side of Occam's razor works to justify the positing of a non-neurological factor for explanatory purposes.

The operation of the principle of parsimony in the resolution of the ultimate issue concerning man's difference precisely parallels its operation in the resolution that we reached in the preceding chapter of the pivotal issue in this controversy. But the two cases are not exactly alike. In the case of the issue concerning the psychological difference between man and other animals, when the principle of parsimony worked to show that something over and above the power of perceptual thought was needed to explain linguistic behavior, we had, in the power of conceptual thought, the factor that was needed. Here, however, if the principle of parsimony works to show that some non-neurological factor is required to explain conceptual thought, we are left with a puzzling question. What is the nature of this other factor that is required, in addition to and in cooperation with the brain, in order to explain the psychological difference between men and other animals?

It seems evident that no other material factor—no other bodily organ, no other physiological mechanism or process—is needed to supplement the power of the brain and nervous system to provide an adequate explanation for conceptual thought. The non-neurological factor must, therefore, be an immaterial power of some sort. Since the word "immaterial" is as negative in its connotation as the word "non-neurological," we have hardly advanced very far in solving the puzzle. Yet we may not be able to go very much further than this in answering the question. We can, of course, have recourse to such traditional terms as *mind*, *intellect*, or *reason*, and, by using them, say that the hypothesis to be tested here is whether conceptual thought can be adequately explained by reference to the action of the brain alone or can be adequately explained only by reference to the action of the mind or intellect in conjunction with the brain. But this statement must itself be made more precise by adding two qualifications: *first*, that the mind is *existentially and causally distinct* from the brain; and *second*, that its action is the action of an immaterial power and not of anything that can be described as a bodily organ.

When we have thus stated the position that is taken by those who affirm man's radical difference in kind (i.e., by those who deny that the action of the brain is the sufficient condition or adequate explanation of conceptual thought), we cannot go much further in specifying the character of the non-neurological (i.e., non-physical, non-bodily) factor. So far as we are able to conceive it, it remains essentially negative in character, and whether we call it "mind" or "intellect" or refer to it as an "immaterial factor" or an "immaterial power," the question at issue, the opposite answers given to it, and the evidence and arguments offered in support of them, remain exactly the same.

However, there is one further point that must be made and made as clearly and emphatically as possible. The word "mind" or "intellect," as used above to designate the immaterial factor or power that, according to one position on the issue, must be posited in order to explain conceptual thought, *does not include the power of perceptual thought.* Let me stress this by spelling it out in the following way: (1) non-linguistic animals have the power of perceptual thought; (2) the assumption that the brain *is* the organ of perceptual thought, we saw earlier in this chapter, not only underlies all ways of stating the question at issue, but it is also adopted by opposite answers to that question; (3) in other words, all the phenomena of the perceptual order—sensations and sensory affects, sensitive memories and memory-images, perceptions and perceptual abstractions—can be adequately explained by reference to neurological factors and processes and, therefore, need no supplementary immaterial factor to complete the explanation; (4) hence, if the word "mind" or "intellect" is used to designate the immaterial factor that one answer to the question claims is needed to explain conceptual thought in man, these words cannot be univocally used to designate anything that is thought to enter into the make-up or constitution of non-linguistic animals.

Of course, the word "mind"—though perhaps not the word "intellect"—can be used in *quite another sense* to designate the kind of intelligence that non-linguistic animals possess, whereby they are able to solve problems by trial and error or insight, generalize from experience, achieve perceptual abstractions, learn to respond to cues, etc. Since both men and non-linguistic animals have the power of perceptual thought, in which sensitive intelligence and its related abilities reside, both men and other animals have minds *in this sense*, and in this sense mind is *not* an *immaterial (non-physical)* factor or power that is *existentially and causally distinct* from the brain and nervous system. But if mind in the sense of an immaterial or non-physical factor or power must be posited, as a factor over and above the central nervous system, in order to explain man's unique possession of conceptual thought, then non-linguistic animals are totally bereft of mind in the sense indicated.

In the light of the foregoing analysis of the one issue that remains, it seems reasonable and appropriate to refer to the answer that asserts the adequacy of a neurological explanation of conceptual thought as the *materialist* position on the issue; and to the opposite answer, which asserts the need for an additional and immaterial factor, as the *immaterialist* position. The two positions, thus named, represent opposed philosophical theories or hypotheses. Each has arguments to advance in its own favor, objections to raise against its opponent, and replies to the objections raised against itself. And both must submit alike to the test of empirical evidence that may falsify the one or tend to confirm the other.

(2)

It would be a happy circumstance if the whole matter could be left as just described. The issue is clear, the alternatives uncomplicated, the opposed answers squarely opposed. Unfortunately, the word "materialist" that I have used to name one of the two positions has connotations that either are not relevant to this issue or are wide of the mark; so, too, the word "immaterialist," especially the connotation that the mind, or the non-physical factor posited, is a relatively autonomous substance that is united with the body as a motor might be attached to or detached from the chassis of an automobile, or as a pilot is related to the ship that he steers.

In addition, the issue as stated above involves two conflicting hypotheses: on the one hand, the hypothesis of mind as a non-physical factor that operates in conjunction with a bodily organ such as the brain, and, on the other hand, the hypothesis of the brain alone as the sufficient condition of conceptual thought. It would be natural, therefore, for many readers who are acquainted with the philosophical literature of the mind-body problem to suppose that the controversy about the difference in man has, in its ultimate issue, now landed us squarely in the midst of that muddle.

That, fortunately, is not the case. The central questions in the mind-body problem, either in its classical formulation in the seventeenth, eighteenth, and nineteenth centuries or in the much improved versions of it that are now current, deal mainly, and sometimes exclusively, with the mind in that sense of the term in which it is common to man and other animals. Since mind in that sense of the term is equivalent to the power of perceptual thought and covers the domain of sensory phenomena, we are not at all concerned with the mind-body problem in that sense of the word "mind." It is only on the periphery of the traditional mind-body problem that there are occasional questions about the relation of body to mind in the other sense—the sense in which it is posited to explain conceptual thought and, through it, man's unique possession of propositional speech.

These questions are variously stated, but I hope that I can show that they can all be reduced to the one question that I have stated as the ultimate issue in this controversy about the difference of man—especially to that form of the question which asks whether the brain is the sufficient, or only a necessary and not sufficient, condition of conceptual thought. When the one aspect of the mind-body problem with which we are here concerned is thus clarified, we will also, I think, be able to avoid having commerce with most of the traditional isms that complicate and sometimes obfuscate the discussion of the problem—hypotheses that go by such names as "psychophysical parallelism," "psychophysical interactionism," "occasionalism," "epiphenomenalism," "double-aspect theory," "monistic materialism," and "dualism." Merely to recite this list of isms is like exhuming a whole series of corpses in the last stages of decay.

For the purpose of the present inquiry, the only question that concerns us is whether conceptual thought can be adequately explained in neurological terms. The hypothesis that it can be is currently called "the identity hypothesis," and when I call the position that adopts that hypothesis the "materialist position," I mean materialism in a sense that is acceptable to the exponents of the identity hypothesis and not the monistic or reductive materialism that they so explicitly reject. The opposite hypothesis, that I have called the "immaterialist position," might also be called "the non-identity hypothesis," since it affirms mind as an immaterial power that is existentially and causally distinct from the brain and nervous system. If the identity hypothesis ultimately proves to be the right answer, then the mind-body problem, both in its traditional form and in the special aspect of it that concerns us, will have been solved. But if the non-identity hypothesis should ultimately prevail, there would still be difficult questions to answer about the immaterial power or factor that must be posited, in addition to the brain, in order adequately to explain conceptual thought—such questions as precisely how it is related to the brain, how it co-operates with the brain, and so on.

While these questions are not to be dismissed out of hand as unimportant or as pseudo-problems, they are important and genuine problems *only if and after* the non-identity hypothesis is established. Since they are consequent upon its establishment, they have no place whatsoever in arguments *pro* or *con* bearing on its establishment. It makes no difference to the truth or falsity of the non-identity hypothesis whether these consequent problems can ever be satisfactorily solved. Hence, our present consideration of the issue with respect to which the identity hypothesis (the materialist position) and the non-identity hypothesis (the immaterialist position) are the opposed answers need not deal at all with the difficult questions that would have to be faced if the non-identity hypothesis were ever established.

Let me repeat: the only question with which we are concerned is whether the manifest and psychological difference in kind between men and non-linguistic animals is superficial or radical. To that question, the materialist exponents of the identity hypothesis answer: only *superficial*; the immaterialist exponents of the non-identity hypothesis answer: *radical.* The first answer is entirely compatible with the general continuity of nature and with the special evolutionary principle of phylogenetic continuity. The second answer is not compatible with the principle of phylogenetic continuity as that would apply to the origin of man. If an immaterial power must be posited to explain man's having conceptual thought and, through it, a propositional language, the emergence of man on earth cannot be genetically accounted for in the same way that genetics accounts for the origin of other species; and so the principle of phylogenetic continuity is violated and the general continuity of nature is breached—at this one point at least.

If the difference in kind between man and non-linguistic animals is radical, is it the *only* radical difference of kind in nature—the only break in the continuity of nature? It was once thought that the line that divided non-living from living things and the line that divided animal life from plant life sharply separated things that were radically different in kind. But the accumulation of scientific data bearing on these matters more and more favors the opposite view. While the manifest properties of animate and inanimate bodies are such that it would be incorrect to describe them as differing in degree rather than in kind, nevertheless, current advances in biochemistry and in molecular biology strongly suggest that the difference in kind is superficial, not radical; i.e., it does not involve any new factors—any factors other than those operative in the realm of inorganic things. Hence, it seems reasonable to expect that in the not too distant future a living organism capable of reproducing itself will be synthetically produced in the laboratory. As for the difference between plant and animal life, that too, in terms of the manifest properties of these two types of living organisms, appears to be a difference in kind, not degree (even allowing for the difficulty of classifying certain unicellular organisms, and such borderline cases as the sensitive plant). But here, even more overwhelmingly than with regard to the difference between living and non-living things, the weight of the scientific evidence supports the conclusion that the difference in kind is only superficial, not radical. The principle of phylogenetic continuity is not violated by the emergence of animal life.

(3)

This conclusion is strengthened by the support it receives from the philosophical theory that is now called "the identity hypothesis." According to this theory, as I indicated earlier, the power of perceptual thought can be adequately explained in neurological terms: the brain is the sufficient condition for the occurrence of all psychic phenomena that are sensory in character, including such sensory residues as memories and images, and such perceptual attainments as perceptual abstractions. To account for the existence or reality of such phenomena, no causes need be sought beyond the physical or material factors that are operative in neurological mechanisms and processes.

The argument for the identity hypothesis, boiled down to its essentials, involves three steps. (1) All the empirical evidence now available shows that the brain is a necessary condition of sensory or perceptual occurrences and processes, i.e., the latter have never been found to occur without the accompaniment of brain events or processes. (2) In view of the fact that the psychic phenomena in question can be experimentally produced by activating the central nervous system in certain specified ways, brain action is not only a necessary condition in the sense of *sine qua non*, but also the productive cause of the psychic phenomena in question. (3) Since there is no need for an additional cause or a cause of another type to explain the phenomena, the principle of parsimony operates to make the action of the brain not merely a necessary, but the sufficient condition of sensory or perceptual occurrences or processes—everything that can be ascribed to the exercise of the power of perceptual thought.

I will expound and examine this argument more fully in the next section, where we will be concerned primarily with its extension to the sphere of conceptual thought. For the moment, I wish only to say that I can see nothing wrong with it so far as it applies to the sensory or perceptual order. With the one exception of the difficulty of explaining parapsychic phenomena, such as ESP, in neurological terms, the exponents of the identity hypothesis seem able, in my judgment, to answer all the objections and resolve all the difficulties that have been raised against them or that they confront themselves with (and the evidence for parapsychic phenomena is itself so dubious or questionable that it hardly constitutes a serious difficulty at this stage of scientific investigation). [1]

I said a moment ago that the identity hypothesis, as applied to sensory or perceptual occurrences and processes, confirms the view that the difference between animals with sensory or perceptual powers and plants without them is only a superficial, not a radical, difference in kind. The converse is equally true: all the scientific evidence that now supports that view and, with it, the phylogenetic continuity of plant and animal life, also confirms the identity hypothesis, so far as it applies to sensory or perceptual phenomena. Hence, those among contemporary philosophers who oppose the identity hypothesis on the sensory or perceptual level, in addition to propounding philosophical objections or difficulties (which they do), must also give reasons for thinking, contrary to the best scientific evidence available, that the difference between animals with sensory or perceptual powers and plants without them is a radical difference in kind—a difference that violates the principle of phylogenetic continuity. *This they do not do.* [2]

The identity hypothesis thus has a clear and substantial advantage over the non-identity hypothesis with respect to the explanation of sensory or perceptual phenomena. I can find no reason for hesitating to say that, in the light of all relevant evidence and arguments, it is much the *truer* of the opposed philosophical theories, so far as that can be judged in the light of the arguments *pro* and *con*. But since the question is not a philosophical one, but a mixed question involving science as well as philosophy, the confirmative weight of the scientific evidence cannot be ignored. When this is taken into account, it greatly increases the truth of the identity hypothesis relative to that of the opposing hypothesis, insofar as both apply to psychic occurrences or processes that are common to man and non-linguistic animals.

The only problem that remains, therefore, is which of the conflicting hypotheses is true with respect to those psychic occurrences or processes that are to be found only in man—the formation and use of concepts, the making of judgments and of inferences; in short, the occurrences or processes that take place when men exercise their power of conceptual thought. How far do philosophical arguments *pro* and *con* go toward resolving the issue that is constituted by these opposed hypotheses? Can it be resolved philosophically; and if not, how can it be resolved? Since the issue to be resolved is the ultimate issue concerning the difference of man (i.e., the issue whether man's difference in kind is only a superficial or is a radical difference in kind), the rest of this chapter as well as Chapters 13 and 14 are devoted to it. To guide the reader in following the course of the argument, let me outline the steps I now propose to take.

In Sections 4 and 5 of this chapter, I will consider the philosophical arguments for and against the identity hypothesis or the materialist position with regard to conceptual thought. In Sections 6–9, I will consider the philosophical arguments for and against the non-identity hypothesis or the immaterialist position with regard to conceptual thought. In both cases, I can do no more than summarize the gist of arguments, objections, and answers to objections as these appear in the vast and ever-growing literature on this subject. (A bibliography of relevant books and papers prepared by Professor Feigl and confined to recent publications runs to 359 items. [3]) Substantiation and, in some cases, amplification of points made in the text will be supplied in the notes. The reader who does not wish to pursue the matter further can ignore the notes; they are provided for the reader whose interest in the matters treated is great enough to sustain reading considerably further.

(4)

Among contemporary proponents of the identity hypothesis, the leading figures include such philosophers as Gilbert Ryle of Oxford; Herbert Feigl, Director of the Center for the Philosophy of Science at the University of Minnesota; Wilfrid Sellars of Yale; Kenneth Craik, late Fellow of St. John's College, Cambridge; J. J. C. Smart and U. T. Place, both of the University of Adelaide, South Australia; Hilary Putnam of M.I.T.; Stephen Pepper of the University of California; and Anthony Quinton of Oxford. [4] While it is not inappropriate to call all of them materialists in the sense that they deny autonomous existence or causal efficacy to anything immaterial, it is important to record their unanimous rejection of the crude and philosophically untenable doctrine that is associated with the name of materialism across the centuries, and that has been given some currency in our own time through its adoption by psychologists who are metaphysical as well as methodological behaviorists. The proponents of the identity hypothesis refer to such materialism as "reductive materialism" because it denies the reality of the psychical, treats it as illusory, or converts the language used for describing such phenomena into just another way of speaking about physical occurrences or processes.

In attacking such reductionism, which goes to the extreme in identifying the psychical with the physical, proponents of the identity hypothesis are, of course, joined by their opponents. [5] That is to be expected from those who oppose the identity hypothesis; it could hardly be otherwise. But the fact that proponents of the identity hypothesis reject the reductive identification of the psychical with the physical calls attention to the non-reductive sense of identity that distinguishes these philosophers from the crude materialists whom they criticize. It is of critical importance to the understanding of their hypothesis to get this sense of the term as clear as possible.

Two things are analytically inseparable if the meaning or understanding of the one is indistinguishable from the meaning or understanding of the other. Two things are existentially inseparable if, though analytically or logical distinguishable, they never occur or exist in separation from one another. Such existential inseparability may be either necessary or contingent: *necessary* if it is intrinsic to the nature of the things conjoined, so that it is impossible to conceive the occurrence of the one without the accompaniment of the other; *contingent*, if it is simply a matter of empirical fact that whenever the one occurs, we also always find the other.

Now in the strictest meaning of the word "identity," two things, if they are distinguishable in any way, cannot be identical, for strict identity, as Leibniz pointed out, is the identity of indiscernibles, and *indiscernibilty negates twoness in any respect.* Hence, wherever we have both analytical and existential inseparability, we have the strict identity of a thing with itself, not the identity of two things. In its most extreme form, the reduction of the psychical to the physical is an identification that annihilates the psychical as having any independence in meaning or existence. But if the psychical and the physical are analytically or logically distinguishable, so that what is properly said of the one cannot be properly said of the other, then their twoness is not obliterated even if they are existentially inseparable from one another. To speak of them as identical when they are only existentially inseparable from one another is, of course, a much weaker sense of identity than is connoted by the identity of indiscernibles, and that sense is further weakened if the existential inseparability is empirical and contingent rather than *a priori* and necessary.

It is in this weakest possible sense of identity that the identity hypothesis asserts the identity of the psychical and the physical. Some confusion and misunderstanding might have been avoided if the word, so far removed in meaning from its strict sense, had not been used at all, and the doctrine had been described as a moderate or non-reductive materialism that (1) asserted the empirically known and contingent concurrence (in a one-one relationship) of the psychical and the physical (more particularly, the concurrence of sensory or perceptual phenomena with brain states or processes); and (2) asserted the physical to be the sufficient condition of the psychical, i.e., the action of the brain and nervous system to be the sufficient condition of the happenings that are described as sensations, feelings, images, memories, perceptions, and as conceptions, judgments, and inferences.

The step from the first to the second of these two assertions is accomplished by applying the principle of parsimony, a step that is explicitly acknowledged by the best expositors of the identity hypothesis or the non-reductive materialist position. [6] According to Professor Feigl, it is the taking of this step that distinguishes the identity hypothesis from such other views of the mind-body relationship as psychophysical parallelism and epiphenomenalism, which start from the same first premise; namely, that there is a one-one relationship and concurrence between physical and psychical states or events. [7] As I pointed out earlier, the principle of parsimony is used to reject as unnecessary the appeal to any causal conditions other than neurological occurrences or processes, in order to explain the so-called "mental" states or events that are paired with these neurological occurrences or processes in one-to-one correspondence. Not only do the so-called "mental" states or events fail to occur in the absence of brain states or processes (which means that brain action is a necessary or *sine qua non* condition of their occurrence), but nothing more or other than brain states or processes is needed for their occurrence (which means that brain action is the sufficient condition for their coming to be or happening).

With significant exceptions that will be noted in a moment, the critics of the identity hypothesis attack it exclusively on the level of what I would call "subhuman or animal mentality"—the level of sensory and perceptual phenomena that are common to both linguistic and non-linguistic animals. [8] Similarly, when the proponents of the identity hypothesis enumerate objections or difficulties that they then try to answer or resolve, these are without exception on the level of sensory and perceptual phenomena. Of the ten problems that Professor Feigl regards as serious enough to discuss in detail, not one is on the level of conceptual thought; the same is true of the eight objections that Professor Smart is at great pains to answer. [9] We need spend no time on these refinements of the theory since, as I remarked earlier, the theory is sufficiently well established as the truer of the two competing hypotheses with regard to all phenomena on the sensory or perceptual level.

Turning now to the level of conceptual thought, where the relative truth of the competing hypotheses bears directly on the precise character of man's difference in kind from non-linguistic animals, we must observe two things: first, that the general framework of argument for the identity hypothesis remains exactly the same on this level as on the perceptual level; and second, that within the same general framework, a few authors, notably Wilfrid Sellars and Kenneth Craik, advance arguments specifically directed toward establishing the first premise of the identity hypothesis on this level; namely, the existential inseparability and factual concurrence of brain processes and conceptual processes. Other authors in this group who mention the process of conceptual thought do no more than assume that the arguments they have already advanced on the level of perceptual thought apply with as much force to conceptual thought as well.

Sellars pivots his discussion of the problem on a comparison of Descartes and Hobbes. In his view, Hobbes treated the relation of conscious thought to neurophysiological processes as identical with the relation of conscious sensations to sensory states of the brain. Descartes, on the other hand, "not only refused to identify [conceptual thinking] with neurophysiological process, he did not see this as a live option, because it seemed obvious to him that no complex neurophysiological process could be sufficiently analogous to conceptual thinking to be a serious candidate for being what conceptual thinking 'really is.'" As between Hobbes and Descartes, Sellars thinks that advances in science and philosophy favor Hobbes. "In the light of recent developments in neurophysiology," he writes, "philosophers have come to see that there is no reason to suppose that there can't be neurophysiological processes which stand to conceptual thinking as sensory states of the brain stand to conscious sensations." [10]

The only argument that Sellars offers for this view of the matter turns on the analogy between conceptual thought and propositional speech: concepts or thoughts are related to one another as words and sentences are related to one another. But "to point to the analogy between conceptual thinking and overt speech," he remarks, "is only part of the story, for of equally decisive importance is the analogy between speech and what sophisticated computers can do, and finally, between computer circuits and conceivable patterns of neurophysiological organization. All this," he adds, "is more or less speculative, less so now than even a few years ago. What interests the philosopher is the matter of principle. . . ." And on that decisive point, Sellars concludes that "if thoughts are items which are conceived in terms of the roles they play"—analogous to the roles that words and sentences play in propositional speech—"then there is no barrier *in principle* to the identification of conceptual thinking with neurophysiological process." [11]

Craik's argument, though expressed in different terms, closely resembles that of Sellars. The fundamental feature of neural machinery and also of calculating machines, in Craik's view, is their ability to "parallel or model external events" in their order and relationship. [12] The order and relation of thoughts, as symbolized in words or numbers, also models or parallels the order and relationship of external events; in such modeling or paralleling, their truth consists. Hence, Craik is persuaded that it is reasonable to hypothecate the identifiability of conceptual thinking with neurological processes. Accordingly, "general meaning or meaningfulness . . . would be the power of words to symbolize things and events through the neural events which parallel those things and give rise to words and images." [13]

In a later book, commenting on this hypothesis as to the nature of thought, Craik confesses that it is yet far from being established that "ideas and neural patterns" can be viewed "as if they were almost synonymous"; that is not possible, he says, "in the present stage of physiology and psychology." Nevertheless, he repeats his conviction about the underlying principle of the identity hypothesis as applied to conceptual thought: "I see no reason to suppose," he writes, "that concepts and reasoning are fundamentally different from the mechanisms of physical nature." [14]

(5)

The opponents of the identity hypothesis as applied to conceptual thinking do not deny that neurological processes may be an indispensable or *sine qua non* condition of conceptual thought, but they argue that the meanings—or, in their language, the "intentionalities"—which are identical with concepts and which confer significance on the names or designators that we use in propositional speech cannot be adequately explained in neurological terms; and so the action of the brain and nervous system is not the sufficient condition of conceptual thought. Professor Popper's way of saying this is summarized in his thesis that "no causal physical theory of the descriptive and argumentative functions of language is possible"; in other words, no neurological or mechanical explanation can be given of the meanings involved in our use of designative names, and even less so of the meanings involved in the sentences whereby we express inferences. [15] Professor Price of Oxford, in a discussion of papers on the mind-body problem by Anthony Quinton, also of Oxford, and John Beloff of Edinburgh, points out that "if Brentano is right in saying that all mental events have intentionality and that no physical events have it, this would seem to be a conclusive objection to the Identity Hypothesis." [16] A lengthy appendix in the volume that contains Professor Feigl's comprehensive essay on the mind-body problem deals with "intentionality and the mental"; it contains correspondence between Professors Chisholm and Sellars on the subject, in which Professor Chisholm of Brown University spells out the point made above by Professor Price; namely, that the intentionality of thoughts makes it impossible to identify thoughts with brain states, in any sense of identification that would make brain states or processes the adequate explanation or sufficient condition of conceptual thought. [17]

Replying to Chisholm, Sellars reiterates the position that he took in his earlier paper on the subject. He calls attention to the fact that "the analogy between the way in which thoughts are connected with one another and with the world . . . and the way in which overt linguistic episodes are so connected . . . makes it sensible to envisage the identification of thoughts *in their descriptive character* with neurophysiological episodes in the central nervous system." [18] The intentionality characteristic of thoughts, in Sellars' view, can be adequately explained by the semantics of overt verbal behavior. [19] Professor Putnam goes further in pointing out, against Chisholm's thesis concerning intentionality, that structural linguistics and empirical semantics can account for all linguistic behavior without any reference to intentionality, meaning, or concepts. Should Chisholm contend that a behavioristic semantics which omits intentionality cannot succeed in explaining human language, that, according to Putnam, would be irrelevant even if true; because "if *any* semantical theory can fit human language, it has to be shown why a completely *analogous* theory would not fit the language of a suitable machine." [20]

In his consideration of Brentano's thesis about the identification of the intentional with the mental and its non-identifiability with the physical, Anthony Quinton discusses and criticizes the views of Popper and Chisholm noted above. He concludes by trying to explain why, in his judgment, Brentano's thesis does not rule out the identity theory.

> Its immediate victim is behaviorism. It aims to prove that there is more to thinking and meaning than verbal and other behavior, that there are mental processes . . . over and above such behavior. . . . But the identity theory does not deny that mental events and states . . . are distinct from verbal and other behavior. It takes them, after all, to be causally related to such behavior. What it does maintain is that every such introspectibly discriminable mental state is also a discriminable brain state. Now if such brain states are not irreducibly intentional, does it follow that they cannot be identical with mental states? It does not, because the identity theory does not regard the physical and mental descriptions of states of mind as *logically* equivalent. Only a contingent identity is claimed for physical states of the brain and introspectible states of mind. [21]

Professor Feigl reaches the same conclusion: that Brentano's thesis, even if true, poses no serious difficulty for the identity hypothesis as applied to conceptual thought. [22]

To summarize the discussion that we have just surveyed, I would call the reader's attention to three points.

(1) The positive argument for the identity hypothesis, as advanced by Sellars and Craik, has its crux in the parallelism or analogy between the order and relation of concepts in thought and the order and relation of the verbal elements in propositional speech. Turning on that crux, the argument proceeds as follows: a similar parallelism can be found between the order and relation of verbal elements and the order and relation of neural events or of computer states; it should, therefore, be possible to explain

language in neurological or mechanical terms; and if that is possible, it should be possible to explain conceptual thought in neurological or mechanical terms. Sellars and Craik do not assert that a completely satisfactory or adequate explanation has yet been given; they merely contend that they see *no difficulty in principle* about giving one.

(2) The opponents of the identity hypothesis, especially Popper and Price, base their criticism of it on the intentionality or meaning that constitutes the elements of conceptual thought: concepts are the intentions or meanings through which all signs, both verbal and non-verbal, get their significance. They then argue as follows: since that which is mental is intentional and that which is physical is not, they cannot be identified; nor can an adequate physical explanation be given of the intentionality that is constitutive of the elements of conceptual thought.

(3) Against such criticism, the defenders of the identity hypothesis point out that their theory does not call for the analytical inseparability or indistinguishability of the mental and the physical—the intentional and the non-intentional. It asserts only that they are existentially inseparable in an empirical and contingent manner. This being so, the action of the brain is at least a necessary condition of conceptual thought; and there is good reason to suppose that it is also the sufficient condition, in view of the purely mechanistic explanations of man's propositional speech that can now be given by structural linguistics and empirical semantics.

(6)

In Section 4, we saw the necessity for distinguishing between the identity hypothesis and the extreme form of materialism that is reductive; only the moderate materialism of the identity hypothesis is tenable and defensible. Here it is necessary to distinguish an extreme form of the immaterialist position from the more moderate hypothesis that, in the light of available scientific evidence, is tenable and defensible, as the extreme form of immaterialism is not. In considering the philosophical dispute on the issue of whether man's difference in kind is radical or superficial, we shall be concerned only with the conflict between the two hypotheses that, while opposed on philosophical grounds, are equally compatible with the scientific evidence that is germane to the issue.

Of the philosophers cited in Chapter 4 as affirming man's radical difference in kind, two—Plato and Descartes—are representatives of the extreme immaterialist position, and two—Aristotle and Aquinas—are exponents of the more moderate view. Two points characterize the extreme position: (1) the mind, intellect, or rational soul is conceived as an immaterial substance, united to the body in the manner in which two relatively autonomous entities might be conjoined; e.g., as the motor is united with the chassis or as the pilot is united with the ship—the ghost in the machine. The resulting unity is one of association rather than of being or existence. Hence, (2) the body is not even a necessary, much less the sufficient, condition for the existence and functioning of the mind, intellect, or rational soul: the latter can exist in separation from the body, and when they are conjoined, the relation between acts of the mind and acts of the body is a one-many or many-one rather than a one-one relationship.

The proponents of the identity hypothesis would, of course, deny the truth of these two propositions, but so would the adherents of the moderate immaterialist position. Unfortunately, most of the contemporary philosophers who have adopted the identity hypothesis in one form or another are unacquainted with the moderate immaterialist position. Beginning with Ryle, they proceed on the incorrect assumption that all opponents of materialism espouse the ghost in the machine. So far as the moderate immaterialists are concerned, they are attacking a straw man, just as much as the immaterialists would be doing if they attacked the materialist position conceived solely in its extreme reductive form. It is additionally unfortunate that the contemporary philosophers who reject the identity hypothesis do so without adequate knowledge or understanding of the arguments that have been advanced on their own side of the issue—arguments that not only operate against the identity hypothesis but also against the ghost in the machine. [23]

In contradistinction to the extreme form of the immaterialist position, as that is typified by the doctrines of Plato and Descartes, the moderate form of it, typified by the doctrines of Aristotle and Aquinas, can be defined in terms of the following three propositions. (1) Bodily events or processes, particularly brain states or processes, are a necessary—an indispensable or *sine qua non*—condition of mental acts, such as the acts of forming and using concepts, of making judgments and inferences. They stand in a one-one relationship, not a one-many or a many-one relationship. This is affirmed as a matter of empirical fact and, therefore, as a contingent, not a necessary, connection. But (2) brain action is *not the sufficient condition or sole cause* of the aforementioned mental acts. The arguments relative to this proposition try to show that it *cannot* be. (3) The additional cause required for the explanation of these acts is the mind or intellect conceived not as an immaterial substance, but as a power possessed by man, differing from all of his other powers in *one respect and one respect only*; namely, that it is an immaterial power not embodied in a physical organ, such as the stomach, the eye, or the brain. According to this third proposition, it is the immateriality of the power of conceptual thought that must be posited in order to explain the mental acts that cannot be adequately explained in neurological terms alone.

In other words, just as earlier the principle of parsimony was used to justify positing man's possession of the power of conceptual thought in order adequately to explain his possession of a propositional language, so here, the proponents of the moderate immaterialist view contend, the principle of parsimony can be used to justify positing the immateriality of that same power in order adequately to explain the mental acts which the identity hypothesis tries to explain solely in neurological terms. Thus we see that the two moderate positions on the ultimate issue about man's difference in kind completely agree on one proposition and appeal to the same principle as the basis for their disagreement on another. They agree on the proposition that the action of the brain is an indispensable or *sine qua non* condition of the mental acts to be explained (i.e., conception, judgment, inference). They disagree about whether anything in addition to brain action need be posited to explain these acts.

Since both sides affirm man's possession of the power of conceptual thought, the basic difference between them lies in the way they conceive this power: either (a) as a power of the brain, in which case brain action is the sufficient condition of the acts in question, or (b) as an immaterial or non-physical power associated in its action with the power and action of the brain, in which case brain action is only a necessary and not the sufficient condition of the acts in question. In their disagreement on this crucial point, both sides appeal to the principle of parsimony, one using its negative edge to deny the need to posit anything beyond brain action, the other using its positive edge to justify the need for positing the immateriality of the power of conceptual thought. [24]

Within the framework of these agreements on the empirical facts and on the controlling principle, the one point in dispute is sharply defined and the debate of it should be better conducted than most philosophical controversies are. Unfortunately, as we shall see, that is not the case, largely for reasons of ignorance and misunderstanding on both sides. The contemporary exponents of the identity hypothesis, like the contemporary philosophers who criticize them, are unacquainted with the arguments for the immateriality of the mind or intellect conceived not as a substance, but as a power, i.e., the power of conceptual thought. And most of the scholastic philosophers alive today who might uphold the position of Aristotle and Aquinas in this dispute seem to be unacquainted with the identity hypothesis and the arguments for it; they, for the most part, continue to attack the straw man of extreme or reductive materialism; in addition, they do not know how to marshal their own arguments in a way that might make them intelligible to contemporary ears.

Before I attempt to supplement the contemporary discussion by adding the crucial argument for the immaterialist position that is not represented in it, let me briefly comment on two points that do appear in the current literature—one critical, the other constructive.

The first point is the one made by such writers as Price, Brandt, Beloff, and others in their criticism of the identity hypothesis. They heed the cautionary statements of the exponents of that hypothesis that (1) the inseparability of mental acts from the action of the brain is only existential, not analytical; and that (2) the existential inseparability is only contingent insofar as it is empirically known, not necessary as it would be if it could be known *a priori*. These qualifications, in their opinion, so weaken the meaning of identity that the force of that term is totally lost. With it removed from the dispute, all that is left then is the proposition on which both sides can agree; namely, that the action of the brain is a necessary or *sine qua non* condition of mental acts. [25]

The second point is the one that is introduced into the discussion by Popper, Price, Chisholm, and others, as was pointed out in the preceding section. [26] It involves the thesis that these authors attribute to Brentano—that intentionality or reference is the exclusive property of mental acts; it does not belong to the order of physical events, nor can it be produced by purely physical conditions or occurrences. Accordingly, brain states or processes cannot be the sufficient condition or sole cause of such mental acts as conception, judgment, and inference, all of which are intentional acts. Let me spell this out by one further statement of the point. The act of digesting is not a mental act in the sense defined; it is not intentional; it can, therefore, be the act of a bodily organ, such as the stomach. The act of forming concepts and the act of using them to make judgments and inferences are mental acts; they are intentional; they cannot, therefore, be the acts of a bodily organ such as the brain or central nervous system. [27]

I have, for a reason that will presently become clear, omitted reference to acts of perception, memory, and imagination. According to the identity hypothesis, these are acts of the brain and its sensory appendages. According to such contemporary philosophers as Price and Chisholm, these are intentional acts and so they cannot be acts merely of the brain and its sensory appendages, as digestion is an act of the stomach. But according to Aristotle and Aquinas, the acts of perception, memory, and imagination are not intentional acts of the same type as the acts of conception, judgment, and reasoning, and so they can be acts of the brain and its sensory appendages in exactly the same way that digestion is an act of the stomach, whereas the intentionality of conception, judgment, and inference is such that these acts cannot be acts of the brain as seeing is the act of the eye and the brain, or as memory and imagination are acts of the brain.

In short, according to Brentano and his contemporary followers, it is intentionality *as such* that distinguishes the mental from the physical; but according to Aristotle, Aquinas, and those who understand their doctrine, as Brentano, Price, Chisholm, and others obviously do not, it is only a certain type of intentionality that is the exclusive property of the mental; i.e., it is only a certain type of intentional act that cannot be the act of bodily organs such as the sense organs and brain. The contemporary philosophers who, in the dispute about the identity hypothesis, refer to Brentano's thesis, appear to think that Brentano is the original source of the insight about the intentionality of mental acts. It is difficult to understand their thinking so, for I would have supposed that it is a matter of common knowledge that Brentano was reared in the tradition of scholastic philosophy and that his doctrine of the intentionality of mental acts goes back through Aquinas to Aristotle, where it originated.

Knowing only Brentano's incorrect statement of the doctrine of intentionality, his contemporary followers repeat his mistake. If the intentionality of sensory or perceptual acts were the same as the intentionality of conceptual acts, they would be mental acts *in the same sense*; from this it would follow that mind is present, *in the same sense*, in non-linguistic animals with perceptual powers and in man with both perceptual and conceptual powers; and it would then further follow that perceptual acts as well as conceptual acts cannot be acts of bodily organs, as digestion is an act of the stomach: in which case, as a final consequence, it would follow that a radical difference in kind exists between plant life, on the one hand, and animal and human life, on the other, but that the difference between man and non-linguistic animals is at most only a superficial difference in kind.

If Brentano's statement of the Aristotelian doctrine were correct, we would expect Aristotle and Aquinas to maintain that the acts of perception, memory, and imagination are not acts of such bodily parts as the sense organs and the brain, any more than conceptual acts are. Anyone who will take the trouble to examine their writings can soon find out that they say no such thing. On the contrary, they assert as explicitly as possible that all sensory acts, including the acts of the interior sensitive powers —the acts of perception, sensitive memory, imagination, and cogitation—are acts of bodily organs. [28] In their view, only conceptual acts—such as the acts of understanding or concept-formation and the acts whereby concepts are used in judgments and inferences—cannot be merely acts of the brain, though they *never occur without* acts of the brain, since the exercise of the sensitive powers is empirically discovered to be an indispensable condition for man's exercise of his intellectual or conceptual power. [29] Hence, they attribute immateriality only to man's intellectual or conceptual power, and not to his sensory or perceptual power; they posit the immateriality of the conceptual power in order to explain conceptual acts, but they see no reason to posit the immateriality of the perceptual power in order to explain perceptual acts. [30] And though they acknowledge that both perceptual and conceptual acts are intentional, they regard the intentionality of conceptual acts and the intentionality of perceptual acts as analogical, not univocal; and so what is true of the one (i.e., the immateriality requisite to explain the intentionality of conceptual acts) need not be true of the other. [31]

Still another important point remains to be made. The contemporary philosophers who appeal to Brentano's doctrine of intentionality merely re-assert his thesis that intentionality belongs to the order of mental acts and not to the order of physical acts; but, to my knowledge, they fail to give reasons for this assertion, i.e., they fail to advance arguments to show why intentionality cannot be present in purely physical acts. This abstention from argument would be justified and appropriate if the proposition about the immateriality of the intentional were self-evident. Descartes, for example, regards it as self-evident that matter cannot think, and so, in view of the fact that thinking is going on, he asserts without further argument that thinking must be done by an immaterial substance—a substance to which thinking is as intrinsic as extension is to a material substance or body. But if it is not self-evident that matter cannot think, as Locke holds and as most contemporary philosophers maintain, then arguments must be offered for positing the immateriality of that which thinks. And the proposition about the immateriality of the intentional is certainly even less capable of being regarded as self-evident than the proposition that matter cannot think. [32]

(7)

The arguments required to establish the proposition that matter cannot think (i.e., that conceptual acts cannot be acts of the brain) were first formulated by Aristotle and Aquinas and, to my knowledge, are to be found only in the philosophical tradition that stems from them. Furthermore, they are arguments specifically designed to justify attributing immateriality *only* to the power of conceptual thought, *not* to the perceptual powers as well; i.e., these arguments do not try to establish the immateriality of the intentional as such, but only the immateriality of that type of intentionality which is to be found in the mental acts of conception, judgment, and inference.

I have purposely used the word "arguments" in the plural because, as a matter of historic fact, there are at least three distinct reasons advanced by Aristotle and, following him, by Aquinas as the grounds for attributing immateriality to the intellect, the power that they call the power of understanding and that we have been referring to as the power of conceptual thought. In whichever way it is named, the acts of this power are the same—the act of concept-formation and the acts of using concepts to make judgments and inferences. In what follows, however, I will confine myself to summarizing only one of the aforementioned arguments, because of the other two, in my judgment, one is fallacious, and the other appeals to empirical observations that are questionable and will remain so until they are made with the technique and precision of modern scientific investigation. [33]

Before summarizing the one argument that seems to me still to have philosophical cogency, there is one final observation I would like to make. It concerns the somewhat paradoxical character of introducing an argument drawn from Aristotle and Aquinas into the dispute of the mind-body problem as that has developed in modern thought since the time of Descartes. Opinions on this subject that I have harbored for many years have recently been confirmed by a penetrating and scholarly essay of Professor Wallace I. Matson of the University of California, entitled "Why Isn't the Mind-Body Problem Ancient?" [34]

Professor Matson points out that the Cartesian and post-Cartesian formulation of the mind-body problem, as well as the various solutions of it that have been advanced under the names of the various isms enumerated earlier in this chapter, would have mystified the ancient Greeks. "The Greeks," he writes, "did not lack a concept of mind, even of a mind separable from the body. But from Homer to Aristotle, the line between mind and body, when drawn at all, was drawn so as to put the processes of sense perception on the body side." [35] Hence, in the sense of mind in which most contemporary exponents of the identity hypothesis use that term (i.e., to stand for sensory or perceptual acts or experiences), Aristotle and his predecessors would have "subscribed to this theory," as Professor Matson says, not as one solution to a philosophical puzzle, but rather as an obvious truth that no Greek ever gainsaid or even could have thought of challenging. "Indeed, in the whole classical corpus," Matson tells us, "there exists no denial of the view that sensing is a bodily process throughout"—not only sensing, but all the acts and manifestations of the perceptual power that is common to men and non-linguistic animals (i.e., memory, imagination, etc). [36]

These observations seem to me much more completely true of Aristotle than any other Greek philosopher. Plato, for example, would have understood Descartes much better than Aristotle could have, especially the Cartesian separation of mind and body into existentially distinct substances and the Cartesian view of the mind's independence of the body. So, too, Democritus would have understood Hobbes much better than Aristotle could have, especially the Hobbesian identification of mind with body that is a precursor of the identity hypothesis in contemporary thought about the mind-body problem. To Aristotle, Descartes and Hobbes would have seemed relatively unintelligible extremists who, like Plato and Democritus with whose doctrines he was acquainted, mixed truth with untruth—the one by not seeing the dependence of even intellectual or conceptual mind on body, the other by not seeing that bodily processes cannot adequately explain intellectual or conceptual acts as they can fully explain sensory or perceptual ones.

In the hylomorphic doctrine that is Aristotle's most original contribution, it is impossible for the mind-body problem to arise, either on the perceptual or on the conceptual level. And after it has arisen in Cartesian or post-Cartesian terms, it is impossible to translate it back into Aristotelian terms in order to pose the problem in a way that an Aristotelian could understand well enough to try to solve it. The point is not that there is no Aristotelian solution to the mind-body problem; the point is rather that, within the framework of Aristotelian metaphysics and psychology, there can be no mind-body problem.

In the hylomorphic view of being and becoming, of inanimate and animate nature, and of man, the twin pairs of polar principles

—matter and form, potency and act—lead to the conception of the soul as nothing but the form and first actuality of an organic body having the potentiality of life; and all vital operations, from digestion and locomotion to imagination and conceptual thought, are the second acts (or actualizations) of the living organism's powers or potentialities. In this view, the soul is inseparable from the organic body of which it is the form, just as the seal impressed on the wax is inseparable from the wax; and this applies to the human or rational soul just as much as it applies to the sensitive souls of brute animals, and to the vegetative souls of plants. What is true of soul as the form or act of the organic body as a whole is also true, with one exception, of the parts of the soul, i.e., each of its various powers is the power of a part of the body, a living organ. Thus, the power of digestion is embodied in the stomach; the power of vision, in the eye and brain; the power of memory or imagination, in the brain; and so on.

The one striking exception, according to Aristotle, is the power of understanding or intellection—the power of conceptual thought. This one power (distinctive of the rational soul that is the form of the human body) belongs to the living or besouled man in exactly the same way that his power of digestion or his power of perception does; but unlike all his other powers, this one power is not the power of any bodily organ. It alone is an immaterial power; its acts are not the acts of any bodily organ; yet its acts never occur without the accompaniment of sensory or perceptual acts, especially acts of imagination and memory, that are themselves acts of corporeal powers, i.e., acts of the sense organs and of the brain. [37]

The immateriality of the intellectual or conceptual power does not create a mind-body problem for Aristotle; for, as I just remarked, this immaterial power, no less than the other corporeal powers, belongs to man the living organism, composite of matter and form; it functions co-operatively with other corporeal powers (i.e., affects them and is affected by them), especially man's sensory or perceptual powers; and it cannot function in any other way because man is a unity both in existence and in operation.

I hope that this brief digression into Aristotelian theory has now explained why I regard it as paradoxical that Aristotle and his follower Aquinas should supply us with the one argument for the immateriality of the power of conceptual thought that fits into the contemporary dispute of the mind-body problem as a mixed question, involving both science and philosophy, so far as that problem involves the question whether conceptual thought can be adequately explained in neurological terms (i.e., whether the action of the brain is the sufficient cause of conceptual thought), and so directly bears on the question whether man's difference in kind from non-linguistic animals is radical or only superficial. I also hope that this much too brief account of Aristotelian theory will prepare the reader for an equally over-brief summary of the argument itself, which I will now attempt to make. As is so often the case with Aristotle, it is pithily and, perhaps, even somewhat obscurely condensed in a short sentence or two. [38] On the other hand, the argument is spelled out in great detail and with many elaborations in a number of treatises by Aquinas. [39]

The brief version of it that I will now present necessarily omits the metaphysical reasons and the psychological distinctions that make it understandable and persuasive. Hence, I have placed in the notes to this chapter a much more extensive statement of the argument and one that is couched in terms that may make it more intelligible and persuasive to contemporary readers than would the language and ratiocination of Aristotle and Aquinas. I do this in order to give this argument its proper place in the contemporary discussion of the brain's relation to conceptual thought. So far as I can judge from my own fairly extensive reading of the contemporary literature on this subject, the argument is totally unknown. [40] I can do something about making it known, but whether, in the present climate of philosophical speculation, I can make its subtleties and distinctions intelligible is another question.

(8)

The argument in its bare bones hinges on two propositions. The first proposition asserts that the concepts whereby we understand what different kinds or classes of things are like consist in meanings or intentions that are universal. The second proposition asserts that nothing that exists physically is actually universal; anything that is embodied in matter exists as an individual; and as such it can be a particular instance of this class or that. From these two propositions, the conclusion follows that our concepts must be immaterial. If they were acts of a bodily organ such as the brain, they would exist in matter, and so would be individual. But they are universal. Hence, they do not and cannot exist in matter, and the power of conceptual thought by which we form and use concepts must be an immaterial power, i.e., one the acts of which are not the acts of a bodily organ.

The reasoning that supports the first proposition is as follows. Our common or general names derive the meanings they carry from the concepts we have. The meaning of a common or general name is universal in its denotation and its connotation; that is to say, a common or general name always signifies a class of objects, never any particular instance or member of the class. Therefore, the concept that confers meaning on a common or general name must be a universal meaning—an act of the mind which has an intentionality that is universal. Were it otherwise, the concepts that we form when we exercise our power of conceptual thought would not enable us, as they do, to understand what it is like to be a dog, or a poodle, or a quadruped—or an electron, a galaxy, and so on.

The second proposition is supported by the facts of common experience. The objects of our common experience are all individual things, i.e., this individual dog, or poodle, or quadruped. One and the same individual object may be a whole variety of particulars according as it is a member of a whole variety of classes; the object lying at my feet is this one unique individual thing, but is many particulars, for it is this particular dog, this particular poodle, this particular quadruped. The same holds true of objects outside the domain of common experience, such as the theoretical entities that are the posited objects of scientific knowledge. Each elementary particle moving about in a cyclotron is that one individual particle, though this individual particle may be a particular electron, and that individual particle may be a particular neutron.

The facts just stated lead to the generalization that all physical objects, whether they are objects of common experience or objects of scientific knowledge, are individual things. This generalization can be stated in the following proposition and its converse:

the proposition is that whatever exists physically (i.e., whatever is embodied in matter) exists as an individual; and the converse proposition is that whatever exists as an individual exists physically. Since these two propositions state empirical generalizations, they are capable of being falsified by a single negative instance. But no negative instance has yet been found; no one has ever produced an existent object of common experience or of scientific knowledge that is at once physical or material in its mode of existence and also universal in character (i.e., a class of things rather than an individual thing).

The argument then reaches its conclusion as follows. Our concepts are universal in the character of their intentionality. Hence they do not exist physically; they are not embodied in matter. Since our concepts are acts of our power of conceptual thought, that power must itself be an immaterial power, one not embodied in a physical organ such as the brain. The action of the brain, therefore, cannot be the sufficient condition of conceptual thought, though it may still be a necessary condition thereof, insofar as the exercise of our power of conceptual thought depends on the exercise of our power of perception, memory, and imagination, which is a corporeal power embodied in our sense organs and brain. [41] (If it can be shown that any other animal, such as the dolphin, has the power of propositional speech and, therefore, the power of conceptual thought, the argument just stated would lead to the same conclusion about the dolphin; namely, that it had an immaterial power and that the action of the dolphin brain may be a necessary, but cannot be the sufficient, condition of the dolphin's engaging in propositional speech and conceptual thought.)

(9)

Proponents of the identity hypothesis, as we noted earlier in this chapter, raise a number of objections or difficulties against their own position and then undertake to answer or resolve them. Opponents of the position have advanced additional criticisms. In the give-and-take of contemporary discussion, the adherents of the identity hypothesis have found occasion to reply to some of these. But the non-identity hypothesis that I have described as a moderate immaterialism—the theory of intellect or mind developed by Aristotle and Aquinas—appears to be totally neglected in the contemporary discussion. From Ryle on, the only theory of mind that the exponents of the identity hypothesis hold up for ridicule or refutation is the Platonic or Cartesian form of extreme immaterialism that they interpret as positing the ghost in the machine, and against which they argue, in terms of the principle of parsimony, that the ghost need not be posited in order to explain human behavior, including linguistic behavior and conceptual thought. This adverse argument does not, of course, apply to the Aristotelian or Thomistic form of moderate immaterialism. In fact, the proponents of that position claim that the principle of parsimony works in the opposite direction to justify positing the immateriality of the power of conceptual thought in order to explain the universal intentionality of its acts.

Because the moderate immaterialism of Aristotle and Aquinas is totally neglected or ignored in the contemporary discussion, we cannot look for criticisms of it, or objections to it, in current philosophical literature. Aquinas, however, did himself raise one objection against his own theory; and at least two others can be readily thought of. I will now present these three objections, together with replies that are consonant with the position to be defended.

First objection and reply. The clinical data of brain pathology, especially brain injuries that are accompanied by disorders of speech and by the loss of understanding, show the involvement of the brain in the processes of conceptual thought; just as other brain injuries causing blindness or deafness show the involvement of the brain in perceptual processes. Hence, the one set of processes, like the other, must be a function of the brain. This objection is raised by Aquinas, who mentions the interference with conceptual thought that results from brain injuries, as well as the interference that results from the effect of toxic substances and fatigue poisons on the action of the brain. [42]

His reply consists in pointing out that there is no inconsistency between admitting the involvement of the brain in conceptual thought and asserting the immateriality of conceptual thought. All that the evidences from brain pathology show is that the brain is a necessary condition of conceptual thought; and in order to deny that the brain is the sufficient condition of conceptual thought, one does not have to deny that it is a necessary condition.

The error of the obection consists in treating conceptual and perceptual processes as wholly alike in being functions of the brain; i.e., in treating *visual* blindness (loss of sight) as if it were the same as *conceptual* blindness or *agnosia* (loss of understanding). [43] To treat them as the same is to ignore the argument for the immateriality of conceptual thought. The objection can hardly invalidate an argument that it ignores.

Second objection and reply. The human infant is not born able to exercise the power of propositional speech. It is only in the course of maturation that that power comes into operation and develops with exercise. The infant's first use of names or designators and his first utterance of sentences do not occur until, with growth, his brain reaches a certain magnitude. Hence, it would appear that there is a critical threshold in the continuum of brain magnitudes, above which the human being has and below which he lacks propositional speech. But the presence of propositional speech is our only objective evidence of the presence of conceptual thought; and so it can be argued that engaging in conceptual thought depends, as engaging in propositional speech depends, on a certain brain magnitude. [44]

The reply to this objection, like the reply to the preceding one, concedes that conceptual thought depends on the brain, and especially on its having a certain magnitude. However, all that this shows is that the brain, or a certain magnitude of it, is a necessary condition of conceptual thought. The argument for the immateriality of conceptual thought, the whole point of which is to show that the brain is not the sufficient condition of conceptual thought, remains untouched by this objection.

Third objection and reply. It has been conceded that animals and machines are capable of perceptual abstractions. Rats can learn to react to individually different triangles *as if* they all had some characteristic in common (their triangularity) that is not shared by other visible shapes; and some success has been achieved in getting machines to recognize different shapes in an apparently discriminating manner (i.e., react in one way to square shapes, and in another to triangular shapes). It would thus appear that animals and machines are able to apprehend universals—classes or kinds of objects. [45] But unless an immaterial power is to be attributed to subhuman animals and to machines, it would seem to follow that an immaterial power need not be posited to explain man's apprehension of classes or kinds of objects. Hence, even if it is granted that the concepts whereby we know kinds or classes are universal intentions, that does not justify our positing the immateriality of the power of conceptual thought.

The reply to this objection turns on preserving the distinction that was made in Chapter 10, between perceptual abstraction and concept-formation. Let me repeat it briefly here.

A perceptual abstraction, as attained by men or other animals, is an acquired disposition to perceive a number of sensible particulars as being of the same kind or as sufficiently similar to be reacted to in the same way; it is also a disposition to discriminate between similar and dissimilar particulars. It is not a disposition to recognize a single perceived particular as being of a certain kind, for the recognition of a single perceived particular as being of a certain kind is inseparable from the understanding of the kind itself. These related acts of recognition and understanding presuppose more than perceptual abstraction; they presuppose concept-formation. In a laboratory rat that has learned a food cue, a perceptual abstraction or generalization enables it to perceive that this shape and this shape (e.g., triangular shapes) but not that shape or that (e.g., circular shapes) are sufficiently alike to serve as the cue for a certain response. But such perceptual generalization and discrimination does not dispose the rat to recognize that this shape by itself is a triangle or to understand triangularity when no triangular shapes are perceptually present. Only a man, having the concept of triangularity, can recognize this perceived shape as being an instance of triangularity, and can, in the absence of any perceived shape, understand triangularity and the distinction between it and circularity. By means of a perceptual abstraction, like that attained by the laboratory rat, a man can also perceive a number of sensible particulars as similar shapes and discriminate between them and dissimilar shapes, but his recognition that the similar shapes are all triangles and that the dissimilar shapes are circles derives from his concepts of triangle and circle, which operate in conjunction with his perceptual abstractions. [46]

The central point here is that perceptual abstractions do not function in the same way in man, on the one hand, and in non-linguistic animals and in machines, on the other; because in man they operate in conjunction with concepts, and in other animals and machines, they do not. Now it is only the intentionality of concepts that is universal. It is only through concepts that we are able to understand kinds or classes of objects; and it is only through concepts in conjunction with perceptual abstractions that we are able to recognize this perceived object as being of a certain kind or class that we understand. Perceptual abstractions by themselves, functioning in the absence of concepts as they do in animals and machines, can do no more than enable the animal or machine to discriminate between perceived particulars according to whether they are sufficiently alike or sufficiently different to warrant this or that reaction. [47]

Since, unlike concepts, perceptual abstractions do not have an intentionality that is universal in character, immateriality need not be attributed to the power of which they are acts. This holds true for all other acts of the power of perceptual thought, such as the acts of memory and imagination. Hence, even if these acts have intentionality, as all cognitive acts do, the type of intentionality they have is such that they can be acts of a bodily organ. It is only an intentionality that is universal in character and that is characteristic of conceptual acts, but not of perceptual acts, which warrants attributing immateriality to a cognitive power. Hence, the objection might have some force against the position held by Brentano and those who adopt his thesis that all cognitive acts have intentionality in the same sense; but it has no force against the position of Aristotle and Aquinas, who distinguish between the intentionality of conceptual and the intentionality of perceptual acts, and regard them as only analogous because the one is universal in character and the other is not.

CHAPTER 13

The Three Prongs of the Cartesian Challenge

(1)

THE EFFORTS of the philosophers to resolve the ultimate issue in the controversy about man falls far short of success. Neither side appears to be able to persuade the other that it has indisputable grounds for deciding the question whether the brain is the sufficient or only a necessary condition of conceptual thought. That, I presume, will not come as much of a surprise to those who have grown accustomed to the irresolution—even the irresolvability—of difficult philosophical issues. But what may come as a surprise is the possibility of circumventing the stalemate by taking another tack and submitting the opposed philosophical issues to the infirmative or confirmative effect of scientific evidence that may be forthcoming in the next half century or a little beyond.

Before I describe the logical detour that I have in mind, I think I can explain why it is unlikely that the well-developed argument for the immaterialist position, however cogent it may appear to be in its own terms, will fail to persuade the proponents of the identity hypothesis that brain action may be the necessary, but cannot be the sufficient, condition of conceptual thought. And, on the other side, I think I can also say why the identity hypothesis, no matter how well it is defended in its own terms, will appear to its opponents to have avoided or evaded the crux of the issue.

From the point of view of the moderate materialists who espouse and defend the identity hypothesis, the argument for the immateriality of conceptual thought rises from a nest of metaphysical subleties and involves metaphysical distinctions and assertions that make its cogency questionable for anyone who is inclined to challenge the terms in which the argument is couched. If this is true of the condensed version of the argument presented in Chapter 12, it is even more true of the more elaborate formulation of the argument presented in Note 41 to that chapter. The problem of the universal (i.e., how and where universals exist) has always been one of the thorniest questions in the metaphysics of being and of knowledge; no less so is the problem of individuation; and when these problems are further complicated by questions about how the act of knowing relates the knower to the known, we cannot overestimate the difficulties and complexities of a theory that must solve these problems in order to reach a conclusion concerning conceptual thought in relation to mind and matter.

This would be so even if the pervasive attitude of contemporary thought were not anti-metaphysical—even if the argument were not beset by all the misunderstandings, dismissals, and puzzlements that would constitute the first line of criticism by those who have explicitly or implicitly adopted the principles of the analytic or linguistic philosophy that is regnant today. The contemporary frame of mind being what it is, it is very unlikely that the argument for the immateriality of conceptual thought can be sympathetically read by those among living philosophers who oppose the conclusion it reaches. Since it is philosophically possible to withhold assent from the conclusion even when the argument is understood in its own terms, how much more so is that the case when the argument is not understood or, worse, misunderstood.

From the point of view of the moderate immaterialists who oppose the identity hypothesis solely on the ground that conceptual thought cannot be identified with the action of the brain, the defense of the identity hypothesis simply misses the mark. One way or another, it bypasses the crucial question about the place of meanings or intentions in the scheme of things—the type of universal meanings or intentions that constitute conceptual thought and that are the source of meaningfulness in everything else, especially the meanings acquired by the originally meaningless vocables or notations that comprise the common or general names in human language. If that which is meaningless cannot become meaningful except through that which is, in its very nature and existence, a meaning, the question about how and where meanings exist would seem to be an inescapable one. Yet, as the moderate immaterialists see it, this is precisely the question that the proponents and defenders of the identity hypothesis not only fail to answer, but also appear deviously to evade—either by calling it irrelevant, as Feigl does, or by suggesting, as do Sellars, Craik, Putnam, and Smart, that the language of computing machines holds out the hope for a purely mechanical solution of of the problem of human language that will remove the immaterialist sting from the question about meanings or intentions.

Proponents of the Aristotelian and Thomistic theory of conceptual thought would certainly insist that the question of meanings or intentions, far from being irrelevant, is the very crux of the issue. They would dismiss the hope expressed by Sellars, Craik, Putnam, and Smart as a conjecture rather than an argument; in addition, they would regard the basis for it as *unsound in principle*. To use something like Chomsky's structural linguistics together with something like Ziff's empirical semantics as a means for devising a linguistic system, entirely devoid of meanings, that will make it possible for a computing machine to be programmed to perform linguistically *as if* it had concepts or meanings, even though it does not—to succeed in doing this, the opponents of the identity hypothesis would contend, proves nothing except that men are ingenious in the technological tricks they can perform with machines. [1] Of course, it is possible that they do not understand the treatment of meaning by the proponents of the identity hypothesis any better than the proponents of that hypothesis understand the Aristotelian and Thomistic argument for the immateriality of universal meanings or intentions. But, granting for the moment that they can and do understand it, it should be clear that, even so, they would find it unpersuasive.

This, then, is the stalemate to which we are brought by the best arguments that have so far been mustered on both sides of the issue about whether man's difference in kind from other animals and from machines is radical or superficial. While allowing for the possibility that a better philosophical argument may be forthcoming in the future, one that will be so persuasive as to resolve the issue, I think it is fair to say that the philosophical dispute up to the present leaves the issue unresolved; and I would expect agreement on this point from anyone who understood both sides of the dispute well enough to understand why neither side is persuaded by the other.

What is our situation, then? Do we have to wait for that better philosophical argument to be invented and for that improvement in the intellectual atmosphere which would render its cogency and conclusiveness generally persuasive? I am happy to say that I think there is another way out of our present impasse. It lies in what I have called a logical detour that finds a way around the roadblock set up by opposed philosophical arguments, neither of which is yet prepared to yield to the other. If we can reach a conclusion that resolves the issue by taking another tack, we can then look back and see why the reasons on one or the other side of the philosophical dispute should have prevailed, if only we had understood them better.

The signpost pointing to this logical detour is nothing other than the principle of parsimony, on the force and relevance of which both sides of the philosophical dispute agree perfectly. Both sides agree that the immateriality of conceptual thought need not be posited *if* conceptual thought can be adequately explained in terms of purely material factors, such as the action of the brain or the action of mechanical devices; both sides agree that *unless* it can be so explained, there is justification for positing the immateriality of conceptual thought. In addition, both sides agree that material factors, such as are involved in the action of the brain, are *at least* a necessary condition of conceptual thought, and so contribute *in part, at least,* to explaining it. The crux of their disagreement, as we have seen, lies right here: the proponents of the identity hypothesis hold that brain action is *more than a necessary condition*; the proponents of the immateriality of conceptual thought deny that it is. Within the framework of these agreements, by what other means than philosophical argument can it be determined whether brain action is or is not the sufficient condition and the adequate explanation of conceptual thought?

If one excludes divine revelation or religious dogma as the source of a conclusive answer to the question, the only other source to which we can turn is science and technology. But how can science and technology provide something like a resolution of the issue that opposed philosophical arguments have left unresolved? By finding experimental evidence or by devising mechanical artifacts that will bring the principle of parsimony into operation in one way or the other—either making it *unnecessary* or making it *unavoidable* to posit the immateriality of conceptual thought.

The philosophical insight that underlies this way of trying to resolve the issue was first expressed by Descartes when he resorted to a *reductio ad impossibile* form of argument in order to defend what he himself regarded as a clear and distinct idea, or self-evident truth; namely, that matter cannot think (i.e., cannot think conceptually). Since this proposition was for him axiomatic, he knew that no reasons need be or can be given for its truth: one does not try to prove what is self-evident; one cannot. But for anyone who holds a proposition to be axiomatic or self-evident, it is always possible to argue against those who fail to see its truth by challenging them to come up with empirical evidence showing that it is not true. Descartes challenged his opponents to do what he himself thought to be impossible—a form of argument that logicians describe as a *reductio ad impossibile.*

The force of the Cartesian challenge, as an indirect argument for the immateriality of conceptual thought, is in no way lessened by rejecting, as Aristotle and Aquinas would reject, the error Descartes made in supposing it to be a self-evident truth that matter cannot think. Even though Aristotle and Aquinas, and anyone else who shares their view, offer a direct argument for a conclusion that they regard as demonstrable, not self-evident, they would have no hesitation in employing the indirect argument concocted by Descartes for the purpose of persuading those who might not be persuaded by the direct argument, which certainly describes the condition of adherents of the identity hypothesis. The latter, for their part, gladly take up the challenge of the indirect argument, since they think that empirical evidence is able to confirm their hypothesis and falsify the proposition that conceptual thought is immaterial. Certainly, to whatever extent they acknowledge their failure to persuade their opponents of the truth of the identity hypothesis by direct argument, they should try to overcome that failure by successfully meeting the challenge of the indirect argument.

The indirect argument, which I will henceforth refer to as the Cartesian challenge, has other advantages beyond circumventing the philosophical impasse. For one thing, its simplicity is comforting to those who have little taste or aptitude for philosophical disputation and metaphysical reasoning. For another, it should be immediately intelligible to the scientists who are concerned with this issue, intelligible in a way that the direct arguments *pro* and *con* are not likely to be. It speaks to them in their own terms and lays down the kind of challenge that they regard themselves as able to meet. Last but not least, the fact that the indirect argument aims at confirming one of the opposed philosophical conclusions and at falsifying the other, together with the fact that it seeks to do this by means of scientific data or technological results, shows more clearly than anything else that the question about how man differs is a mixed question, and not a purely philosophical one.

(2)

In Part V of the *Discourse on Method*, Descartes asserts that it is quite possible for a machine or automaton perfectly to simulate the behavior of subhuman animals of the highest order, such as the primates, precisely because in his view all animals except man lack the power of conceptual thought, to which Descartes gives the name "reason." "If there had been machines possessing the organs and outward form of a monkey or some other animal without reason, we should not have had any means of ascertaining that they were not of the same nature as those animals." [2] But, Descartes goes on to say, it is impossible for a machine or automaton perfectly to simulate the behavior of man. He gives two reasons for maintaining this, only the first of which need here be stated. It runs as follows:

> If there were machines which bore a resemblance to our body and imitated our actions so far as it was morally [i.e., practically] possible to do so, we should always have two very certain tests by which to recognize that, for all that, they were not real men.
>
> The first is that they could never use speech or other signs as we do when placing our thought on record for the benefit of others. For we can easily understand a machine's being constituted so that it can utter words, and even emit some responses to action on it of a corporeal kind, which brings about a change in its organs; for instance, if it is touched in a particular part, it may ask what we wish to say to it; if in another part, it may exclaim that it is being hurt and so on. But it [could] never happen that it [would] arrange its speech in various ways, in order to reply appropriately to everything that may be said in its presence, as even the lowest type of man can do. [3]

To which Descartes then adds the following cautionary remark: "We ought not to confound speech [i.e., propositional speech] with natural movements that betray passions and may be manfested by animals." [4]

We know that the reason why Descartes maintained that no machine will ever be built that can engage in human conversation, exhibiting thereby its power of conceptual thought, is one with his explanation of the fact that no animal except man has propositional speech; namely, the presence of an immaterial power in man that is absent from both machines and other animals. The acts of reason (or, what is the same, the acts of conceptual thought), Descartes declares, can "not be in any way derived from the power of matter." Since, in his view, brute animals are nothing but living mechanisms composed entirely of material parts or organs, they are without mind or reason. Stressing this as the radical difference in kind between men and brutes, Descartes writes:

> It is a very remarkable fact that there are none so depraved or stupid, without even excepting idiots, that they cannot arrange different words together, forming of them a state-

ment by which they can make known their thought; while, on the other hand, there is no other animal, however perfect and fortunately circumstanced it may be, which can do the same. . . .

This does not merely show that the brutes have less reason than men, but that they have none at all, since it is clear that very little is required in order to be able to talk. . . . [5]

The nub of the indirect argument can, therefore, be expressed in the following challenge: "Show me an animal or a machine that can engage in conversation, either with another machine or with another animal or with a human being, and I will either have to concede that matter organized in a certain way can think conceptually, or I will have to posit the operation of an immaterial power in the machine or in the sub-human animal."

Translated into terms that fit the present state of science and technology, the Cartesian challenge can be somewhat expanded so that it has three distinct prongs. The first prong is a challenge to the neurologist to give an adequate explanation of conceptual thought in terms of brain action. The second prong is a challenge to the zoologist to discover a non-human species of animal the members of which engage in conversation with one another, or that can be taught to engage in conversation with members of the human species after we have found some means of translation between the propositional language of that species and our own. (This prong of the challenge, it must be noted, is not met by training circus or laboratory animals to respond to human words; or to imitate the sounds or even the verbal sequences of human speech, for parrots and myna birds can do that. [6]) The third prong is a challenge to the technologist to produce a machine, specifically not a computer but an artifact that, without being programmed to do so, can engage in conversation with human beings, using as a means not "computer talk," but an ordinary natural language such as English.

I have two reasons for setting forth the Cartesian challenge as a three-pronged affair. One is that all three points seem to me to be involved in the challenge that emerges from Descartes' statement of the indirect argument. The other reason is that each of the three prongs has a distinct and different interest in view of claims now being made by neurologists, zoologists, and technologists. However, as we shall see, it is only the third prong—the challenge to the technologist—that may result in a decisive resolution of the issue, one way or the other. Even if the neurologist were to do the very best he can to meet the challenge addressed to him, it would still be possible to maintain that conceptual thought involves an immaterial power. And if the zoologist should ever be able to show that the bottle-nosed dolphin, for example, has a propositional language that should enable us, by translation, to engage in conversation with him, it would still be possible to conclude that the bottle-nosed dolphin, like man, has the power of conceptual thought because his constitution, like man's, involves an immaterial power. But the third prong, in my judgment, provides no escape hatch of that sort. If a robot can be built that meets the Cartesian challenge by successfully passing what I am going to call "the conversational test," then, unless one were inclined to posit pixies, it would be impossible still to assert the immateriality of conceptual thought.

In the two following sections of this chapter, I will briefly consider the first and second prongs of the Cartesian challenge. They do not deserve as much attention as the third prong, which in my judgment is not only the most serious, but the only one that can promise results that may be decisive one way or the other. I will, therefore, devote the whole of Chapter 14 to it.

(3)

No neurologist claims, in the present state of his science, that he can give a satisfactory neurological explanation of conceptual thought that has the support of decisive experimental or clinical data. Leading neurologists are quite frank and explicit on the confession of their ignorance of the brain's action in the performance of simple acts of memory. [7] When it comes to conceptual thought, which is much more complex than memory, they acknowledge even more plainly their inability at present to give a neurological explanation of it.

K. S. Lashley, late Professor of Neuropsychology at Harvard University, was especially attentive to the problems raised for the neurologists by the serial order, the mental set, and the conceptual intentions or meanings involved in human speech, but he did not advance even a tentative hypothesis about the underlying brain action. In addition, he made a point of insisting that the mechanics of machine language or "computer talk" gives us no hint about the neurological mechanisms involved in propositional speech and conceptual thought. [8] And J. M. Nielsen, Clinical Professor of Neurology and Psychiatry at the University of Southern California, who has devoted himself to the clinical study of aphasia and agnosia, declares that there is no clinical or experimental evidence of a brain center for conceptual thought. [9]

Among the neurologists, the most speculative is Lord Russell Brain, who has proposed some conjectures about how our cerebral cortex may operate when we understand the meaning of words and when we think conceptually, using words to do so. But even he asks: "Is it likely that physiology will ever throw any real light upon the relationship between the brain and the mind?" His answer is as follows:

> I believe that, working in conjunction with psychology, it will. I can only guess where present advances seem to be leading us. . . . My guess is that in the nervous system we are looking at the threads while with the mind we perceive the patterns, and that one day we may discover how the patterns are made out of the threads. [10]

Let us adopt Lord Brain's hope, one that is naturally shared by Lashley, Arbib, McCulloch, and others concerned with the neurology of propositional language and conceptual thought. [11] Let us suppose that future advances in neurology, both on the side of theory and on the side of experimental or clinical evidence, provide us with much more knowledge than we now possess of how our brain works when we engage in conceptual thought and exercise our power of propositional speech. The question remains: Will it ever be possible to show by experimental or clinical neurology that the working of the brain—granted that we understand how it works as well as that can be understood—is more than a necessary condition of conceptual thought?

The answer must be negative. An affirmative answer would beg the question that is at issue, for it would assume the correctness of the identity hypothesis that, beyond being a necessary condition, the action of the brain is the sufficient condition of conceptual thought. But this is precisely what must be shown. As Sellars points out, the most we can hope for from future neurological research and theory is a showing that neurophysiological processes are "sufficiently analogous to conceptual thinking to be a serious candidate for being what conceptual thinking 'really' is." [12] If this were to be shown, that would remove the chief obstacle to identifying conceptual thinking with the action of the brain. But removing this obstacle does not by itself solve the problem, especially if any reasons can be given on the other side, as they can be, for maintaining that brain action may be a necessary, but cannot be the sufficient, condition of conceptual thought.

Were there no reasons whatsoever for supposing that the universal intentions in conceptual thought cannot be materially embodied in brain processes, then the better the neurologist's account of how the human brain works when men engage in conceptual thought, the more it would confirm the identity hypothesis. But in view of the philosophical dispute over the identity hypothesis, in which arguments are advanced against it that it does not satisfactorily answer, additional neurological evidence and improved neurological theory cannot decisively show that brain action is the sufficient cause of conceptual thought. No matter how far the neurologist can go in demonstrating, experimentally or clinically, the dependence of conceptual thought upon brain processes, that dependence may mean no more than that the brain is a necessary condition of conceptual thought. Furthermore, no matter how far he can go in showing the structural parallelism between brain processes and thought processes, the analogy between them is no more than an analogy; it is not an identity, even though it may have the effect of removing an obstacle to identifying thought processes with brain processes.

(4)

The neurologists leave us with one question for which we must turn to the zoologists for an answer. Whatever knowledge we may have of how the brain works when we engage in conceptual thought and propositional speech, we still have to ask what difference between the human brain and the brains of other animals explain *their lack* of propositional speech and conceptual thought. The answer now universally given to this question is that the brains of the highest mammals are of such magnitudes in size and complexity that, with one possible exception, they all fall below a critical threshold in the quantitative continuum, above which propositional speech occurs, as in the case of man, and below which it does not, as in the case of other mammals. [13]

The one exception mentioned above is the bottle-nosed dolphin. A number of zoologists, pre-eminently Dr. John Lilly, think that the relative brain weight of the dolphin is so close to the ratio between the brain and body weight of man that it should be possible to communicate with the dolphins by establishing some two-way translation between human and dolphin language. If this can be done, it would show, according to Dr. Lilly, that dolphins had the power of conceptual thought. The assumption here to be tested is either that the dolphins already have a language of their own which men can learn and use to converse with them, or that the dolphins have large enough brains to be taught a human language. On either assumption, the test calls for a two-way conversation between men and dolphins, a conversation that exhibits conceptual thought as much as a conversation between men, or at least between an adult and a small child. [14]

Dr. Lilly recognizes all the difficulties to be overcome in making a test of this sort, but he is hopeful that it can be done and will turn out to be successful. Let us ask, therefore, what we would learn from the results of the test that he envisages, first if it fails, and second if it succeeds.

If the test fails, the negative result can be interpreted as merely a failure to overcome the difficulties already seen to be inherent in the effort of men to engage in conversation with a non-human species. Failure would *not decisively show* that the dolphins lacked enough brain power to engage in propositional speech. [15]

If the test succeeds, the positive result would be open to two interpretations. Though the positive result might help us to ascertain more precisely the critical threshold in the continuum of brain magnitudes, above which propositional speech can occur, it would not by itself be decisive as to whether a certain magnitude of brain is *the sufficient* or only *a necessary* condition of propositional speech and conceptual thought. The point being made here is exactly the same point that was made earlier with regard to the correlation between stages in human brain growth and the first appearance and subsequent development of propositional speech in the human child. [16]

Hence, if dolphins ever converse with us in a manner that exhibits their power of conceptual thought, we would be left with these two possible interpretations of the fact: either (1) a certain magnitude of brain is the sufficient condition of conceptual thought, in which case there is no need for an immaterial power in order to explain it; or (2) a certain brain magnitude is a necessary, but not the sufficient, condition of conceptual thought; and so, in the dolphins as well as in man, an immaterial power must be operative.

If, for the reason just given, experiments with the bottle-nosed dolphin cannot decisively resolve the issue, then *a fortiori* no other zoological evidence can decide the question: first, because, among the higher mammals, only the dolphin has a relative brain weight that approximates the relative brain weight of man; second, because similar efforts with other animals, even if successful, would be open to the same interpretations that apply to a successful outcome of efforts with the dolphin.

That being so, only one source of decision is left to us—that which may be provided by the technologists in their effort to produce machines that simulate human intelligence, including man's power of conceptual thought as that is manifested in propositional speech. This brings us to the third and last prong of the Cartesian challenge.

CHAPTER 14

The Third Prong: From Descartes to Turing

(1)

IN ORDER TO be precise about the nature of the challenge that is flung across the centuries from Descartes to the technologists of our own day, four preliminary clarifications are necessary.

In the first place, it is necessary to distinguish between computers that are programmed to perform in certain ways and what I am going to call "robots"—machines built for the puropse of simulating human intelligence in its higher reaches of learning, problem-solving, discovering, deciding, etc. [1]

We can eliminate from further consideration all computers that are completely programmed. The programmed computer does only what it is programmed to do. The program that is put into it by man determines its performance—a certain output on the basis of a certain input. It can be programmed only for performances that are logical. Its chief superiority to man lies in its speed and its relative freedom from error. Its chief utility is in serving man by extending his power, just as a telescope or a microscope does. [2]

Robots in principle are different from programmed computers. Instead of operating on the basis of predetermined pathways laid down by programming, they operate through flexible and random connections. They may have what Turing calls "infant programming"—some fixed connections that are like those built into the human infant at birth. But for the purpose of simulating human intelligence in its higher reaches, the robot must be able to learn from its own experience and must be teachable, as the human being is. Like human beings and unlike computers, robots must be capable of making errors that are not wholly explicable by mechanical defects, as are the errors of a programmed computer.

In the second place, we must distinguish between simulation and what is called "replication." The attempts to construct mechanical models that operate in the same way that the human brain operates are efforts at replication. Most of these efforts up to the present have not gone beyond the stage of mathematical theory and the drafting board; a few actual models, such as the McCulloch-Pitts nerve net, have been constructed. These attempts to replicate the action of the central nervous system have been criticized by leading neurologists on two grounds: first, on the ground tht we do not yet know enough about the action of the CNS to attempt its mechanical replication; and second, on the ground that all such efforts are severely limited by the crucial difference between the electrochemical action of the CNS and the purely electrical action of the mechanical models. [3]

In contrast to replication, the simulation of human behavior by machines consists in achieving the same end result in the way of performance but not achieving it in the same way. Thus, for example, airplanes simulate the flight of birds, but the mechanics of flight are not the same in both cases, though both bird and airplane obey the same laws of aerodynamics. Machines have been built to simulate trial-and-error learning, pattern-recognition, chess and checker playing, working with hypotheses, carrying out a systematic search for solutions to a problem; but in all these cases the machine—whether a programmed computer or something more like a robot—achieves the result without the working of its machinery replicating the neurophysiological processes of the human being who accomplishes the same result. [4]

We can ignore replication and concern ourselves only with simulation; for the Cartesian challenge only calls for a machine that can simulate conceptual thought as that is exhibited in the flexible and unpredictable give-and-take of human conversation. It is possible to enumerate a whole series of differences between machines and men, beginning with the fact that machines are not alive, but though such differences may be significant for the problem of replication, they do affect the problem of simulation. In short, if a machine were to engage in conversation with men, using an ordinary language such as English and using it as men use it, the Cartesian challenge would be met, even if the machine otherwise differed from men in many and various respects.

In the third place, we must distinguish, in this field of technology, between actual achievements and theoretical promises for the future. As might be expected, the claims that are made both with respect to mechanical devices now actually in operation and also with respect to the theoretical possibilities that will be realized in the future, range from the very modest at one extreme to the most extravagant at the other. [5] The explanation of the deficiencies in existing apparatus, where they are admitted, tends to support the prediction that the machines of the future will come much closer to simulating human intelligence than any now in existence. [6]

The magnitude of the human brain in componentry (number of neurons) is a very large number—from 10^{10} to 10^{11}. And the magnitude of the circuitry (number of connections) is very much larger. The magnitude of existing machines is very much smaller —both in componentry (number of transistors—10^{3}) and in circuitry. Until machines are built that more closely approximate the magnitude of the human brain—as, for example, the magnitude of the dolphin's brain does—it is unreasonable to expect an unprogrammed robot to simulate the most characteristic of human performances, such as learning a language like English and using it conversationally. The only further point that need be made here is that there is no reason in principle to deny the possibility of building a robot that will have a componentry and a circuitry equal in magnitude to, or even greater than, that of the human brain.

No one, not even the most extravagant among the technologists, claims that a robot now exists that can meet the Cartesian challenge; though, as we shall see presently, there are many theoreticians in this field who do not hesitate to predict that one will be produced in the future.

In the fourth place, and finally, we must carefully note that the challenge to future technologists is very precise. It does not call for the production of a robot whose performance will provide us with an answer to the loose and unclear question, "Can machines think?" The literature concerned with computers and robots quite properly dismisses that question as so loose and ambiguous that there is no way of deciding what the correct answer is. In its use by psychologists, neurologists, computer technologists, and philosophers, the word "think" has so many meanings in its application to animals, men, and machines, that if anyone asks, "Can animals think?" or "Can machines think?" the answer must be "Yes"—in some senses of the word, and probably also "No"—in other senses of the word. No one has yet produced an acceptable definition of human thinking *in all its variety* that will serve as a standard for measuring the success of efforts to produce a robot that will simulate the whole range of human thinking. [7]

Fortunately, in order to make a critical test of artificial or machine intelligence, it is not necessary to do what it might always be impossible to do; namely, *gain general acceptance for a definition of human thinking in all its variety*. The Cartesian challenge to the technologists calls for a very specific performance that would sufficiently indicate that the robot had the power of conceptual thought, by virtue of the fact that the robot could use propositional language conversationally.

What justifies our inference that men have the power of conceptual thought and that other animals lack this power? It is the fact that men have and animals lack propositional speech. This being so, we would be equally justified in attributing the power of conceptual thought to an unprogrammed robot that was able to engage in conversation in English; and by the same token, we would be justified in saying that a robot failing this test did not have the power of conceptual thought, no matter what other intelligent or apparently "thinking" behavior the robot manifested.

(2)

In the light of the foregoing clarifications, and with this prong of the Cartesian challenge made as sharp as possible, we are now in a position to appreciate the remarkable fact that an English mathematical genius just recently deceased, A. M. Turing, has picked up the gauntlet thrown down by Descartes more than three centuries ago. Turing's widespread fame in the world of computers and robots—and the currency of such phrases as "Turing's game" and "Turing's machine"—centers on his claim that it is mathematically possible to conceive a robot that will successfully meet Descartes' challenge.

"Turing's machine" is a mathematically conceivable robot of the future that will be able to play Turing's game as well—or almost as well—as men can play it. "Turing's game" is a conversational affair using an ordinary language, such as English. It is derived from a game in which all the players are human beings. Two of the players are behind a screen; one of them is a male, the other female. The third player is the interrogator who asks the hidden participants questions in an effort to determine which one is male, and which is female. The questions (*unlimited as to content or variety*) are submitted in typewritten form and answers return in typewritten form, so that tone of voice is eliminated as a clue. The hidden players are *not required to tell the truth* in answering. They can say anything that they think will serve to prevent their being detected. The Turing version of this game simply substitutes a robot for one of the human beings. All the rules of the game remain the same, but the problem becomes one of determining which hidden participant is a human being, and which a robot. [8]

If he were confronted with Turing's game, Descartes would say that no machine could ever be built that would be able to participate in it at all, much less be able to play it as effectively as a human being. Turing's claim, on the contrary, is that a robot participant in his game is now theoretically conceivable and that, with the development of technology, his theoretical model can some day be actually produced in the form of a machine that will use an ordinary language, such as English, with the conversational flexibility and resourcefulness required to play the game effectively.

Among competent scientists and technologists, there are many differences of opinion about Turing's claim, ranging from dismissal of it as unfounded to endorsement of it as sound. For reasons already given, we can ignore the type of criticism which says that human thinking involves much more than the ability to play Turing's game effectively. It may, indeed; but playing Turing's game would satisfy our criterion for attributing to the robot that played it the power of conceptual thought. We can also ignore those who point out the numerous difficulties that have so far been encountered in programming computers to use an ordinary language such as English; or those who go further and maintain that such programming is inherently impossible. That, too, may be the case; but Turing's machine will not be a programmed computer; it will be a robot with no more than infant programming, a robot able to learn English and learn how to use it conversationally. [9]

One further comment: the question is not whether Turing's mathematical theorizing is sound. It is rather whether the robot that he envisages will ever come into existence and operate as intended. *Only if and when it does will the third prong of the Cartesian challenge be successfully met.*

(3)

Let us for the moment suppose that Turing's claim is validated at some future date. *Would the significance of this fact be entirely clear, or would there be some ambivalence about it?*

In the case of the dolphins, we observed that success in engaging them in conversation could be interpreted in two ways. We would have to admit that they had the power of conceptual thought, for the same reason that we attribute it to man. But, as we saw, experimental success with the dolphins would not be decisive with regard to the question whether the brain, or a certain magnitude of brain, was the sufficient, or only a necessary, condition of conceptual thought.

Can there be more than one interpretation of success in producing Turing's machine? *Theoretically, the answer is affirmative.* On the one hand, we could say that an immaterial factor is present in the machine as well as in man, in view of the fact that both have the power of conceptual thought, and conceptual thought involves an immaterial factor (at least according to the direct argument expounded in Chapter 12). On the other hand, we could say that since the machine is entirely material in its constitution, and since the machine exhibits the power of conceptual thought, no immaterial factor is required, either for the robot's performance or for man's.

But while both answers are logically possible, the first can be dismissed as fanciful rather than serious, for it involves an invocation of ghosts or pixies. After all, we built the machine step by step, and every component that entered into its construction was a material component. To give the first answer seriously, we would have to claim—not seriously, I hope—that while we weren't looking, an immaterial factor crept in and hid itself in the works.

We are thus left only with the second interpretation of success in the production of Turing's machine; and, according to that interpretation, no immaterial factor is needed to explain the possession—by a machine or by a man—of the power of conceptual thought as exhibited in the indefinitely variable and, therefore, unpredictable turns of human conversation. The Cartesian challenge would be satisfactorily met. More than that, the conclusion of the direct argument for the immateriality of conceptual thought would be falsified by observable facts, and we would be obligated to re-examine the premises and the reasoning to discover the source of the error. [10]

CHAPTER 15

The Future Resolution of the One Remaining Issue

(1)

WE ARE now in a position to sum up—both with regard to where we are at present and where we can expect to be in the foreseeable future on the question of how man differs from everything else on earth. Let us break that question down into its several parts and deal with each in turn.

(1) With regard to whether man differs in kind or degree from other animals, the available evidence now supports the answer that man differs in kind; but it is necessary to remember that this conclusion is tentative in the sense that it is based on evidence now available, and so does not preclude the possibility that evidence of a contrary tenor may be forthcoming in the future.

We are obliged to ask ourselves, therefore, what effect contrary evidence would have, should it ever be discovered and be generally agreed upon to the same extent as the fact that only man has propositional speech is now agreed upon. The easiest way of doing this is to suppose that, at some future date, it is discovered that other animals—the bottle-nosed dolphin, the chimpanzee, or even the dog—can engage in propositional speech to some degree. Let us suppose, in other words, that this or that species of subhuman animal passes the conversational test. Let us further suppose that this power is *not* found in *all* subhuman animals, but only in *some*. What would follow from general agreement about the facts here being supposed?

In the first place, we would have to say that man differed only in degree, not in kind, from the subhuman species that manifested the power of propositional speech to some degree. In the second place, we would have to say that man, together with these other species that also possessed the power of propositional speech, differed in kind from the rest of the animal world that totally lacked the power in question. In the third place, we would have to attribute the power of conceptual thought not only to man but also to whatever other species possessed the power of propositional speech, while still denying it to the rest of the animal world that lacked this power. In the fourth place, attributing the power of conceptual thought to one or more species other than man, we should be inclined to look for evidence that they also had the power of toolmaking, of history-making, of law-making, etc.—all the powers, in short, that have their root in the power of conceptual thought. We shall presently be concerned with the practical consequences that might follow from such possible future discoveries and from the inferences or conclusions to which they would give rise.

(2) Let us consider next the question whether the difference in kind between man and other animals is superficial or radical. This question, as we have seen, involves the question whether man's power of conceptual thought can be adequately explained in terms of neurophysiological processes; in other words, whether the human brain is not just a *necessary*, but is by itself *the sufficient* condition of man's having the power of conceptual thought.

With regard to this question, our examination of the scientific evidences and the philosophical arguments now available made the following points clear. The philosophical arguments for the moderate materialism of the identity hypothesis try to support the answer that the brain is the sufficient condition, and that the difference in kind is, therefore, superficial, involving a critical threshold in a continuum of degrees in brain magnitudes. The philosophical arguments against the identity hypothesis and for a moderate immaterialism try to support the opposite answer;

namely, that the brain is only a necessary, but not the sufficient condition, and hence, that an immaterial power is required to explain conceptual thought. If that is the case, man's difference in kind is radical.

The opposed philosophical arguments, as we have seen, are deadlocked in the sense that neither of the opponents has as yet been able to persuade the other, or is likely to in the near future. The scientific data at present available leave the philosophical issue unresolved; there is no neurological evidence that definitely favors one side rather than the other. In addition, we have seen why future neurological research cannot ever by itself be decisive on the question whether the brain is a necessary or the sufficient condition of conceptual thought. Finally, we have seen that the future does contain the possibility of efforts by technologists to build a robot that will meet the Cartesian challenge—a robot that will be able to play Turing's game successfully; or, in other words, a machine that will use an ordinary language such as English and engage in conversation with men.

The future, therefore, contains two distinct possibilities. One is that a machine will pass the conversational test and, by so doing, will decisively falsify the immaterialist hypothesis, leaving the materialist position in command of the field. If that result is reached, the answer to our second question must be that the difference in kind between men and other animals is *only superficial.*

The other possibility is that, with repeated trials, machines will fail to pass the conversational test and, by failing to do so, will confirm the truth of the immaterialist hypothesis, or at least add weight to the argument it brings to bear against the materialist position—the position that predicts a machine's success in the conversational test. If that result is reached, the answer to our second question must favor the other alternative; namely, that the difference in kind between men and other animals is *radical.*

(2)

The future must bring about the realization of one of these two possibilities. Since they exhaust the alternatives, that is a certainty. Hence, it is equally certain that the future holds a resolution of the ultimate question about man—whether his make-up does or does not involve an immaterial power; and, accordingly, whether he differs radically or only superficially in kind from other things. Since the certain promise of a relatively decisive answer, one way or the other, carries with it theoretical and practical consequences of the greatest importance, let us look closely and carefully at the logic of the alternatives.

The opposed philosophical positions that constitute the ultimate issue in the mixed question about man can be regarded as hypotheses, each with a different prediction about the future outcome of efforts to produce a Turing machine that will succeed in passing the conversational test that is the third prong of the Cartesian challenge.

The immaterialist position predicts failure in the Turing venture. If its proponents are reasonable rather than dogmatic in their espousal of it, they should be open to the falsification of their hypothesis. So far as I can see, success in the Turing venture would falsify the immaterialist hypothesis. That, in turn, would have one further consequence: if, with the falsification of the immaterialist view, the action of the brain is acknowledged to be the sufficient condition of conceptual thought, then we must conclude that man's difference in kind from other animals is only superficial, not radical. It is generally agreed that man's power of conceptual thought is the root of all the observed behavioral differences in kind between man and other animals: not only his sentence-making, but his toolmaking, his history-making, his law-making, his institution-making, etc. Hence, if his having the power of conceptual thought does not require us to assert the proposition that man differs radically in kind from nonlinguistic animals, we must embrace the other alternative; namely, that he differs in kind *only superficially*.

The materialist position predicts success in the Turing venture. It would, therefore, be strongly confirmed by the eventuality of success. But, unlike the immaterialist position, *it cannot be falsified by failure*. As we saw in the case of the projected experiment with dolphins, repeated failures, while discouraging, can always be attributed to experimental deficiencies or obstacles, and need not be interpreted as definitely showing that the dolphins lack the capacity for propositional speech. So here, likewise, failure in the Turing venture can always be attributed to technological inadequacies or to obstacles that have not yet been overcome in practice *even though, in principle, they are not insuperable.* Nevertheless, if the effort is made time and time again, and success is not achieved, such repeated failures do have some logical effect.

The logical principle that becomes operative, then, is Popper's principle that a theory or hypothesis which is repeatedly put to the test and is not falsified gains in credibility, i.e., it acquires an increasing degree of relative truth. It tends more and more to be confirmed in its truth, even though it can never be completely confirmed with finality as having incorrigible and indubitable truth. In the light of the principle just stated, we would be justified in saying that the immaterialist hypothesis, by submitting itself to a decisive test in terms of the third prong of the Cartesian challenge, would gain some measure of relative truth through the failure of each serious attempt of a Turing machine to pass the conversational test. However, the number of attempts that can be made is as indefinitely large as the amount of time in which men can make the effort. Hence, there is no point at which it can be said that the technologists have definitely failed to meet the Cartesian challenge.

On the other hand, if the proponents of the materialist position are as reasonable as we expect the immaterialists to be, then repeated trials and failures in the Turing venture should have the effect on them of diminishing the credibility—the relative truth—of the identity hypothesis in proportion as it tends to confirm the immaterialist hypothesis and to increase its relative truth.

The future of the mixed question about the difference of man thus involves two major alternatives: (1) eventual success in the Turing venture will decisively settle the question, or will come as close to doing that as can be expected in matters of this kind; (2) with attempt after attempt being made, repeated failure in the Turing venture will progressively confirm the truth of the immaterialist position and, with it, the truth of the proposition that man differs radically in kind from other intelligent animals and from apparently intelligent machines. [1]

The certainty that one of these two alternatives will be realized in the future impels me to assess in advance the consequences—both theoretical and practical—that follow from the realization of one or the other of these alternatives. What difference does it make to us if man differs *only superficially* in kind from other animals? What difference does it make to us if man differs *radically* in kind from other animals and from machines? These are the questions I will attempt to answer in the third and last part of this book.

Part Three

The Difference It Makes

CHAPTER 16

To Whom It Makes a Difference

(1)

THE SUMMING UP in the preceding chapter together with the logical assessment of the alternatives that the future holds sets the stage for the problem to which we now turn—the problem of determining the practical and the theoretical consequences that flow from opposite answers to the questions about how man differs.

Just as the question itself is divided into two parts, so the problem of the consequences must be divided into two parts. The first part of the problem asks what difference it makes whether man differs from other animals in kind or only in degree. Although our present answer to the question of how man differs is that he differs in kind, we have allowed for the possibility that contrary evidence may be forthcoming in the future; and so we are concerned with the consequences of finding out that man differs only in degree. In addition, we must consider the difference it makes which of the other pair of alternatives is true—that man differs in kind but only superficially, or that man differs radically in kind from other things.

The second part of the problem concentrates on that same pair of alternatives—on the difference it makes whether the materialist or the immaterialist hypothesis is true, and, with that, whether the difference in kind, between man and other things, is superficial or radical. Here we can take no position at present, in the light of available evidences and arguments. But with an eye on the certainty that one or the other position will be confirmed in the future, we are concerned now to consider the consequences that then would follow alternatively on one side and on the other.

The consequences with which we are concerned may be either practical or theoretical. By *practical* consequences, I mean effects in the realm of action, either directly on conduct or on the principles that underlie conduct or that are appealed to in order to justify conduct. By *theoretical* consequences, I mean effects in the realm of thought, either by entailment or by opposition. What other propositions (opinions or beliefs) are affected by the conclusion that man's difference in kind is radical, or by the conclusion that it is only superficial? What is entailed by either conclusion? What is precluded as contrary to either conclusion?

In Chapter 17, we will deal with the practical consequences of all the alternatives that we have considered. In Chapter 18, we will restrict our attention to the choice between saying that the difference between man and other things is only a superficial difference in kind and saying that it is a radical difference in kind. It is only this set of alternatives—involving the truth of the materialist hypothesis, on the one hand, and of the immaterialist hypothesis, on the other—that has serious consequences in the realm of theory, affecting some of man's fundamental convictions and beliefs.

(2)

Different attitudes can be and are taken toward the problem of drawing practical consequences from the fact that man differs from other animals in kind or only in degree.

On the one hand, there are those who maintain that the difference between the way in which we treat men and the way in which we treat other animals is not at all dependent on or affected by how man differs from other animals. Our differential conduct toward man and beast is emotionally, not rationally, motivated; or if it is not wholly emotional, its reasons are purely reasons of expediency, not reasons of principle. [1] If the fact is that men and other animals differ in kind, we can, of course, use that to justify the different kinds of treatment we accord men and other animals. But if the fact is that men and other animals differ only in degree, we can find other ways of justifying our differential treatment of men and other animals. It might suffice to argue that one kind of treatment is appropriate for members of our own species, and another kind for other species, even if all the differences among species are only differences in degree. In short, the ultimate reason why we treat men as we do, or attribute to them a certain respect or dignity that we deny other animals, or excoriate the enslavement, exploitation, and consumption of men, but not of animals, is that we simply *like* the results that such policies produce for ourselves and our fellow men. If the facts of the matter tend to support such policies, well and good; but if they do not, no matter, for we can find other ways, equally good, of justifying the policies we *like* or think it *expedient* to act on.

On the other hand, there are those—and I am one of them—who maintain that sound policies for the conduct of our relations with our fellow men and for our quite different treatment of other animals must be based on the nature of man, on the nature of other animals, and on the character of the difference between them. For example, I would say that if man differs only in degree from other animals, then a sharp line cannot be drawn to separate the world of persons from the world of things; in fact, the distinction between person and thing becomes meaningless or at best arbitrary if there are only differences in degree, since that distinction is either a distinction in kind or no distinction at all.

I would maintain, furthermore, that the special dignity and respect accorded persons and not accorded things is based on an argument that involves two premises—one a normative or "ought" premise, the other a factual or "is" premise. The normative premise consists in the proposition that persons *ought* to be treated in a certain way, different from the way in which we treat things: their lives and liberties ought to be respected; we ought not to use them merely as means (we ought not to make chattel slaves of them; we ought not to consume them as food, etc.) The factual premise consists in the proposition that men are persons and other animals are things. I am not saying here what must be true in order to establish the proposition that men are persons and that other animals are things. I am content to rest my case here on the point that if men and other animals differ only in degree, the whole distinction between person and thing evaporates and we are left with no argument of this sort to justify our differential treatment of men and other animals. [2]

At this point, we must face the obvious objection from the man who takes the other attitude toward such matters. He claims that we do not need an argument of this sort to justify our conduct; we can find other ways of doing it, just as good. I cannot deny that other ways of justifying our conduct are possible. I know they have been used. I can only deny that they are *just as good*. These other ways of justifying our conduct are all *ad hoc*. They are all rationalizations of what we want to do rather than reasons of principle. Those who want to do opposite things can always find ways of rationalizing—and thus justifying—their opposite purposes. Thus, for example, if we want to treat men differently from animals even though they differ only in degree, we can justify this by saying that men all belong to the same species. But if some men want to treat other men as men now treat animals (using them as means, enslaving them, or killing them for expediency's sake), they can also justify this by saying that, even though all men belong to the same species, nevertheless, some men are superior in degree to other men, and so superior men are justified in treating inferior men as men treat other animals who are inferior in degree.

In contrast, when we confine ourselves to justifying our conduct by appealing to normative principles and the facts of the case, we cannot justify opposite lines of conduct. If the principles and facts dictate one line of conduct, they preclude support for or justification of the opposite. This is the one clear advantage of conduct that is *principled* over *unprincipled* conduct even though the latter can be justified in some *ad hoc* fashion. [3]

Within the scope of this book, I cannot argue further for the position that I am here taking; namely, that conduct should be principled and that, when it is, the facts of nature have practical consequences. My further analysis of the practical consequences of saying that man differs in kind or only in degree will be of interest only to those who agree with me about this. Those who do not will, of course, continue to say that it makes no practical difference at all how in fact man differs from other animals—whether in kind or in degree.

CHAPTER 17

The Consequences for Action

(1)

As an initial step toward determining the consequences for action that flow from asserting or denying man's difference in kind, I propose to examine some contemporary views of the matter—the opinions of a number of scientists and philosophers who have faced up to this problem in one way or another.

Let me present first the warning given us by Dr. John Lilly with regard to the possibility that, in the not too remote future, we will be able to engage in a two-way conversation with the bottle-nosed dolphin. If and when this occurs, according to Dr. Lilly, we will have to attribute to dolphins the same kind of intellectual power that we attribute to men and deny to other non-linguistic or non-conversational animals. In other words, though men and dolphins may differ in the degree of their common intellectual power, they will stand on the same side of the line that divides animals that have such power from animals that totally lack it. Men and dolphins together will differ in kind from other animals. [1]

Would this possible state of facts, if realized, have any practical consequences? Dr. Lilly thinks it would. He writes:

> The day that communication is established, the [dolphin] becomes a legal, ethical, moral, and social problem. At the present time, for example, dolphins correspond very loosely to conserved wild animals under the protection of the con-

> servation laws of the United States and by international agreement, and to pets under the protection of the Society for the Prevention of Cruelty to Animals.
>
> [But] if they achieve a bilateral conversation level corresponding, say, to a low-grade moron and well above a human imbecile or idiot, then they become an ethical, legal, and social problem. They have reached the level of humanness as it were. If they go above the level the problem becomes more and more acute, and if they reach the conversational abilities of any normal human being, we are in for trouble. Some groups of humans will then step forward in defense of these animals' lives and stop their use in experimentation; they will insist that we treat them as humans and that we give them medical and legal protection. [2]

Let us consider next the view expressed by Professor Michael Scriven of the University of California in his Postscript to an article on "The Mechanical Concept of Mind." He is concerned with the question whether a robot that is successful at playing Turing's game can also pass the test that would require us to attribute consciousness to it. "With respect to all other performances and skills of which the human being is capable," Scriven writes, "it seems to me clear already that robots can be designed to do as well or better." But with respect to this special performance—the one that would be the test of the robot's consciousness—Scriven says that he was not certain at the time of writing the article; however, in the postscript which he added, he tells us that he is, "upon further deliberation, confident that robots can in principle be built that will pass this test too, because they are in fact conscious." [3]

We need not agree with Scriven's prediction about the behavior of some future robot in order to take account of his comment on the practical consequences of his prediction's coming true. On the outcome of his prediction depends, in his judgment, "not only the question of matching a performance, but . . . also the crucial ontological question of the status of a robot as a person and thence the propriety of saying that it knows or believes or remembers. . . . If it is a person," Scriven goes on to say, "of course it will have moral rights and hence political rights." [4]

I turn next to the reflections of Professor Wilfrid Sellars on what it means to be a person rather than a thing and on the criteria for drawing the line that divides persons from things. Sellars writes:

> To think of a featherless biped as a person is to think of it as a being with which one is bound up in a network of rights and duties. From this point of view, the irreducibility of the personal is the irreducibility of the "ought" to the "is." But even more basic than this . . . is the fact that to think of a featherless biped as a person is to construe its behavior in terms of actual or potential membership in an embracing group each member of which thinks itself a member of the group.

Such a group, according to Sellars, is a community of persons. From the point of view of each of us as an individual, the most embracing community of persons to which we belong includes "all those with whom [we] can enter into meaningful discourse. . . . To recognize a featherless biped or dolphin or Martian [Sellars might have added, "or robot"] as a person is to think of oneself and it as belonging to a community"—the group of those who can engage in meaningful discourse with one another. [5]

I call the reader's attention to the criterion of being a person or a member of the community of persons. It is the same conversational test that Lilly and Scriven use for deciding whether dolphins and robots are persons or things. And that same criterion—conversational ability or ability to engage in meaningful discourse—also operates to differentiate man from brute. In other words, the same line that divides man from brute as different in kind also divides person from thing as different in kind. Furthermore, as Lily, Scriven, and Sellars all point out, how we treat a particular entity depends on which side of that line we place it. These authors would, therefore, seem to be maintaining that a difference in kind has practical—legal, ethical, and social—consequences.

I would like, finally, to add the testimony of another philosopher, Professor J. J. C. Smart. Professor Smart, like Professor Sellars, is a moderate materialist. Each in his own way argues that conceptual thought can be entirely explained in terms of neurophysiological processes. Hence, both would deny that man differs radically in kind from other animals or machines, and both would affirm the unbroken continuity of nature. But both also appear to maintain that man differs in kind rather than merely in degree from other animals, and that this difference, which is marked by the possession or lack of "conversational ability," also operates to draw a sharp line between persons and things, with the practical consequence of the differential treatment accorded persons and things. [6] Sellars makes all these points more explicitly and clearly than Smart, but it is, nevertheless, instructive to observe Smart moving in the same direction. He writes:

> A scientist has to attend seriously to the arguments of another scientist, no matter what may be that other scientist's nationality, race or social position. He must therefore at least respect the other as a source of arguments and this is psychologically conducive to respecting him as a person in the full sense and hence to considering his interests equally with one's own. [7]

The moral obligation of one scientist to another, here recognized by Smart, can be generalized into the moral obligation of one person to another. The other to whom we owe respect, the other whom we ought to treat "as a person in the full sense," is here being defined as the giver or receiver of arguments. Interpreted broadly yet without violence to the essential point, the giver or receiver of arguments is one who can enter into meaningful—one might even say "rational"—discourse. Hence, the line that Smart draws between persons and things is the same line that differentiates man from brute; and, like Sellars and the others, he attaches definite moral consequences—respect and other obligations—to being on one side of this line rather than the other.

(2)

The foregoing reference to the opinions of Dr. Lilly and Professors Scriven, Sellars, and Smart indicates some practical consequences of opposed answers to the question about how man differs from other animals—in kind or in degree only. These writers all assume that the difference in kind that is established by man's having, and by all other animals' lacking, the power of propositional speech is only a superficial difference. They assume, in other words, that the power of conceptual thought can be adequately explained in neurophysiological terms, and that its presence in man and not in other animals can be explained by the size and complexity of the human brain, which is above the critical threshold of magnitude required for conceptual thought.

On this interpretation of the observed fact that linguistic animals differ in kind from non-linguistic animals, *is man a person rather than a thing?* The answer is affirmative if, as suggested by the above-mentioned writers, the line that divides persons from things can be drawn by such criteria as conversational ability, the ability to engage in meaningful discourse, and the ability to give and receive reasons or arguments. By these criteria, men are at present the only beings on earth that are persons. All other animals and machines are things—at least in the light of available evidence. The special worth or dignity that belongs exclusively to persons, the respect that must be accorded only to persons, the fundamental imperative that commands us to treat persons as ends, never solely as means—all these are thought to obtain on this theory of what is involved in being a person.

If in the future we should discover that dolphins, too, or certain robots, are persons in the same sense, then they too would have a dignity, deserve a respect, and impose certain obligations on us that other animals and other machines would not. However, if in the future we should discover that man differs from other animals *only in degree*, the line that divides the realm of persons from the realm of things would be rubbed out, and with its disappearance would go the basis in fact for a principled policy of treating men differently from the way in which we now treat other animals and machines.

Other practical consequences would then follow. Those who now oppose injurious discrimination on the moral ground that all human beings, being equal in their humanity, should be treated equally in all those respects that concern their common humanity, would have no solid basis in fact to support their normative principle. A social and political ideal that has operated with revolutionary force in human history could be validly dismissed as a hollow illusion that should become defunct. Certain anatomical and physiological characteristics would still separate the human race from other species of animals; but these would be devoid of moral significance if they were unaccompanied by a single psychological difference in kind. On the psychological plane, we would have only a scale of degrees in which superior human beings might be separated from inferior men by a wider gap than separated the latter from non-human animals. Why, then, should not groups of superior men be able to justify their enslavement, exploitation, or even genocide of inferior human groups, on factual and moral grounds akin to those that we now rely on to justify our treatment of the animals that we harness as beasts of burden, that we butcher for food and clothing, or that we destroy as disease-bearing pests or as dangerous predators?

It was one of the Nuremberg decrees that "there is a greater difference between the lowest forms still called human and our superior races than between the lowest man and monkeys of the highest order." What is wrong *in principle* with the Nazi policies toward Jews and Slavs if the facts are correctly described and if the only psychological differences between men and other animals are differences in degree? What is wrong *in principle* with the actions of the enslavers throughout human history who justified their ownership and use of men as chattel on the ground that the enslaved were inferiors (barbarians, gentiles, untouchables, "natural slaves, fit only for use")? What is wrong *in principle* with the policies of the American or South African segregationists if, as they claim, the Negro is markedly inferior to the white man, not much better than an animal and, perhaps, inferior to some?

The answer does not consist in dismissing as false the factual allegations concerning the superiority or inferiority of this or that group of men. It may be false that, within the human species, any racial or ethnic group is, as a group, inferior or superior. But it is not false that extremely wide differences in degree separate individuals who top the scale of human abilities from those who cluster at its bottom. We can, therefore, imagine a future state of affairs in which a new global division of mankind replaces all the old parochial divisions based upon race, nationality, or ethnic group—a division that separates the human elite at the top of the scale from the human scum at the bottom, a division based on accurate scientific measurement of human ability and achievement and one, therefore, that is factually incontrovertible. At this future time, let the population pressures have reached that critical level at which emergency measures must be taken if human life is to endure and be endurable. Finish the picture by imagining that before this crisis occurs, a global monopoly of authorized force has passed into the hands of the elite—the mathematicians, the scientists, and the technologists, not only those who make and control machines of incredible power and versatility, but also those whose technological skill has mechanized the organization of men in all large-scale economic and political processes. The elite are then the *de facto* as well as the *de jure* rulers of the world. At that juncture, what would be wrong *in principle* with their decision to exterminate a large portion of mankind—the lower half, let us say—thus making room for their betters to live and breathe more comfortably?

Stressing "in principle," the question calls for a moral judgment. Validly to make a moral judgment in a particular case, real or imaginary, we must appeal to a defensible normative principle and one that is applicable to the facts as described. Can we do so in the case that we have been imagining? The facts include not only the scientifically measured ranking of individuals according to degrees of ability and achievement, but also the overarching fact that we have been taking for granted for the purpose of this discussion; namely, that it has been discovered that the psychological differences between men and other animals are all differences of degree. With exceptions that constitute a small minority, men have found nothing morally repugnant in killing animals for the health, comfort, sustenance, and preservation of human life. It seems reasonable to regard as morally sound those policies that have the almost unanimous consent of mankind, including its most civilized and cultivated representatives. By this criterion, we must acknowledge the moral validity of the policy that men have always followed with regard to the killing of animals for the benefit of the human race. If that policy is morally sound, it must reflect a valid normative principle. What is it?

It is indicated by the fact that, with the exception of relatively small numbers of scientists and philosophers, the members of the human race have always interpreted and still do interpret the observation that they alone of all animals have the power of speech as signifying not only a psychological difference in kind between themselves and the brutes, but also the psychological superiority of their own kind. Combining this fact with the policy that men have pursued in their treatment of animals, we can discern the normative principle underlying the action. It is that *an inferior kind ought to be ordered to a superior kind as a means to an end*; in which case there is nothing wrong about killing animals for the good of mankind. The same rule applies to other uses of animals as instruments of human welfare.

Now let us alter the picture by introducing into it the supposition with which we began this discussion—the supposition that it has been discovered that men and other animals differ psychologically only in degree. If, on that supposition, we still think it is a morally sound policy to use animals as means to our own good, including killing them, the underlying normative principle must be that *superiors in degree are justified, if it serves their welfare, in killing or otherwise making use of inferiors in degree.* But that principle, once it is recognized to be sound, cannot be restricted to the relation between men and animals; it applies with equal force to the relation between men of superior and men of inferior degree, especially to those who are at the top and at the bottom of the scale of ability and achievement, since the difference in degree that separates them may be as large as the difference in degree that separates the lowest men from the highest animals. Thus we appear to have reached the conclusion that, given only psychological differences of degree between men and other animals, and given a scientifically established ranking of individuals on a scale of degrees, the killing or exploitation of inferior by superior men cannot be morally condemned.

Is there a flaw in the argument? If there is one, it would appear to lie in the illicit substitution of the relation between superiors and inferiors *in degree* for the relation between a superior and an inferior *kind*. I am not prepared to say that the substitution is illicit, particularly if the superior and the inferior in kind are only superficially different in kind and hence in their underlying constitution differ only in degree. But if the normative principle that subordinates inferiors in kind to the good of their superiors in kind is defensible only when the superiors and the inferiors differ radically in kind, then we cannot validly convert that normative principle into a rule governing the action of superiors in degree with respect to inferiors in degree. Since, in the long history of man's reflective consideration of his action with respect to brute animals, the prevailing view of the difference between human beings and non-human animals has always been that it is not only a difference in kind, but also a radical difference in kind, I think it is reasonable to presume that the conscience of mankind has sanctioned the killing or exploitation of animals on this basis, and not on the view that the difference in kind is only superficial. The latter view, as explicitly formulated in this book, represents the position implicitly held by a relatively small number of scientists and philosophers in very recent times. It can hardly be regarded as generating the almost universal moral conviction that there is nothing reprehensible in the killing or exploitation of animals.

The conclusion that we have now reached has both negative and positive corollaries. On the negative side, the practical consequences may be very difficult to live with. If nothing less than the superiority of human to non-human beings that is based on a radical difference in kind between men and other animals can justify our killing and exploitation of them, we are without moral justification for our practices in this regard, should it turn out, as well it may, that the success of a Turing machine in the conversational game decisively shows that the difference in kind is only superficial. Two future possibilities—the one just mentioned or the possible discovery by psychologists that the difference between men and other animals is only one of degree—would leave us with what, after protracted consideration, might turn out to be an insoluble moral problem. We might have to concede that there is no clearly defensible answer to the question whether we ought or ought not to kill subhuman animals. We would then be forced to treat the problem as one of pure expediency, totally outside the pale of right and wrong. And in that case, would not the problem of how superior men should or should not treat inferior men also cease to be a moral problem, and become one of pure expediency? For those of us who still hold on to the traditional belief that moral principles of right and wrong govern the treatment of man by man, the contemplation of that eventuality is as upsetting as the possibility earlier envisaged—that with the discovery that men and other animals differ only in degree, it would be possible morally to justify a future elite in exterminating the scum of mankind in a global emergency brought on by population pressures that exceeded the limits of viability.

The positive corollary reveals that some of our traditional moral convictions rest on the supposition that men and other animals differ radically in kind. When we affirm the equality of all human beings in virtue of their common humanity, and subordinate to that equality all the differences—and inequalities—in degree between one individual and another, that affirmation involves more than simply asserting that all men belong to one and the same kind, which can be anatomically or physiologically identified. It involves the assertion that men differ from other animals in kind, not only psychologically, but also radically in their underlying constitution. Their superiority to other animals by virtue of such a radical difference in kind is that which gives their equality with one another as members of the human species its normative significance—for the rules governing the treatment of men by men as well as for the rules governing the treatment of other animals by men. The revolutionary social and political ideal of human equality is thus seen to depend for its ultimate validity on the outcome of the test that will decide which of the competing hypotheses about man is nearer the truth. [8]

(3)

We have seen that the line we now draw between men as *persons* and all else as *things* would be effaced by the discovery that nothing but differences in degree separate men from other animals and from intelligent robots. But can it be preserved if the difference, while one of kind rather than of degree, turns out to be only a superficial difference in kind and, therefore, one that is ultimately reducible to, or at least generated by, a difference in degree? Can the special dignity that is attributed to man as a person and to no other animal, and can the rights and responsibilities that are usually associated with that dignity, continue to be defended as inherently human if man is not radically different in kind from everything else?

Dr. Lilly and Professors Scriven, Smart, and Sellars have presented us with what I shall call a diminished view of what it means to be a person. For them, men are persons by virtue of their distinctive power of conceptual thought, manifested by propositional speech—and so also will dolphins and robots deserve to be ranked as persons if and when they, too, manifest their possession of conceptual thought by conversational or linguistic performances comparable to man's. In an etymologically warranted sense of the word "rational," talking animals are rational, and non-talking animals are brute; for the Greek word "logos" and its Latin equivalent "ratio" connote the intimate linkage of thought and word that is manifested in propositional speech. But if the difference between rational and brute animals solely and ultimately depends upon a difference in degree that places the talking animal above and the non-talking animals below a critical threshold in a continuum of brain magnitudes, such criteria as conversational ability, ability to engage in meaningful discourse, or ability to give and receive arguments may not suffice to establish men as the only persons in a world of things, with the dignity or moral worth that attaches to personality and with all the moral rights and responsibilities that appertain thereto. This began to become clear in our consideration of the hypothetical case that we explored dialectically in the preceding section. The argument there led us to the conclusion that the age-old prohibition against treating men as we have for ages treated animals, and the basic equality of men that rests not only on their all being the same in kind but also on their superiority in kind to animals, not just superiority in degree, cannot be defended—at least, not adequately—except on the ground that men differ *radically* from other animals and other things.

The reason why this is so can be made clearer by going back to the conception of personality as the bearer of moral worth, moral rights, and moral responsibility, which originated in classical antiquity with Plato and Aristotle and with the Roman Stoics, which developed under the influence of Christianity in the Middle Ages, and which, as reformulated in the eighteenth century, especially by Kant, prevailed in Western thought until very recently. As contrasted with the minimal or diminished view advanced by a number of contemporary writers, the traditional view conceived a person as a rational being with free choice. Rationality by itself —if that is nothing more than the power of conceptual thought as manifested in propositional speech—does not constitute a person. A dolphin or a robot would not have the moral worth or dignity that demands being treated as an end, never merely as a means; would not have inherent rights that deserve respect; and would not have the moral responsibility to respect such rights, if the dolphin or robot was nothing more than a talking animal by virtue of having the requisite brain power for speech. Nor would a man! On the traditional view, a person not only has the rationality that other animals and machines lack; he also has a freedom that is not possessed by them—the freedom to pursue a course of life to a self-appointed end and to pursue it through a free choice among means for reaching that end.

I think the traditional view is correct as against the minimal view that has recently been advanced. Man as a person belongs to what Kant calls "the kingdom of ends" precisely because the end he himself pursues and the means whereby he pursues it are not set for him but are freely appointed and freely chosen by himself. His moral rights and moral responsibility stem from the freedom that is associated with his rationality, not just from his rationality itself. If the power of conceptual thought that constitutes his rationality can, according to the identity hypothesis, be adequately accounted for in neurophysiological terms, then man's rationality does not carry with it the freedom of choice that is requisite for his having the moral rights and responsibility that comprise the dignity of a person. The power of conceptual thought elevates man above the world of sense, the world of the here and now; but the power that elevates him above the world of physical things and makes him a person is the power of free choice which, as Kant puts it, involves "independence of the mechanism of nature." [9] Such independence can be man's only if the psychological power that is distinctive of man involves an immaterial or non-physical factor and can, therefore, operate with some independence of physical causes.

The freedom of free choice is properly called a "contra-causal" freedom when "contra-causal" is understood not as the total absence of causality, but as the presence of a non-physical causality. This does not mean total independence of physical causes; it means only that the act of free choice cannot be wholly explained by the action of physical causes. As will be pointed out in Chapter 18, one of the theoretical consequences of affirming the materialist hypothesis is the denial of free choice. If the brain is the sufficient condition of conceptual thought and if, therefore, there is no reason for positing an immaterial or non-physical factor as operative in man, then man may have other freedoms, just as brute animals do, but he does not have that freedom of choice which makes him the master of himself and of his own destiny —the course he takes in life from beginning to end. Conversely, the affirmation of free choice presupposes the truth of the immaterialist hypothesis, which posits in man the operation of a non-physical factor, needed not only to explain his power of conceptual thought, but also to explain his contra-causal freedom of choice.

The proposition that man differs in kind, not just in degree, from other animals and from machines represents the conclusion that we have reached in the light of all the evidence that is at present available. This proposition may not be overturned by future findings, but if future experiments with Turing machines decisively show that man's difference in kind is only superficial, not radical, the practical consequences would be almost the same as they would be if future evidence showed that man differed only in degree. The distinction between men as persons and all else as things, and with it the attribution of a special dignity and of moral rights and responsibility to men alone, can be sustained only if man's difference is a radical difference in kind, one that cannot ultimately be explained by reference to an underlying difference of degree.

We saw, in the course of the preceding discussion, that the dignity of man as a person and his moral rights and responsibility rest on his freedom to determine the goal he pursues in life and on his free choice of the path by which to attain it. This throws light on the fact that we do not refer to other animals as engaged in the pursuit of happiness. Their goals are appointed for them by their instinctual drives, and the means they employ to reach these goals are provided either by fully developed instinctive patterns of behavior or by rudimentary instinctive mechanisms that require development and modification by learning. If man were just another animal, differing only in the degree to which his rudimentary instinctive mechanisms needed to be supplemented by learning, the pursuit of happiness would not be the peculiarly human enterprise that it is, nor would there be any ethical principles involved in the pursuit of happiness. There can be an ethics of happiness only if men can make mistakes in conceiving the goal that they ought to pursue in life, and can fail in their efforts by making mistakes in the choice of means. Lacking the power of conceptual thought, other animals cannot conceive, and hence cannot misconceive, their goals; only man with the power of conceptual thought can transcend the perceptual here and now and hold before himself a remote goal to be attained.

To this extent, a difference in kind, even if only superficial, is involved in man's concern with living a whole life well, not just with living from day to day. Other animals do not have this problem. This is just another way of saying that they do not have moral responsibility or moral rights. But if there were only one solution to the human problem of living well—the problem of how to make a good life for one's self—and if that solution were determined for each man by causes over which he had no control, then man would not be master of his life, would not be morally responsible for what he did in the pursuit of happiness, and could not claim certain things as his by right because he needed them to achieve his happiness—the happiness he has a right to pursue in his own way.

This last right, the source of all other rights, would not be the fundamental human right that it is, were man not master of his life, not only able to conceive a remote goal toward which to strive, but also able freely to choose between one or another conception of the goal to seek as well as freely to choose the means of seeking it. More than the power of conceptual thought is thus involved in the pursuit of happiness. Freedom of choice is also involved, and with it a radical difference in kind between men and other animals that have no moral problems, no moral rights, and no moral responsibility. Hence, should a Turing machine of the future succeed in the conversational test, as proponents of the materialist hypothesis predict that one will, the moral aspects of human life will be rendered illusory. Of course, unable quickly to shake off the habit of centuries, men may for some time hold onto the illusion that there are better and worse ways to live; but in the long run the truth will prevail, and men will give up the illusion that there is a fundamental difference between living *humanly* and living as other animals live.

This, in my judgment, is the most serious and far-reaching practical consequence of a decision in favor of the materialist hypothesis concerning the constitution of man, and with it a decision that man's difference in kind is only superficial. Only if the immaterialist hypothesis is confirmed by repeated trials and failures of Turing machines in the conversational test, only if man's difference from other animals and machines is a radical difference in kind, will the truth about man sustain a serious concern on his part with the moral problems involved in the pursuit of happiness—the problem of trying to find out what the distinctively human goods are and the problem of engaging by choice in one or another way of life aimed at a maximization of the goods attainable by man. [10]

(4)

One matter mentioned in the preceding discussion deserves further elaboration. It concerns the role of instinct in human life as compared with its role in the life of other animals. The view we take of the way in which man differs from other animals—in degree only, superficially in kind, or radically in kind—directly affects our understanding of the role of instinct in human life; and so, in the first instance, we are concerned with the theoretical consequences of diverse views of the difference of man. But there are practical consequences, too, though they are less immediate; for according as we understand the role of instinct in human life in one way or another, we may be led to adopt one or another practical policy with respect to the alteration or control of human behavior. A striking example of this is to be found in certain recent popularizations of the findings of ethology concerning the instincts of aggression and territoriality that are operative in fish, birds, and mammals. On the basis of those findings, interpreted in terms of the view that man differs only in degree or at most only superficially in kind, the thesis is advanced that the basic patterns of human behavior underlying the institutions of property, nationalism, and war are determined by these same animal instincts; and, being thus instinctively determined, the human institutions in question are unamenable to alteration or eradication as long as man remains the animal he is. [11]

To state the theoretical problem with clarity, a number of distinctions must be made. First, we must distinguish between that which is innate or unlearned, as indicated by its being species-predictable, and that which is acquired or learned, as indicated by its variable presence or absence in individual members of a given species. Second, we must distinguish between those completely formed instinctive mechanisms that operate effectively without the intervention of learning and those more rudimentary instinctive mechanisms that need to be supplemented by learned behavior in order to be effective in operation. And, third, we must distinguish between instinctive mechanisms, on the one hand, both those that are fully formed and those that are rudimentary, and instinctual drives, on the other hand.

The former are patterns of overt behavior; the latter are conative sources of behavior—sources of energy impelling toward certain biological results. Such are the instinctive drives of sexual or reproductive behavior, self-preservative behavior through feeding or flight, aggressive behavior, and associative behavior. These instinctual drives are innate in the sense of being species-predictable; when activated by specific releasing mechanisms, they impel the animal toward specific objects or conditions that constitute satisfactions of the drive and bring about its temporary quiescence. Though quiescent for a time, the instinctual drive remains as a potency to be aroused again, and when aroused it once again activates patterns of behavior seeking its fulfillment. The behavioral means of fulfillment (1) may consist of fully formed instinctive mechanisms, as in the case of the insects without brains or cerebro-spinal nervous systems, and also as in the case of the cerebro-spinal vertebrates with relatively small brains; or, (2) they may consist of rudimentary instinctive mechanisms supplemented in varying degrees by acquired or learned patterns of behavior, as in the case of the higher mammals with relatively large brains; or, (3) as in the case of man, the means of satisfying instinctual drives when they are operative may consist of overt patterns of behavior that are products of learning or intelligence.

While there seems to be no question that the instinctual drives found in the vertebrates and especially in the mammals are also present in man, the prevailing scientific opinion is that man has no fully formed instinctive mechanisms for the satisfaction of these drives, nor even rudimentary ones as in the case of other higher animals. The only species-predictable behavior in a mature human being consists of such simple reflex arcs as the pupillary, the salivary, the patellar, or the cilio-spinal reflex, together with such involuntary innervations are are produced by the action of the autonomic and sympathetic nervous systems. Men are impelled to overt behavior of certain sorts when in states of fear, anger, hunger, or sexual arousal. This overt behavior will be accompanied by visceral changes—in the glands and in the involuntary musculature—that are set in motion by the autonomic and sympathetic nervous systems. But the behavior itself will consist of voluntary actions that have been learned, that are intelligently organized, and that may be directed to the immediate fulfillment of the drive, to a postponed fulfillment of it, or to its frustration. Such behavior will vary from individual to individual; and in any one individual, it will vary from time to time, though the instinctual drive may be the same and be of the same strength.

The foregoing description of the way in which instinctual drives operate in man as compared with the way in which they operate in other animals is more consonant with the view that man differs in kind than with the view that he differs only in degree; for the difference between the operation of instinctual drives and instinctive mechanisms in other animals and the functioning of instinctual drives in man appears to be one of kind rather than of degree. What other animals do entirely by instinct or by the combination of instinct and perceptual intelligence (i.e., the power of perceptual thought through which animal learning takes place), man does entirely by learning, through the exercise of his perceptual intelligence and especially his power of conceptual thought. The presence of the same instinctual drives in man and other animals does not lead to the same overt performances in man and in other animals when these same drives are operative; nor does the presence of the same instinctual drives in all members of the human species lead all men to behave in the same way when they are activated by the release of instinctual energies.

The power of conceptual thought in man enables him to devise alternative ways of dealing with his instinctual urges. But if all the driving power behind human behavior comes from the instinctual urges that man has in common with other animals, and if man's power of conceptual thought is merely the servant of his instinctual drives, then in its main outlines human behavior is instinctively determined, as animal behavior is to a greater extent and in more detail. For human behavior to be radically different in kind from animal behavior, with respect to the role that instinct plays, man must be radically different in kind from other animals. Not only must the power of conceptual thought enable man to devise diverse ways of dealing with his instinctual urges, but he must have psychic energy not drawn from instinctual sources in order to exercise mastery over them—to sublimate or divert them to non-animal satisfactions, to postpone their gratification for long periods of time, or to subdue and frustrate them entirely if he so chooses. No other animal manifests such mastery of its instinctual urges. In Freudian language, no other animal suffers the discomforts or pains that result from domesticating and civilizing its instincts. Both civilization and its discontents belong only to man: civilization with its technology, its laws, its arts and sciences, because man alone has the power of conceptual thought that produces these elements of human culture; the discontents of civilization, born of the frustration, prolonged postponement, or sublimation of instinctual urges, because man alone exercises some voluntary control over the instinctual drives that he shares with other animals.

Surprising as it may seem, Freud's account of the relation between man's intellect and his instincts presupposes that man differs radically in kind from other animals. I say this with full knowledge that Freud himself, if explicitly asked the question about how man differs, would give one of the opposite answers —either that man differs only in degree or that his difference in kind is only superficial. No other answer fits Freud's explicit commitment to the principle of phylogenetic continuity, and his equally strong commitment to a thoroughgoing determinism that precludes free choice. Nevertheless, when we read *Civilization and Its Discontents*, we find many passages difficult to understand unless man is radically different from other animals that have the same instinctual drives; such as the following:

> Sublimation of instinct is an especially conspicuous feature of cultural evolution; this it is that makes it possible for the higher mental operations, scientific, artistic, ideological activities, to play such an important part in civilized life. If one were to yield to a first impression, one would be tempted to say that sublimation is a fate which has been forced upon

> instincts by culture alone. But it is better to reflect over this a while. Thirdly and lastly, and this seems most important of all, it is impossible to ignore the extent to which civilization is built up on renunciation of instinctual gratifications, the degree to which the existence of civilization presupposes the non-gratification (suppression, repression or something else?) of powerful instinctual urgencies. This "cultural privation" dominates the whole field of social relations between human beings. . . . *It is not easy to understand how it can become possible to withhold satisfaction from an instinct.* [12]

I have italicized the last sentence quoted because I want to call attention to the question that must be answered. *How is it possible for us to withhold satisfaction from an instinct?* What power in us enables us to do so? Freud's answer to that question is, in my judgment, very revealing. It is given in the following passage:

> We may insist as much as we like that the human intellect is weak in comparison with human instincts, and be right in doing so. But nevertheless there is something peculiar about this weakness. The voice of the intellect is a soft one, but it does not rest until it has gained a hearing. Ultimately, after endlessly repeated rebuffs, it succeeds. This is one of the few points in which one may be optimistic about the future of mankind, but in itself it signifies not a little. And one can make it the starting-point for yet other hopes. The primacy of the intellect certainly lies in the far, far, but still probably not infinite, distance. [13]

The foregoing explanation of how men are able to withhold satisfaction from instincts, and to exercise mastery over them in other ways, attributes an autonomy and causal efficacy to the human intellect which it could have only if the power of conceptual thought were an immaterial or non-physical power. Only if he possessed such a power would man be able to choose between diverse ways of gratifying his instincts; be able to decide whether to gratify them or not; and be able, in addition, to seek the gratification of desires that are not rooted in his instinctual urges at all, but arise from his capacities for knowing and for loving, as only an animal with the power of conceptual thought can know or love. [14] Thus, Freud's account of civilization and its discontents and his statement about the power of the human intellect in relation to man's animal instincts appear to lead to a conclusion that runs counter to his own commitments to determinism and to phylogenetic continuity; namely, the conclusion that man differs radically in kind from other animals by virtue of having a non-physical power that gives him freedom of choice and that has sufficient independence of instinctual energies to gain mastery or exercise control over them.

We find the same conclusion implicit in Konrad Lorenz' recent book on aggression; and there, as in Freud, its implicit presence is obscured and contradicted by many things that are explicitly said to the contrary. Lorenz acknowledges the uniqueness of man by virtue of his power of conceptual thought. [15] In addition, he attributes to man, because of his rationality, a "responsible morality" that is not possessed by other animals, and tells us, as Freud does, that "we all suffer to some extent from the necessity to control our natural inclinations by the exercise of moral responsibility." [16] In his discussion of the "behavioral analogies to morality," he clearly indicates that what morally responsible men do by reason, other animals do solely by instinctive mechanisms. [17] Nevertheless, he explicitly denies autonomy to reason; i.e., denies that man has in his constitution any power sufficiently independent of instinctual energies to exercise mastery over them.

> By itself, reason can only devise means to achieve otherwise determined ends; it cannot set up goals or give us orders. Left to itself, reason is like a computer into which no relevant information conducive to an important answer has been fed; logically valid though all its operations may be, it is a wonderful system of wheels within wheels, without a motor to make them go round. The motive power that makes them do so stems from instinctive behavior mechanisms much older than reason and not directly accessible to rational self-observation. [18]

Reason, or the power of conceptual thought, has no driving energy of its own, and no causal efficacy of its own; all its commands or prohibitions draw their effective force "from some emotional, in other words, instinctive, source of energy supplying motivation. Like power steering in a modern car, responsible morality derives the energy which it needs to control human behavior from the same primal power which it was created to keep in rein." [19]

Because, like Freud, Lorenz is committed to determinism and to phylogenetic continuity, he leaves us with the puzzle of how reason and responsible morality can operate to thwart instinctual drives if they lack autonomy, i.e., if all their energy derives from instinctual sources. In addition, there is the further puzzle of how man can have moral responsibility without having a freedom of choice that involves some measure of independence of animal instincts. These puzzles vanish if one holds the view that Freud and Lorenz cannot adopt, because it is irreconcilable with their basic commitments—the view that man differs radically in kind from other animals, and that he has the power of conceptual thought and contra-causal freedom of choice by virtue of having a non-physical or immaterial factor in his make-up, a factor that has a certain measure of autonomy and causal efficacy.

(5)

The reader should not need to be reminded that, at this stage of our inquiries, we do not *know* whether man's difference in kind is superficial or radical; we do not *know* whether the materialist hypothesis or the immaterialist hypothesis is nearer the truth. Such arguments as can be advanced in support of one or the other hypothesis have already been examined; I have not, in the foregoing discussion of the role of instinct in human life, offered any new arguments for the immaterialist hypothesis. My sole purpose has been to see the alternative practical consequences that would follow from a future decision in favor of one hypothesis or the other. Let me summarize what has now become clear.

On the one hand, if man has an immaterial or non-physical factor operative in his make-up and if, with that, he has freedom of choice and some measure of independence of his animal instincts, then the resultant discontinuity between man and other living organisms would require us to desist from trying to explain human behavior by the theories or laws that we apply to the behavior of subhuman animals. In spite of the fact that the same instinctual drives are operative in man and other animals, the radical difference in kind between them would mean that instinct does not play the same role in human life that it plays in the lives of other animals. Man would have a mastery over his instincts that no other animal has; and he could have rational goals, ideals envisaged by reason, beyond the satisfaction of his instinctual needs. We might then look upon the future of man with the optimism that both Freud and Lorenz express, but we would have grounds for that optimism which they cannot reconcile with their scientific convictions. [20]

On the other hand, if determinism and the principle of phylogenetic continuity hold true in the case of man, as they would if man differs only superficially in kind from other animals, then the laws governing and the theories explaining the behavior of subhuman animals would apply without qualification to human behavior. In spite of the fact that man differs in kind by virtue of having the power of conceptual thought, instinct would play the same determining role in human life that it plays in the lives of other animals; and, in that case, we cannot be optimistic about the future of the human race, for so long as man is governed by his animal instincts, his behavior cannot be altered in its broad outlines and in its basic tendencies.

CHAPTER 18

The Consequences for Thought

(1)

THE CONSEQUENCES that we considered in the preceding chapter were mainly, if not exclusively, practical—in the sphere of action. We were concerned there with the effects upon conduct, and on the principles governing conduct, of one or another answer to the question about how man differs. According as we answer that question in one way or another, we sustain or abrogate the distinction between person and thing with all its moral and political consequences; we can adhere to or must abandon traditional views of human equality and freedom, and our whole approach to the problem of human rights, moral responsibility, and the pursuit of happiness is basically altered. These consequences affect the lives of everyone, the ordinary man as well as the man of specialized learning. In contrast, the theoretical consequences to which we now turn our attention —consequences in the sphere of thought, in the domain of scientific theory, philosophical doctrine, or religious belief—primarily affect the man in the academy, not the man in the street.

The thinking of ordinary men may, of course, be ultimately affected by basic changes in the thinking of the learned; and when that occurs, practical consequences—changes in the general tenor of human attitudes and action—may ensue. Let us, however, confine our attention to the theoretical consequences for the sophisticated; that is, to the effects of one alternative or the other on the thinking of the learned. We will first consider the consequences that would flow from an experimental falsification of the immaterialist hypothesis—the hypothesis that the brain is only a necessary, but not the sufficient condition, of conceptual thought, together with its corollary that man differs radically in kind from other animals. We will then consider the consequences that would follow from the failure, after many repeated efforts, to falsify this hypothesis, such failure being interpreted as infirming or casting in doubt the materialist hypothesis and confirming or favoring the relative truth of the immaterialist position.

One further point should be noted. In the preceding chapter, we dealt with the consequences of what we at present know about man's difference, though we did take some account of the future possibility of discovering the very opposite to be the case. In this chapter, we will deal with the consequences not of what we now know, but rather of what we are certain to find out in the future about how man differs.

(2)

The effect of confirming the truth of the materialist hypothesis; or, what is the same, the effect of falsifying the immaterialist hypothesis. There are two questions to consider here, not one. It is not enough to ask what theoretical consequences would follow from experimental success with a Turing machine—a robot that could pass the conversational test and satisfactorily meet the Cartesian challenge. We must also ask in what sphere of learning the theoretical consequences would occur—in science, philosophy, or religion—and, in each case, we must specify the doctrinal commitment of those who would be seriously affected.

To answer the second question first: the most important effects, as I see them, would be in the field of religion. There would also be, I think, one serious consequence in the realm of philosophy. I will come to that later; let us concentrate for the moment on the religious consequences, and ask: *Consequences for whom? For which religious group? What doctrinal commitments define the religious group that would be affected?*

If I cite first the representatives of the "new theology" and those who call themselves "Christian radicals," I must at once call attention to the fact that the views being promulgated by this group of contemporary writers would be affected as seriously by the falsification of the materialist hypothesis as they would be by the falsification of its opposite. The writers I have in mind include not only such eminent Protestant theologians as Bultmann and Bonhoeffer, but also such self-styled Christian radicals as Professors Van Buren, Hamilton, Altizer, and Vahanian—to mention only those who have recently published proclamations of their views. And I would extend the list to include all those Christian thinkers who, in one way or another, approve and promote the secularization of Christianity, or who are engaged in fomenting what Bishop Robinson calls "the new reformation." [1] While all members of this group may not be Christians without religion, as Bonhoeffer describes himself, all are atheists in the sense that their slogan "God is dead" expresses their disbelief in the existence of God as traditionally conceived by orthodox Christianity. The God in whose existence they find it impossible to believe is the God of traditional theism—the supreme being, an infinite and eternal spiritual being, a transcendent as well as an immanent God who is creator, provider, and governor of the cosmos. [2]

The Christian radicals and promoters of the "death of God" movement all agree with the implied negative answer to Robinson's rhetorical question—"Can a truly contemporary person *not* be an atheist?" Why do they think that a truly contemporary person must be an atheist—a disbeliever in the God of traditional theism? The answer lies, in part at least, in their commitment to the naturalism and materialism that is regnant in contemporary thought, and in their rejection of views that they think are incompatible with the main tenets of contemporary science. As a consequence, they are led to deny that anything *im*material or *super*natural exists. The God affirmed to exist by traditional Judaism and by orthodox Christianity (in its Protestant as well as in its Roman Catholic and Greek Orthodox forms) is both a spiritual being and also a supernatural being whose existence transcends the whole natural order. If nothing exists or can exist that is not physical and somehow subject to natural laws, if whatever exists, exists in the cosmos and not apart from it, the supernatural does not exist. Considered in this context, the possible future falsification of the immaterialist hypothesis about man would be welcomed by the new theologians: it would tend to confirm them in their present disbeliefs. Only those among them who are aware that their present commitment to the tenets of scientific naturalism is an "act of faith" on their part would realize that scientific knowledge might be substituted for faith as a result of success by a Turing machine in the conversational test.

In another context, however, the new theologians would—or should—welcome the failure of repeated efforts by Turing machines in the conversational test, and, with it, the weakening of the materialist hypothesis and the strengthening of its contrary. Rejecting traditional theism, the Christian radicals and secularists affirm their belief in a divinity that is somehow manifested in man as a person and in the sphere of interpersonal relationships. This belief leads them to speak of the "transcendence" of the human person, and to conceive man as a being that, though a part of nature, is not wholly natural. If they understood the presuppositions of this view of man, they would realize that it requires them to affirm man's radical difference in kind; for man is wholly natural only if he differs in degree from other animals, or if, while differing in kind, his difference in kind is only superficial. As we have seen, man is not a person in the full sense of that term unless he differs radically in kind from other animals and machines; nor can he be "transcendent," in the sense attached to that word by the new theology, unless his make-up involves the presence and operation of a non-physical or immaterial factor. Hence, if the immaterialist hypothesis were to be decisively falsified in the future, the Christian radicals and secularists might have to abandon not only traditional theism, but also their present notions about the divinity in man.

Conversely, strict logic would lead to a conclusion that might discomfort them—if they ever paid attention to strict logic. For if their belief in the transcendence and divinity of man presupposes man's radical difference in kind from everything else, and if that radical difference in kind carries with it the affirmation of an immaterial or non-physical element in man, then their disbelief in a transcendent and wholly supernatural being that is spiritual should be weakened by the same future findings that would strengthen their belief in the transcendence and divinity of man. Clear recognition of this should lead them to suspect profound inconsistency or incoherence in their various beliefs and disbeliefs. As I will point out presently, the truth of the immaterialist hypothesis renders intelligible and credible belief in a divine person—a wholly spiritual, transcendent, supernatural being—and at the same time it explains the analogical sense in which there is something divine and transcendent about man, i.e., the sense in which man, by virtue of an immaterial element in his make-up, is a *natural person*—the image of God who is a *supernatural person*.

Let us consider another and quite different religious group. It consists of those traditional and orthodox Christians, both Catholic and Protestant, who are fideists. The falsification of the immaterialist hypothesis would have little effect on them.

Fideism involves two things: on the one hand, commitment to a body of religious dogmas; on the other hand, commitment by faith alone and without any regard for the relation between what is affirmed by faith and what is affirmed or denied by the rest of human knowledge. The fideist does not care whether prevailing scientific or philosophical opinions support or oppose the dogmas of his religion. In his eyes, they do not need support from that quarter. And if certain religious dogmas appear to be absurd or unreasonable in the light of secular knowledge, the fideist redoubles his commitment to them, not merely in spite of their being absurd, but precisely because they are absurd. Hence, for the fideist, no change in the state of secular knowledge can affect the dogmas in which he believes or the manner in which he is commited to them. [3]

The one religious group that would be seriously affected by the confirmation of the materialist position, and by the falsification of the immaterialist hypothesis concerning man's nature and radical difference, consists of those traditional Christians (mainly Roman Catholics) who not only are orthodox in their dogmatic commitments but who also try to be philosophical in their understanding of dogmas that they hold by religious faith. The dogmatic theologians in this group conceive the theological enterprise as faith seeking understanding. They look to that part of philosophy which they call "natural theology" to provide rational support for some of the articles of their faith, and to make other articles of faith as reasonable, as intelligible, and as credible as possible. Affirming the unity of truth, they deny that religious truth can exist in a logic-tight compartment unaffected by scientific or philosophical knowledge having a contrary tenor. Unlike the fideists, they regard the slightest apparent conflict between science and religion, or between philosophy and religion, as a matter of the most serious concern—as a challenge to be met or a problem to be resolved. [4]

For this last group, what would be the consequences of the future possibility that we have been considering? The most effective way to answer this question quickly is to turn back to earlier centuries—any period of Christendom prior to the last 100 or 150 years. The dogmatic theology of this earlier period, in most of the Protestant sects as well as in Roman Catholicism, includes four dogmas that we must now consider.

(1) *The dogma of man's personality:* that man and man alone is made in the image of God, and has this special character among all terrestrial creatures by virtue of his having a spiritual aspect, or a non-material component in his nature. [5]

(2) *The dogma of man's special creation:* that the origin of the human race as a whole, and the coming to be of each human individual, cannot be adequately accounted for by the operation of the purely natural causes that are operative in the biological processes of reproduction or procreation, but requires the intervention of divine causality. [6]

(3) *The dogma of individual immortality or of a life hereafter for the individual human person:* that the human soul, unlike the souls of other living things, is capable of subsisting apart from the body, even though for the perfection of human life, it needs to be re-united with the body that God resurrects from the ashes of this earthly life. [7]

(4) *The dogma of free will and moral responsibility:* that man is morally responsible for his compliance with or transgression of God's will by virtue of his having the power of free choice between good and evil, between loving God or turning away from him. [8]

These four dogmas have in common the fact that they all sharply separate man from other terrestrial creatures. No other creature, inert body, plant, or animal is made in the image of God, for none is a person as God is a person. The operation of physical causes in the natural processes of reproduction suffices for the origin of other species of living things, and for the generation of individual members of these species. Only man requires

God's special creative action. No other living thing on earth is vouchsafed individual immortality by God. No other terrestrial creature carries the burden of moral responsibility that is inseparable from freedom of choice.

If now we ask what philosophical conception of man is required to render these four dogmas concerning man's uniqueness reasonable, intelligible, and credible, the answer, *stated in minimal terms*, is as follows. Man must be conceived as different in kind from all other terrestrial things. That difference in kind must be conceived as a radical difference in kind, involving a break in the continuity of nature. That radical difference in kind must be conceived in terms of man's unique possession of an intellectual power that transcends the properties of matter and the operation of physical causes. In other words, man's intellect (i.e., his power of conceptual thought) is the immaterial component in his constitution that makes him a person, requires his special creation, gives him the hope of immortality, and endows him with freedom of choice.

I do not wish to be understood as saying that the truth of the four dogmas can be demonstrated philosophically to constitute a body of natural theology that has the character of *épistēmē*. Far from it. The only point I am trying to make here is much less extravagant. It amounts to no more than this: the truth of the immaterialist hypothesis concerning man's power of conceptual thought, and the truth of its corollary concerning man's radical difference in kind, is the minimal support that philosophy can offer for the four dogmas mentioned above. If the immaterialist hypothesis is true, that at least renders the dogmas somewhat credible, intelligible, and reasonable. What the dogmas assert is at least possible within the framework of all the rest of our philosophical and scientific knowledge.

That being the case, falsification of the immaterialist hypothesis would clearly have serious consequences for the reasonableness of faith in the four dogmas concerning man. If there is nothing immaterial in the constitution of man, if man is continuous with the rest of physical nature, if everything that is distinctive of man can be explained by the magnitude of his brain, then all four of the dogmas are adversely affected, though not in the same way.

It is difficult to see how man can be made in the image of God as a person, if God's personality lies in His spiritual being, and man's personality consists solely in his having the power to engage in meaningful discourse. It is difficult to see why the origin of the human race cannot be accounted for by the natural processes of evolution, or why the generation of the human individual cannot be accounted for by the ordinary processes of procreation. It is difficult to see why man should have any hope of individual immortality or look forward, after death, to a resurrected body and a life in the world to come. It is more than difficult, it is impossible to see how man can have freedom of choice, which involves a kind of causality that is not to be found in the material or physical world.

While it is true that, in the last hundred years or so, Christian theologians, especially those in the Roman Catholic community, have tried to accommodate some of their doctrines to the theory and facts of evolution, none of the accommodations that have been made involves the four dogmas about man. Hence, if the immaterialist hypothesis about man's nature and about his difference in kind should be falsified in the future, the theological consequences for Christians who wish their faith to be reasonable would either be those set forth above or would closely resemble them. [9]

Before we close this discussion of the consequences of the falsification of the immaterialist hypothesis, we must consider briefly the effect of such falsification outside the field of religion and in the realm of philosophy.

I have already touched on the one point that must be made when I said a moment ago that man's freedom of choice is rendered impossible to understand if man's intellectual power is wholly explicable in neurological terms. There is no problem here, of course, for those recent writers who confuse the unpredictability of freely chosen acts with the unpredictability of causally contingent events. For them free choice can occur in any causal sequence and is not found exclusively in human action. [10] But for all the rest, that is, for all the leading exponents of free will in the tradition of Western thought, freedom of choice involves a mode of causality that is not operative in the physical action of bodies or material forces. For those who understand free choice in terms of an immaterial mode of causality, the falsification of the immaterialist hypothesis about man must lead to the denial that man has the power of free choice. Free choice would then become more than difficult to understand; it would become impossible to understand. [11]

This result would, in turn, have serious consequences for moral philosophy, at least for moral philosophers of a certain persuasion. There are many philosophers who hold, as I do, that moral responsibility rests on freedom of choice, and cannot be grounded merely on freedom from external constraint. [12] There are also many who agree with Kant, as I do, that the moral imperative to treat man as an end rests not simply on his being a person able to engage in meaningful discourse, but on his being a person who, through freedom of choice, directs his own life, and so is master of himself. [13]

(3)

The effect of trying to falsify the immaterialist hypothesis, and, after many repeated efforts, failing to do so; thus tending to confirm its relative truth, and to infirm the materialist hypothesis. Let us recall once more the logic of the alternatives. On the one hand, those who espouse the materialist hypothesis concerning man's nature and mode of difference predict a successful outcome of the conversational test. A robot that effectively played its part in the Turing game would show, as nothing else might, that neurological factors and processes suffice to explain propositional speech and conceptual thought. With that shown, the immaterialist hypothesis concerning man's nature and his radical difference in kind would be falsified. While the materialist hypothesis would not be correspondingly proved true beyond doubt, it would be confirmed to so high a degree that it would be, for all practical purposes, true.

On the other hand, those who espouse the immaterialist hypothesis predict that Turing machines will always fail to pass the conversational test. Here we must envisage an extensive number and variety of technological efforts to produce a robot that can effectively play its part in Turing's game. Given such efforts over an extended period of time, and given failure to achieve the desired result, the immaterialist hypothesis would be progressively confirmed by thus being repeatedly put to the test and escaping falsification each time. While the materialist hypothesis would not thereby be falsified, its relative truth would be so far diminished that the scientist or philosopher who still continued to hold it without serious reservations or doubts would be exactly like the dogmatic theologian who is an extreme fideist.

Now let us suppose that this possibility is realized in the future. It should be clear at once that its consequences would take an opposite direction to the ones that flow from the future realization of the alternative possibility. But we must ask as we did before: *For whom would these opposite consequences be serious?* What groups would be adversely affected by confirmation of the relative truth of (a) the proposition that man differs radically in kind from all other animals; (b) the proposition that the brain is only a necessary and not a sufficient condition of man's power of conceptual thought; (c) the proposition that an immaterial power must be posited to explain conceptual thought?

So far as I can see, three groups would be affected: (1) the philosophical proponents of the identity hypothesis, the moderate materialists, for their doctrine excludes the possibility of the existence or operation of an immaterial factor; (2) the scientists, and especially the evolutionists, who in their commitment to naturalism exclude the possibility of any break in the continuity of nature, and therefore exclude all radical differences in kind that would introduce discontinuity into nature; (3) the Christian radicals, the religionless or atheistic Christians, the exponents of the new theology or the new reformation.

I will now comment briefly on the consequences for each of these three groups, dealing with them in the order named.

(1) *The philosophers who are moderate materialists.* It must not be thought that failure to falsify the immaterialist hypothesis after repeated efforts to produce Turing machines able to pass the conversational test would afford the first or only argument against the truth of materialism. In the long history of the controversy about materialism, other arguments have been advanced, and one of these, drawn from common experience, claims to falsify the materialist position. That one is still a matter of grave concern to the most thoughtful of contemporary materialists, such as Wilfrid Sellars and J. J. C. Smart. [14] Nevertheless, it can be

said that the failure of repeated efforts to falsify the immaterialist hypothesis by putting machines to the conversational test would bring a different sort of empirical evidence into the picture; and, if the strict logic of empirical procedures is adhered to, the result could not fail to be regarded as extremely damaging.

(2) *The naturalists and especially the evolutionists.* What is at stake here is not only the unbroken continuity of nature but also the principle of phylogenetic continuity as applied to the origin of man. That principle would be violated if man's nature involves an immaterial component that could not possibly be transmitted by the material factors operative in the genetic process. As a result, a question that most evolutionists now think is solved, at least in principle, would become an open question and, what is more, an embarrassment; for the problem of the origin of man on earth might not be capable of scientific solution.

I mentioned earlier, as one of four articles of orthodox Christian faith about man, the dogma of man's special creation—the dogma that, because of an immaterial factor in man's constitution, neither the human race as a whole nor the individual human person can be generated by the operation of purely natural causes, the kind of causes that operate in the genetic process. If the relative truth of the immaterialist hypothesis is confirmed, the problem of man's origin—both the origin of the race and the origin of the individual—may call for a reconciliation of evolutionary theory with orthodox Christian theology. It is hardly an overstatement to say that most scientists today are unprepared for this eventuality.

In addition, the discontinuity of man with the rest of nature would place an insuperable obstacle in the path of the behavioral sciences, at least insofar as they proceed on the assumption that the laws governing and the theories explaining the behavior of subhuman animals apply without qualification or modification to human behavior. The presence and operation of an immaterial factor in the constitution of man would introduce an element of freedom and unpredictability into human behavior. As we observed in Chapter 17, even though man shares with other animals certain basic instinctual drives, these drives would not operate in the same way in human and subhuman animals if the power of conceptual thought is an immaterial power that endows man with efficacious freedom of choice and permits him to have goals and aspirations beyond his animal needs. Hence, if the immaterialist hypothesis were to be confirmed by the outcome of the Turing test, the discontinuity that would result from man's being radically different in kind would make it impossible any longer to suppose, as natural scientists and especially behavioral scientists now do suppose, that the same laws and the same explanations that apply to the behavior of everything else would not only apply to, but also adequately account for, the behavior of man.

(3) *The Christian radicals for whom God is dead.* If the failure of Turing machines to pass the conversational test greatly strengthens the hypothesis that an immaterial power exists in man and operates in human thought and life, that would—or should—have an effect on the negative faith of those who say that God is dead, at least insofar as their reason for disbelieving in a transcendent God is their disbelief in the reality of immaterial entities—spiritual beings. The confirmation of the relative truth of the immaterialist hypothesis concerning man might even lead to a new proof of the existence of God. For if man's origin cannot be explained by purely natural causes, then the existence of man can be used as a premise in an *a posteriori* argument for the existence of the cause that must be added to all natural causes in order to account for man's genesis on earth. That additional cause would have to be supernatural. [15]

Hence, unless the exponents of the new theology and the new reformation in the Christian community are as much dogmatic fideists as some of their orthodox forebears were, their faith in the proposition that God is dead will be seriously challenged; and the question about the existence of a deity that is a transcendent supernatural being will confront them as an open and embarrassing problem. Confused as the new theologians are, they can only be the worse confounded by whichever alternative comes to pass—by the failure as well as by the success of Turing machines to meet the Cartesian challenge.

(4)

A mixed question is one that requires for its solution a combination of the findings of scientific investigation and the contributions of philosophical analysis and criticism. In such questions, an apparent conflict between scientific opinion and common-sense opinion serves to test the truth of competing philosophical theories by challenging them to resolve the conflict without giving up either the truth of common sense or the truth of science. [16] But the question about man with which this book has been concerned is a very special type of mixed question. Here the solution of the problem of how man differs requires us to consult all relevant scientific data and theories as well as bring philosophical analyses and arguments to bear on the question. But what is most extraordinary here is the fact that we can, with reasonable certainty, predict that future scientific efforts will have the effect either of falsifying a traditional philosophical theory or of confirming its relative truth and infirming the relative truth of its contrary. [17]

The point just made has significance for the difficult question about progress in philosophy. Those who think, as I do, that progress has been and can be made in philosophy are often taxed to offer good and clear examples of advances in philosophical truth. If the future contains the alternative possibilities, one of which must be realized, then the advance that will be made toward a solution of the mixed question about man provides us with a dramatic instance of philosophical progress. Since this advance will be occasioned not simply by the efforts of philosophical inquiry, but by the work of scientists and technologists, it may be atypical. The problem of showing progress in philosophy apart from, or independent, of advances in scientific research may, therefore, remain as perplexing as ever. [18]

There is a certain irony in the shift that will take place from the state of the learned world a hundred years ago to the state it will be in a hundred years hence—when one of these alternative possibilities is realized and generates the theoretical consequences that I have indicated.

A century ago and throughout the last hundred years, the portion of the learned world that was most affected by the changing view of man that came to prevail with scientific advances, especially those in the field of evolution, consisted of adherents to traditional orthodox Christian theology. The thrust of the challenge was mainly, if not exclusively, felt by learned men—philosophers and scientists as well as theologians—who subscribed to certain religious beliefs, among which the four dogmas about man were central. In the last hundred years, the altered view of man has come so generally to pervade the learned world that if now or in the future the immaterialist hypothesis were to be falsified, few would be surprised, and fewer would suffer any serious embarrassment.

A century hence and in the intervening years, if present trends continue and accelerate, the portion of the learned world that would be most shocked by an altered view of man that might come to prevail through the failure of Turing machines to pass the conversational test would be all those who are united in a common disbelief—disbelief in the dogmas of traditional orthodox Christianity. Ideas now thought by them to be dead would come to life again, and questions now thought to be closed would have to be re-opened and faced again. [19]

The beliefs or disbeliefs of the learned eventually filter down and exert an influence upon the lives and conduct of their fellow men. But quite apart from the doctrines that prevail among the learned, the ultimate resolution of the question about how man differs from other things will make a difference—a serious difference—to the future course of human affairs; for the image that we hold of man cannot fail to affect attitudes that influence our behavior in the world of action, and beliefs that determine our commitments in the world of thought.

Notes

NOTES TO CHAPTER 1

1. From *You Shall Know Them* by Vercors, copyright 1953 by Jean Bruller, with permission of Little, Brown and Company, Publishers. A paperback reprint of it has just been published. I heartily recommend Vercors' novel not only for the pleasure of a well-told story, but also for a learned exploration of the criteria involved in differentiating between humans and other animals.

2. The first series of Encyclopaedia Britannica Lectures at the University of Chicago in 1964, published in 1965.

3. See *The Conditions of Philosophy*, Chapter 2, esp. pp. 21–38.

4. See *ibid.*, Chapter 2, pp. 38–42; Chapters 6–7; and Chapter 12, esp. pp. 216–217. Let me stress the two related aspects of every mixed question. On the one hand, philosophy, as we have seen, is indispensable in the clarification of the question and in laying down the criteria for interpreting and judging the relevance and force of the evidence obtained by investigation. On the other hand, since the mixed question is not beyond the scope of investigation, it can never be adequately answered on the basis of common experience alone. Purely philosophical answers to mixed questions are corrigible by science, just as common sense is corrigible when the latter forms opinions about matters on the basis of common experience alone, in spite of the fact that special experience is obtainable and should be sought.

   Not all mixed questions are of the same type. Some arise from an apparent conflict between science and common-sense opinion. These serve to test the truth of competing philosophical theories by challenging them to resolve the conflict without giving up either the truth of common-sense opinion or the truth of science. I dealt in *The Conditions of Philosophy* with a striking example of this type of mixed question, involving a conflict between the common-sense beliefs in the reality of the individual physical objects of common experience and the assertion, by some scientists, of the reality of elementary particles. The mixed question about man is of a different sort. Here the solution of the problem of how man differs requires us to consult all the relevant scientific data and theories and to bring to bear on them the applicable philosophical analysis and arguments. It requires us, in addition, to have recourse to philosophical thought in order to get the question itself properly framed and understood and in order to lay down criteria for interpreting and judging scientific evidence and philosophical arguments in their relation to each other. But what is most extraordinary about the mixed question concerning man, as will become apparent in the concluding chapters of Part Two, is that we can envisage in the future the possibility of scientific efforts that will have the effect either of falsifying a traditional philosophical theory or of confirming its relative truth.

NOTES TO CHAPTER 2

1. *Politics*, I, 13, 1259^{b}37.
2. George and Muriel Beadle, *The Language of Life*, 1966.
3. J. Bronowski, *The Identity of Man*, 1965, pp. 2, 4.
4. *Ibid.*, p. 8.
5. *Ibid.*, p. 48. When, on this page, Bronowski attributes to man the unique gift of conceptual ability, he appears to have forgotten that, on pages 11–12, he had rejected the fallacious assumption that man, if he is to be unique, "must be endowed with uniqueness as if it were a physical gift, from conception."
6. Michael Scriven, *Primary Philosophy*, 1966, pp. 177–178.
7. *Ibid.*, p. 197.

NOTES TO CHAPTER 3

1. For a fuller description of the dialectical method, see *The Idea of Freedom*, Volume I, 1958, pp. xvii–xxiv, and 3–79.

NOTES TO CHAPTER 4

1. *Op. cit.*, Chapter 8, esp. pp. 137–142.
2. The following is an indication of exemplary or capital passages on the point:

   PLATO: *Protagoras*, 320d–322c; *Timaeus*, 42a–c; *Theaetetus*, 185a–186d; *Cratylus*, 399b.

ARISTOTLE: *On the Soul*, II, 3, 414b–415a13 (cf. *ibid.*, III, 3); *History of Animals*, VIII, 1, 588a23–31; *Parts of Animals*, IV, 10, 686a27–32; *Generation of Animals*, I, 23, 731a–30–35; *Nichomachean Ethics*, I, 7, 1097b33–1098a8; *Politics*, I, 2, 1253a7–37; I, 5, 1254b15–23; III, 9, 1280a31–34; VII, 13, 1332b3–6; *Rhetoric*, I, 1, 1355b1–3.

EPICTETUS: *Discourses*, I, 6; IV, 7.

MARCUS AURELIUS: *Meditations*, II, 16; IV, 4; VI, 23; VII, 55.

AUGUSTINE: *City of God*, V, 11; VII, 23; VIII, 6; *On Christian Doctrine*, I, 8.

AQUINAS: *Summa Theologica*, I, 18, 2 ad 2; I, 18, 3; I, 19, 10; I, 59, 3; I, 75, 3; I, 76, 1; I, 76, 4; I, 77, 5; I, 78, 1; I, 83, 1; I, 86, 4 ad 3; I–II, 50, 3 ad 2.

DESCARTES: *Philosophical Works*, trans. by E. S. Haldane and G. R. T. Ross: Volume I, pp. 109–110, 115–118; Volume II, pp. 104–105, 243–245, 343.

SPINOZA: *Ethics*, Part III, Prop. 57, Scholium; Part IV, Prop. 37, Scholium 1.

PASCAL: *Treatise on the Vacuum*, Preface; *Thoughts*, Nos. 339, 344, 346, 358, 365, 418.

LOCKE: *Essay Concerning Human Understanding*, II, i, 10–11; III, i, 1–3; IV, xvii, 2; IV, xviii, 11. Cf. II, xxvii, 8; III, vi, 22.

LEIBNIZ: *Leibniz Selections*, ed. by P. P. Wiener, pp. 339–342, 355–367, 371–372, 390–394, 419, 456–458, 503–508; *The Monadology and Other Philosophical Writings*, ed. by R. Latta, 2nd. ed., pp. 50–57, 126–133; *The Philosophical Works of Leibniz*, ed. by G. M. Duncan, 2nd ed., pp. 279–283, 404–405; *Philosophical Writings*, Everyman edition, pp. 8, 18, 24, 28, 86–87, 99–100. Cf. Bertrand Russell, *A Critical Exposition of the Philosophy of Leibniz*, 1900: pp. 141, 264–266.

ROUSSEAU: *The Social Contract and the Discourses*, Everyman edition, 1913: pp. 183–184, 192–193.

KANT: *Critique of Pure Reason*, trans. by J. M. D. Meiklejohn, pp. 300–301; *Critique of Practical Reason and Other Works on Ethics*, trans. by T. K. Abbott, pp. 63–65, 71–72, 152–153; *Critique of Aesthetic Judgment*, trans. by J. C. Meredith, p. 49; *Critique of Teleological Judgment*, trans. by J. C. Meredith, p. 136, fn. 1.

HEGEL: *Philosophy of Right*, trans. by T. M. Knox, Additions, Nos. 4–5, 10, 22, 121; *Philosophy of History*, trans. by J. Sibree, pp. 8, 33–34, 70.

3. *Op. cit.*, pp. 184, 192–193.

4. *Ethics*, Part I, Appendix; Part II, Prop. 48; Part IV, Preface.

5. See passages cited in note 2, *supra*.

6. *Op. cit.*, Volume I, pp. 109–110, 115–118; Volume II, pp. 104–105.

7. For passages critical of Descartes or in a contrary vein, see Locke, *op. cit.*, II, x, 10; II, xi, 11; Leibniz, *New Essays*, II, x, 10; II, xi, 11; Kant, *Critique of Teleological Judgment*, Sections 66, 78–81.

8. The following indicates passages in which the rational soul is distinguished from the souls of animals and plants, or in which the mind, the reason, the intellect, or the will is distinguished from the senses and the passions, by virtue of its spiritual (its non-physical or immaterial) nature:
   ARISTOTLE: *On the Soul*, I, 1, 403ᵃ3–10; II, 2, 413ᵇ24–30; III, 4–5.
   AUGUSTINE: *Confessions*, VII, 1–2; *City of God*, VIII, 5; *Immortality of the Soul*, Chapters X, XIII–XVI.
   AQUINAS: *Summa Theologica*, I, 75, 2, Resp. and ad 1–3; I, 75, 3; I, 75, 6.
   DESCARTES: *Op. cit.*, Volume I, p. 101; Volume II, pp. 211–212.
   LOCKE: *Op. cit.*, II, xxiii, 18, 32. Cf. *per contra*, IV, iii, 6.
   ROUSSEAU: *Op. cit.*, pp. 183–184.
   KANT: *Critique of Teleological Judgment*, pp. 131–132.
   HEGEL: *Philosophy of Right*, Additions, No. 22.

9. The following indicates passages in which the point is made or adumbrated:
   ARISTOTLE: *Parts of Animals*, IV, 10, 686ᵃ27–32.
   EPICTETUS: *Discourses*, I, 3, 9; II, 8.
   AUGUSTINE: *On Christian Doctrine*, I, 22.
   AQUINAS: *Summa Theologica*, I, 93, 1–6; I–II, Prologue.
   PASCAL: *Thoughts*, No. 430.
   DESCARTES: *Op. cit.*, Volume II, pp. 170–171.
   LEIBNIZ: *Discourse on Metaphysics*, xxxiv–xxxv.
   HEGEL: *Philosophy of History*, pp. 33–34, 333–334.

10. *The Works of William Harvey*, trans. by Robert Willis, pp. 368–369, 425; Montesquieu, *The Spirit of Laws*, I, 1; Adam Smith, *The Wealth of Nations*, Modern Library Edition, pp. 12–15.

11. *Op. cit.*, II, xxvii, 8; III, vi, 22. Cf. *ibid.*, III, vi, 7–11. For Leibniz's critique of Locke's treatment of real and nominal essences, see *New Essays*, III, vi, 22.

12. Though both Locke and Rousseau assert, in a number of passages, that man differs in kind from brute by virtue of intellectual or volitional powers that man alone possesses, they flatly contradict themselves in other passages by asserting that man differs from other animals, especially the primates, *only* in degree. See Locke, *op. cit.*, III, vi, 12; III, x, 17; III, xi, 20; IV, xvi, 12; Rousseau, *op. cit.*, pp. 177–187, 192 ff. In regard to Rousseau, vd. Arthur O. Lovejoy, *The Great Chain of Being*, 1948: p. 235.

13. *Op. cit.*, III, vi, 12. Cf. *ibid.*, IV, xvi, 12. See also Leibniz's commentary on these passages in *New Essays*, III, vi, 12; IV, xvi, 12.

14. *Leibniz Selections*, pp. 184–188, 378; *The Monadology and Other Philosophical Writings*, pp. 36–39, 126–133; *The Philosophical Works of Leibniz*, pp. 33–37. See also Russell's critique of Leibniz with regard to the continuum of forms, in *A Critical Exposition of the Philosophy of Leibniz*, pp. 63–66, 222–223; and Lovejoy's comment on Russell, in *The Great Chain of Being*, p. 355, n. 84.

15. See *The Great Chain of Being*, pp. 253–254, 269–270, 275–277.

16. *Ibid.*, p. 332.

17. *Leviathan*, pp. 18, 22–23, 31, 34–35, 46–47, 130–131, 160–161.

18. See *La Mettrie's L'Homme Machine*, critical edition with an introductory monograph and notes by Aram Vartanian, 1960. Cf. Frederick A. Lange, *History of Materialism*, 3rd ed., trans. by E. C. Thomas, 1925: pp. 75–76; also *A Textbook of Marxist Philosophy*, prepared by the Leningrad Institute of Philosophy, trans. by A. C. Moseley, ed. by John Lewis, pp. 45–50.

19. See Lange, *op. cit.*, Book I, Section 1, Chapters 1–2, 4; Section 3, Chapter 1; Section 4, Chapter 3; Book II, Section 1, Chapter 2; also see Richard Falckenburg, *History of Modern Philosophy*, 1893: pp. 61, 255–256, 593–595; G. V. Plekhanov, *Essays in the History of Materialism*, 1934: pp. 6–7, 91–92. One passage in Ludwig Feuerbach's *Essence of Christianity* asserts that man differs in kind from other animals, and may anticipate the Marxist view of that difference in kind as being merely superficial, not radical (see pp. 1–3). For a critique of Feuerbach on this point, see Friedrich Engels, "German Ideology," in *Handbook of Marxism*, pp. 219–220.

20. *Enquiry Concerning Human Understanding*, Section IX, 82–85; Section XII, Part 1, 118.

21. *Essays*, trans. by Charles Cotton, revised by W. C. Hazlett: Volume 4, pp. 230–240; Volume 5, pp. 13–15. For the passages in a contrary tenor, see Volume 5, pp. 91–93, 188–191.

22. See V. I. Lenin, "The Teachings of Karl Marx," in *Handbook of Marxism*, pp. 538–543; *A Textbook of Marxist Philosophy*, pp. 45–50; Plekhanov, *op. cit.*, pp. 172–175; K. N. Kornilov, "Psychology in the Light of Dialectic Materialism," in *Psychologies of 1930*, ed. by C. Murchison, pp. 243–278.

23. See *Handbook of Marxism*, pp. 211–213; *A Textbook of Marxist Philosophy*, pp. 99–102, 108–112; Plekhanov, *op. cit.*, pp. 205–209, 271–276; Kornilov, *op. cit.*, pp. 246–248.

24. See Kornilov, *op. cit.*, pp. 246–248.

25. See *A Textbook of Marxist Philosophy*, pp. 285–288, 294–297, 348–353; Plekhanov, *op cit.*, pp. 172–175.

26. *Critique of Pure Reason*, pp. 367–376. See reference to Leibniz, p. 374, fn.; see also Lovejoy's comments on Kant in regard to Leibniz in *The Great Chain of Being*, pp. 240–241.

27. *Op. cit.*, VIII, 3, 1043^{b}35–1044^{a}9. An even clearer statement of the hierarchy of species is to be found in *On the Soul*, II, 3, 414^{b}20–31, where Aristotle compares the order of living species, constituted by the vegetative, the sensitive, and the rational soul, to the order of plane figures (triangle, quadrangle, pentagon), between which no intermediates are possible. See also *ibid.*, 414^{a}28–414^{b}20, and II, 4.

28. *Op. cit.*, VIII, 1, 588^{b}4–22. The opening sentence of this passage, which should be read in its entirety, would appear to be contradicted by the following statement in Aristotle's treatise *On Plants*: "It is certainly difficult to find a state intermediate between life and the absence of life" (815^{b}36). But there is no contradiction here, any more than there is between this passage in the *History of Animals* (where Aristotle calls our attention to the scale of degrees of vitality within the plant kingdom and the scale of degrees of vitality, mobility, and sensitivity within the animal kingdom) and the passages in the *Metaphysics* and in *On the Soul* (cited in note 27, *supra*), in which Aristotle asserts the hierarchy of species, a scale not of degrees but of grades of perfection in being, between any two proximate members of which intermediates are impossible. For Aristotle, the fundamental *reality* is the hierarchy and discontinuity of species, though he also acknowledges the *appearance* of continuity in the ascending scale of degrees of vitality by which we pass from lower to higher forms of life; and, in addition, as an empirical biologist, he candidly confesses the difficulty of determining whether a particular specimen is to be classified as a plant or as an animal. In an earlier book, I have tried to show how all these passages dealing with the order of species, and bearing on hierarchy and continuity in nature, can be consistently put together. See *Problems for Thomists: The Problems of Species*, 1940: pp. 52–58, 102–109, 260–263. Professor Lovejoy, aware of the apparently conflicting texts in Aristotle on hierarchy and continuity, leaves the apparent contradiction unresolved (see *The Great Chain of Being*, pp. 55–58). Professor Toulmin likewise tends to find two quite disparate and irreconcilable views in Aristotle—one held by Aristotle the metaphysician and the other by Aristotle the empirical biologist (see *The Discovery of Time*, 1965: pp. 44–45, 50–52).

29. For the passages in Aquinas that comment on and adopt the Aristotelian conception of the hierarchy of species and the Aristotelian observations of continuity in the scale of degrees manifested by the forms of life, see *Summa Theologica*, I, 5, 5; I, 47, 2; I, 76, 3; I, 76, 4; I, 78, 1; *Summa Contra Gentiles*, II, 91; II, 95; IV, 41; *Disputed Questions on the Soul*, Q.1, A.7. I have dealt with these pas-

sages, along with the comparable ones in Aristotle, in *Problems for Thomists: The Problem of Species* (see pages cited in note 28, *supra*).

NOTES TO CHAPTER 5

1. Robinet's *Philosophical Considerations on the Natural Gradations of the Forms of Being* was published in 1768. For an available summary of Robinet's views on the continuity of nature and on the unreality of kinds, see Lovejoy, *The Great Chain of Being*, pp. 269–270, 275–279.

2. *Histoire Naturelle* (1749), I, 38. Cf. Lovejoy, *op. cit.*, pp. 229–230, 283–286.

3. See Lovejoy, *op. cit.*, pp. 230–231, 233, 235.

4. See note 1, *supra.*

5. See Lovejoy, *op. cit.*, pp. 235, 272.

6. *Essay Concerning Human Understanding*, III, vi, 12; IV, xvi, 12.

7. *The Social Contract and the Discourses,* Everyman edition, pp. 177–187, 192 ff. Cf. Lovejoy, *op. cit.*, p. 235.

8. See Lovejoy, *op cit.*, p. 197.

9. I am indebted to Professor Lovejoy for this insight. See *op. cit.*, Chapter IX; and cf. S. Toulmin and J. Goodfield, *The Discovery of Time*, Chapter 8.

10. See *Origin of Species and The Descent of Man*, Modern Library edition: p. 361.

11. For a fuller discussion of apparent differences in kind, the reader is referred back to Chapter 2, pp. 23–24.

12. See Darwin, *op. cit.*, pp. 86–96, 98–100, 275–277, 351–352, 370. Cf. A. J. Cain, *Animal Species and Their Evolution*, 1954: p. 182.

13. *Op. cit*, p. 370.

14. See Ernst Mayr, *Animal Species and Evolution*, 1963: pp. 89, 110, 338, 348–349, 403, 428, 431, 449, 450, 480–482, 516–518, 546–547, 554–555, 586–587, 620; Julian Huxley, *Evolution, The Modern Synthesis*, New York, 1942: pp. 154–155, 171–173; A. J. Cain, *op cit.*, pp. 69, 72–73, 130, 132–133, 135, 168, 176, 179, 181–182.

15. See Mayr, *op. cit.*, pp. 422–424; Julian Huxley, *op. cit.*, pp. 164–165, 168–170.

16. T. Dobzhansky, *Mankind Evolving*, 1962: p. 203. Cf. G. G. Simpson, *The Major Features of Evolution*, 1953: pp. 379–380, 384, 389.

17. See Dobzhansky, *op. cit.*, pp. 183, 186, Mayr, *op. cit.*, pp. 358–359, 422–423, and esp. 424; Julian Huxley, *op. cit.*, pp. 164–165, 168–170; and A. J. Cain, *op. cit.*, p. 130.

18. *Genetics and the Origin of Species*, 1937: p. 259. Cf. his *Mankind Evolving*, p. 186, written almost thirty years later.

19. See *op. cit.*, pp. 389–391.

20. *Antiquity of Man* (1863), Everyman edition, pp. 392–393. The whole of the concluding chapter is worth reading.

21. See Loren Eiseley, *Darwin's Century*, 1958: p. 267.

22. See A. E. Wallace, *Contributions to the Theory of Natural Selection*, 1871: Chapter 10. Cf. Eiseley, *op. cit.*, pp. 304–313.

23. *Man's Place in Nature and Other Anthropological Essays*, 1898: p. 155. See *ibid.*, pp. 157–208 for Huxley's discussion of the Engis and Neanderthal skulls.

24. *Op. cit.*, p. 494–495. Cf. *ibid.*, pp. 446, 911–912, 472–473.

25. *Ibid.*, pp. 512–513.

26. See *ibid.*, pp. 461–464.

27. *Ibid.*, p. 465. Cf. Eiseley, *op. cit.*, pp. 288–289; 323; and see also MacDonald Crichtley, "The Evolution of Man's Capacity for Language," in *Evolution After Darwin*, ed. by S. Tax, 1960: Volume II, pp. 290–291, 307–308.

28. See *op. cit.*, p. 431. Cf. *ibid.*, pp. 431–432, 541, 912.

29. See *ibid.*, pp. 513–514, 520–521.

30. See *ibid.*, p. 521; and cf. *ibid.*, pp. 911–915.

31. *The Creed of Science*, 1881: p. 161. Cf. Eiseley, *op. cit.*, pp. 257, 345–346.

NOTES TO CHAPTER 6

1. See T. Dobzhansky, *Mankind Evolving*, 1962: Chapter 7, *Evolution, Genetics, and Man*, 1961: pp. 325–334; G. H. R. von Koenigswald, *The Evolution of Man*, 1963: pp. 69–70, 86–87, 113–114, 119, 130; Richard Carrington, *A Million Years of Man*, 1963: pp. 49 ff., 76, 79–122; W. E. Le Gros Clark, *History of the Primates*, 1961: pp. 13–20, 46–75, 102–137, 144–158, 168–176; *The Antecedents of*

Man, 1960: pp. 343–349; Ernst Mayr, *Animal Species and Evolution*, 1963: pp. 628–658; L. S. B. Leakey, "The Origin of the Genus Homo," in *Evolution After Darwin*, 1960: Volume II, pp. 17–31; S. L. Washburn and F. Clark Howell, "Human Evolution and Culture," in *ibid.*, pp. 35–53; Cesare Emiliani, "Dating Human Evolution," in *ibid.*, pp. 64–65.

See also L. S. B. Leakey, *Adam's Ancestors*, 1960: Prologue and Chapters I, X–XII; *The Progress and Evolution of Man in Africa*, 1961; Raymond Dart, *Adventures with the Missing Link*, New York, 1959: Chapters II, XI, XIV–XV; Pierre Teilhard de Chardin, *The Appearance of Man*, 1965; W. E. Le Gros Clark, *Man-Apes or Ape-Men?*, 1967.

As this book goes to press, recent fossil finds and much more sensitive methods of dating them give a greater antiquity to both hominid and proto-hominid life on earth. Recent finds in China appear to indicate that *Homo erectus* may go back a million years, and the australopithecines may have existed two million years ago. In addition, very recent discoveries support the possibility that there may be only two species of fossil man—*Homo erectus* and *Homo sapiens*—and that *Homo erectus* may have lived on earth from over one million years ago to as recently as 35,000 years ago, while *Homo sapiens*, to which living man belongs, may date back as far as 500,000 years. See William H. Howells, "Homo Erectus," in *The Scientific American*, Volume 215, No. 5, November, 1966, pp. 46–53.

2. *The Origin of Species and The Descent of Man*, Modern Library edition: p. 541.

3. See Julian Huxley, *Evolution, The Modern Synthesis*, 1942: pp. 569–572; *The Uniqueness of Man*, 1943: Chapter I; *Evolution in Action*, 1953: pp. 103–111; T. Dobzhansky, *Mankind Evolving*, 1962: Chapters 8, 12; G. G. Simpson, *The Meaning of Evolution*, 1949: Chapter XVII; Ernst Mayr, *op. cit.*, pp. 623–624, 650, 656–658; Bernard Rensch, *Evolution Above the Species Level*, 1960: pp. 305–307, 340–341; W. E. Le Gros Clark, *Antecedents of Man*, 1960: pp. 347–349; *History of the Primates*, 1960: pp. 119–120; Richard Carrington, *op. cit.*, pp. 58–59, 62–68; Kenneth P. Oakley, *Man the Tool-Maker*, 1964: pp. 4–5, 125–126, 130, 132; Pierre Teilhard de Chardin, *The Appearance of Man*, 1965: Chapter XVII, *The Phenomenon of Man*, 1959: pp. 164–171, 194–198. See also the papers by Leakey and by Washburn and Howell, in *Evolution After Darwin*, cited in note 1, *supra*.

For a discussion of the significance for human speech of the exclusively human asymmetry of dominance in the cerebral cortex, see Dobzhansky, *Mankind Evolving*, pp. 200–201; Washburn and Howell, *op. cit.*, p. 51; Warren S. McCulloch and Warren M. Brodey, "The Biological Sciences," in *The Great Ideas Today, 1966*, pp. 330–331.

4. See passages cited in note 3, *supra.*

5. For criticism of the interpretation of the South African fossils and artifacts, see von Koenigswald, *op. cit.*, pp. 69–70; Dobzhansky, *Mankind Evolving*, pp. 174–175, 193–194; Le Gros Clark, *History of the Primates*, pp. 102 ff., 118–119; *Man-Apes or Ape-Men*?; Oakley, *op. cit.*, p. 5; Carrington, *op. cit.*, pp. 76, 79; G. G. Simpson, "The Biological Sciences," in *The Great Ideas Today, 1965*; pp. 298–299; Mayr, *op. cit.*, pp. 628–631.

6. See Oakley, *op. cit.*, pp. 4, 125–126; Carrington, *op. cit.*, pp. 64–68; Dobzhansky, *Mankind Evolving*, pp. 208–210, 332, 339; Julian Huxley, *The Uniqueness of Man*, pp. 3–4, 15–16, 27–29; *Evolution in Action*, pp. 107–109; *Evolution, The Modern Synthesis*, pp. 569–572; S. L. Washburn and V. Avis, "Evolution of Human Behavior," in *Behavior and Evolution*, ed. by Simpson and Roe, 1958: pp. 428–435; Le Gros Clark, *Antecedents of Man*, pp. 347–349; *History of the Primates*, pp. 119–120; Dart, *op. cit.*, pp. 216–217, 223–224; Leakey, in *Evolution After Darwin*, Volume II, pp. 28–30; Washburn and Howell, in *ibid.*, pp. 44–46, 49–53; M. Crichtley, in *ibid.*, pp. 296–297, 302–306.

7. *Op. cit.*, p. 283.

8. *Ibid.*, p. 284.

9. *Ibid.*, p. 286.

10. *Ibid.*, pp. 284–285.

11. *Ibid.*, p. 286.

12. *Op. cit.*, p. 624. Cf. *ibid.*, p. 638.

13. *Ibid.*, p. 623.

14. *Ibid.*, pp. 623, 650.

15. *Ibid.*, p. 658.

16. *Mankind Evolving*, p. 203. Cf. *Evolution, Genetics, and Man*, p. 338.

17. *Evolution, Genetics, and Man*, p. 340.

18. *Mankind Evolving*, pp. 208, 210.

19. *Ibid.*, p. 332.

20. *Evolution, Genetics, and Man*, p. 340; *Mankind Evolving*, pp. 210–211.

21. *Evolution, The Modern Synthesis*, p. 556.

22. *The Uniqueness of Man*, pp. 3–5. Cf. pp. 15–32 *passim.*

23. *Evolution in Action*, pp. 107–109.

24. *Evolution, The Modern Synthesis*, pp. 570–571.

25. *Op. cit.*, pp. 305–307.

26. See the references to Washburn and Avis, Washburn and Howell, Oakley, Clark, and Dart, in note 6, *supra*.

27. *Op. cit.*, Chicago, 1964: pp. 227–232.

28. *Op. cit.*, 1927: pp. 266–267. Cf. W. H. Thorpe, *Science, Man and Morals*, 1965: p. 105; W. R. Thompson, "Social Behavior," in *Behavior and Evolution*, p. 293.

29. Oakley, *op. cit.*, pp. 125–126; Carrington, *op. cit.*, pp. 64–65; Mayr, *op. cit.*, pp. 634–635, 650; Rensch, *op. cit.*, pp. 306–307, 340; Dobzhansky, *Mankind Evolving*; pp. 208–210; Julian Huxley, *Evolution in Action*, pp. 103–111; *Evolution, The Modern Synthesis*, pp. 571–572; *The Uniqueness of Man*, p. 3; Le Gros Clark, *History of the Primates*, pp. 119–120; Dart, *op. cit.*, pp. 216–217, 223–224; Washburn and Avis, in *Behavior and Evolution*, pp. 423–425, 435; Washburn and Howell, in *Evolution After Darwin*, Volume II, p. 152.

30. See the references to Oakley, Carrington, Dobzhansky, Julian Huxley, Washburn and Avis, Washburn and Howell, Clark, Leakey, Dart, and Crichtley cited in note 6, *supra*. See also Mayr, *op. cit.*, p. 650; Schaller, *op. cit.*, pp. 224–227; Thorpe, *op. cit.*, p. 69. Cf. Kohler, *op. cit.*, Chapters 4–5.

31. See Dobzhansky, *Mankind Evolving*, p. 339; Julian Huxley, *Evolution in Action*, pp. 110–111; Rensch, *Evolution Above the Species Level*, p. 306; Carrington, *A Million Years of Man*, pp. 62–63; Washburn and Howell, in *Evolution After Darwin*, Volume II, pp. 52–53. Cf. Thompson, "Social Behavior," in *Behavior and Evolution*, pp. 291–308.

32. See Dobzhansky, *Mankind Evolving*, pp. 210–211; *Evolution, Genetics, and Man*, p. 340; Julian Huxley, *Evolution in Action*, pp. 107–108; *The Uniqueness of Man*, p. 4; Mayr, *Animal Species and Evolution*, pp. 624, 656; Rensch, *Evolution Above the Species Level*, pp. 306–307; Simpson, *The Meaning of Evolution*, p. 286; Crichtley, in *Evolution After Darwin*, Volume II, pp. 293–294; Schaller, *The Year of the Gorilla*, pp. 230–231.

33. See Oakley, *Man the Tool-Maker*, p. 126; Dobzhansky, *Mankind Evolving*, p. 218; Carrington, *A Million Years of Man*, pp. 58–59.

34. See Dobzhansky, *Mankind Evolving*, p. 339; Huxley, *Evolution in Action*, pp. 107–108; *Evolution, the Modern Synthesis*, p. 575; Simpson, *The Meaning of Evolution*, p. 290.

35. See Oakley, *op. cit.*, pp. 126–132; Carrington, *op. cit.*, pp. 58–59; Dobzhansky, *Mankind Evolving*, pp. 214, 217–218; Julian Huxley, *Evolution in Action*, pp. 107–108. Cf. Thorpe, *op. cit.*, pp. 89–92. It should be noted that, here and elsewhere, Thorpe fails to distinguish between instinctive performances, on the one hand, and learned performances, on the other. To compare the instinctive behavior of the bower-birds of Australia in decorating their nests, with the non-instinctive decorative behavior of men, is to treat as comparable performances that are incomparable. Hence the behavior of the bower-birds is totally irrelevant to the point here under consideration. For a fuller discussion of this point, see *infra* Chapter 8.

36. See Oakley, *op. cit.*, pp. 4, 125–126; Carrington, *op. cit.*, pp. 67–68; Mayr, *op cit.*, p. 658; Rensch, *op. cit.*, p. 306; Schaller, *op. cit.*, pp. 217, 228–229; Dobzhansky, *Evolution, Genetics, and Man*, pp. 207, 338; Julian Huxley, *Evolution in Action*, pp. 107–109; *The Uniqueness of Man*, p. 3. Cf. John C. Lilly, *Man and Dolphin*, New York, 1961: pp. 256–265; and for passages in a contrary vein, see W. H. Thorpe, *Learning and Instinct in Animals*, 1963: pp. 132–133, 391–393.

37. See Schaller, *op. cit.*, pp. 217, 228–229; Kohler, *op. cit.*, pp. 266–267; Oakley, *op. cit.*, pp. 1–3; Julian Huxley, *Evolution in Action*, pp. 107–108. Cf. Leslie White, "Four Stages in the Evolution of Minding," in *Evolution After Darwin*, Volume II, pp. 239–249.

38. *Evolution in Action*, p. 104.

39. *Ibid.*, p. 109.

40. *Evolution, Genetics, and Man*, p. 338.

41. *Mankind Evolving*, p. 207.

42. *Man the Tool-Maker*, p. 4.

43. Quoted by Schaller in *The Year of the Gorilla*, p. 227.

44. *Evolution Above the Species Level*, p. 306.

45. *Ibid.*, pp. 340–341, 344–345. Cf. *ibid.*, pp. 349–352, in which Rensch makes the principle of continuity in nature the basis for a thorough-going panpsychism, allowing for differences only in degree between lower and higher forms of life. See William James's critique of panpsychism in *The Principles of Psychology*, 1891: Volume I, Chapter VI.

46. *A Million Years of Man*, pp. 64–65, 67–68.

47. See von Koenigswald, *op. cit.*, p. 119; Le Gros Clark, *History of the Primates*, pp. 108, 118, 158; Dobzhansky, *Mankind Evolving*, pp. 175, 177–179, 200–202; Julian Huxley, *Evolution in Action*, pp.

107–109; Mayr, *op. cit.*, 634–637, 652; Rensch, *op. cit.*, 306–307, 332; Washburn and Howell, in *Evolution After Darwin*, Volume II, pp. 50–53; Washburn and Avis, in *Behavior and Evolution*, pp. 424–425; Crichtley, in *Evolution After Darwin*, Volume II, pp. 303–305, 308. Cf. John Lilly, *op. cit.*, pp. 278, 284–285. "Of all animals," wrote Aristotle in the 4th century B.C., "man has the largest brain in proportion to his size" (*Parts of Animals*, II, 7, 653ᵃ28).

NOTES TO CHAPTER 7

1. *Op. cit.*, 1951: p. 6. For a thorough-going critique of the behaviorist position on the distinction between learned and innate behavior, see Konrad Lorenz, *Evolution and the Modification of Behavior*, 1965. Cf. Adolf Portmann, *Animals as Social Beings*, 1964: Chapter 5.

2. See Konrad Lorenz, *King Solomon's Ring*, 1952; W. H. Thorpe, *Learning and Instinct in Animals*, 1963; *Science, Man and Morals*, 1965.

3. Ernest R. Hilgard, "Psychology After Darwin," in *Evolution After Darwin*, 1960: Volume II, p. 270.

4. See *ibid.*

5. See R. H. Waters, "The Historical Background of Comparative Psychology," in *Comparative Psychology*, ed. by F. A. Moss, 1942: pp. 18–29; C. J. Warden, T. N. Jenkins, and L. H. Warner, *Introduction to Comparative Psychology*, 1934: pp. 9–21; Donald Hebb, *A Textbook of Psychology*, 1958: pp. 259–263.

6. *Op. cit.*, p. 3. Cf. Hebb, *The Organization of Behavior, a Neuropsychological Theory*, 1949.

7. *Method and Theory in Experimental Psychology*, 1953: p. 638. Cf. *ibid.*, pp. 655–656, 681.

8. "Levels in the Psychological Capacities of Animals," in *Philosophy for the Future*, ed. by R. W. Sellars, V. J. McGill, and M. Farber, 1949: p. 274.

9. *Op. cit.*, in *Behavior and Evolution*, p. 278. Cf. *ibid.*, p. 282.

10. *The Evolution of Human Nature*, p. 327.

11. See *op. cit.*, p. 279. Cf. *ibid.*, pp. 277–279.

12. See H. F. Harlow, "The Evolution of Learning," in *Behavior and Evolution*, pp. 278–279, 283; "Primate Learning," in *Comparative Psychology*, ed. Calvin Stone, 1955: p. 234; "Thinking," in *Theoretical Foundations of Psychology*, ed. by H. Helson, 1951:

pp. 493–496; Donald Hebb, *A Textbook of Psychology*, 1958, pp. 29–30, 46–48, 188, 206–210, 260–261; Charles E. Osgood, *op. cit.*, Chapter 15 *passim*; Henry W. Nissen, "Axes of Behavioral Comparison," in *Behavior and Evolution*, pp. 193–195; T. C. Schneirla, *op. cit.*, pp. 245, 275–280; N. R. F. Maier and T. C. Schneirla, *Principles of Animal Psychology*, 1935: pp. 469–479; W. T. Heron, "Complex Learning Processes," in *Comparative Psychology*, ed. by F. A. Moss, pp. 265–271–275; John Paul Scott, *Animal Behavior*, 1963; pp. 127–130, 182–184, 219; Robert Leeper, "Cognitive Processes," in *Handbook of Experimental Psychology*, ed. by S. S. Stevens, 1964: pp. 754–755. Other scientists—sociologists, anthropologists, and physiologists—concur in the view held by the comparative psychologists, that man differs only in degree from other animals: see, for example, F. H. Hankins, *Introduction to the Study of Society*, 1928: pp. 56–327; Ralph Linton, *The Study of Man*, 1936: pp. 60, 68, 70; Alexander Goldenweiser, *Anthropology*, 1937: p. 39; A. J. Carlson, "Dynamics of Living Processes," in *Nature of the World and Man*, ed. by H. H. Newman, 1926: pp. 477–479.

13. *Op. cit*, pp. 350–351.

14. *Op. cit.*, p. 326. Cf. *ibid.*, pp. 309, 323–325, 327–329, 358, 360–361, 368, 401–405, 446–448, 453–456. Anyone who reads these pages carefully will end up being utterly perplexed as to just where Professor Herrick stands on the question whether man differs from other animals in kind *as well as* in degree, or *only* in degree.

15. In *Scientific American*, Volume 212, No. 1, January, 1965, pp. 92–100.

16. *Ibid.*, p. 92.

17. *Ibid.*, p. 99.

18. *Ibid.*, p. 97.

19. *Ibid.*, p. 100.

20. See Robert S. Woodworth and Harold Schlosberg, *Experimental Psychology*, 1965: pp. 589–613, 814 ff.; Maier and Schneirla, *op. cit.*, pp. 446–449, 452–453, 455–458, 460, 465, 469–479; Schneirla, *op. cit.*, pp. 275–280; Hebb, *op. cit.*, pp. 29–30, 52–59, 188 ff., 203–205, 260–261; Harlow, in *Behavior and Evolution*, pp. 279 ff.; in *Theoretical Foundations of Psychology*, pp. 457–460, 463, 465, 470; in *Comparative Psychology*, ed. by Stone, pp. 216–217, 228–229, 231–232; Heron, in *Comparative Psychology*, ed. by Moss, pp. 251–254, 257, 271; Heinrich Klüver, *Behavior Mechanisms in Monkeys*, 1961: pp. 326–328, 344–345, 355.

21. *Op. cit.*, p. 283.

22. *Ibid.*, p. 288.

23. For a brief summary of the experimental work and its findings, see Hebb, *A Textbook of Psychology*, pp. 170–177.

24. See Osgood, *op. cit.*, pp. 663–666, 679, 681–682; Schneirla, *op. cit.*, p. 279; Leeper, *op. cit.*, pp. 754–755; Heron, *op. cit.*, pp. 254–257, 271–274; Herrick, *The Evolution of Human Nature*, pp. 401–405; Harlow, in *Behavior and Evolution*, pp. 278, 282; in *Theoretical Foundations of Psychology*, pp. 493–496; in *Comparative Psychology*, pp. 232–234; Henry W. Nissen, "Phylogenetic Comparison," in *Handbook of Experimental Psychology*, pp. 353–354, 376–378, 380; Gregory Razran, "Evolutionary Psychology: Levels of Learning—and Perception and Thinking," in *Scientific Psychology*, ed. by B. B. Wolman and E. Nagel, 1965: pp. 209–219, 233–245.

25. *Op. cit.*, in *Behavior and Evolution*, p. 193.

26. *Ibid.*, p. 195. Cf. Nissen's essay, cited in note 24, *supra.*

27. *A Textbook of Psychology*, p. 211.

28. For a critique of over-simplified stimulus-response formulations, see Osgood, *op. cit.*, pp. 653–656, 663; Hebb, *A Textbook of Psychology*, pp. 46–48, 60–61, 260–263.

29. Hebb, *ibid.*, pp. 209–210.

NOTES TO CHAPTER 8

1. *Politics*, I, 2, 1253ᵃ9–14.

2. *On Interpretation*, Chapters 1–4.

3. *The Uniqueness of Man*, p. 3. As we have noted in Chapter 6 *supra*, the paleoanthropologists and evolutionary biologists, without exception, affirm the proposition that man and man alone has a propositional language or syntactical speech—man and man alone names things and makes sentences. (For textual references on this point, see Chapter 6, note 29.) Agreement on this point extends to the comparative psychologists, the ethologists, the neurologists, and other students of human and animal behavior. See Charles E. Osgood, *Method and Theory in Experimental Psychology*, pp. 681–682; Donald Hebb, *A Textbook of Psychology*, pp. 6, 207–211; Harry Harlow, "The Evolution of Learning," in *Behavior and Evolution*, pp. 278; Henry W. Nissen, "Axes of Behavioral Comparison," in *ibid.*, pp. 193, 195; William R. Thompson, "Social Behavior," in *ibid.*, pp. 293–294; Lawrence Z. Freedman and Anne Roe, "Evolution and Human Behavior," in *ibid.*, p. 462; T. C. Schneirla, "Levels in the Psychological Capacities of Animals," in *Philosophy for the Future*, pp. 275–277, 279; Otto L. Tinklepaugh,

"Social Behavior of Animals," in *Comparative Psychology*, ed. by F. A. Moss, p. 391; John Paul Scott, *Animal Behavior*, Chapter 9; C. Judson Herrick, *The Evolution of Human Nature*, pp. 209, 324–325, 368; George B. Schaller, *The Year of the Gorilla*, pp. 217, 228–229; Konrad Lorenz, *King Solomon's Ring*, pp. 76–78; Henry Nissen, "Phylogenetic Comparison," in *Handbook of Experimental Psychology*, p. 354; W. H. Thorpe, *Learning and Instinct in Animals*, p. 132; John C. Lilly, *Man and Dolphin*, 1961: Appendix Two; K. S. Lashley, "The Problem of Serial Order in Behavior," in *Cerebral Mechanisms in Behavior*, ed. by L. A. Jeffress, 1951: pp. 113–118; Ward C. Halstead, "Brain and Intelligence," in *ibid.*, pp. 255, 259; Lord Russell Brain, *Mind, Perception, and Science*, 1951: pp. 23–30, 38–41; Warren S. McCulloch and Warren M. Brodey, "The Biological Sciences," in *The Great Ideas Today, 1966*, pp. 330–331; Adolph Portmann, *Animals as Social Beings*, pp. 96–97.

4. See Karl von Frisch, *The Dancing Bees*, 1953. For a penetrating commentary on the difference between the instinctive sentence-making of the honey bee and the intelligent sentence-making of man, see Jonathan Bennett, *Rationality*, 1964. If the honey bees were to make the statements that they do make not by instinct, but as a result of learning, calculation, and inference, they would need a brain as large as man's, and would possess a degree of intelligence well above the human average. See also Scott, *op. cit.*, pp. 232–238; T. Dobzhansky, *Mankind Evolving*, pp. 209–210; Julian Huxley, *Evolution in Action*, p. 103.

5. *King Solomon's Ring*, pp. 76–77.

6. See Donald Hebb, *A Textbook of Psychology*, pp. 123–126, and 129–130, esp. p. 126. With regard to the differentiation between innate and learned behavior, see N. Tinbergen, *The Study of Instinct*, Konrad Lorenz, *Evolution and Modification of Behavior*, Adolf Portmann, *op. cit.*, Chapter 5; Irenäus Eibl-Eibesfeldt, "Experimental Criteria for Distinguishing Innate from Culturally Conditioned Behavior," in *Cross-Cultural Understanding*, ed. by F. C. S. Northrop and H. H. Livingston, 1964, pp. 297–307.

7. *Science, Man and Morals*, p. 90.

8. See *ibid.*, pp. 89–92.

9. *Ibid.*, p. 99.

10. *Ibid.*, pp. 101–102. In this context, Thorpe returns to one of his favorite themes—that man differs only in degree from other animals, not in kind. He writes: "We have evidence that animals can use conceptual symbols, but to a limited degree; and that here, as in so many other instances, the difference between the mind of animals and men seems to be one of degree—often the degree of abstraction that can be achieved—rather than one of kind." This, of course,

does not prevent him from writing in a contrary vein in other contexts. In another place in the same book, he says: "I strongly disagree with [C. H.] Waddington's argument that because man evolved as a physical being, he cannot then know any other realms of existence. The animal mind is undoubtedly an efficient instrument for carrying out the essential biological activities; and insofar as man's mind is of the same class of organization, the same thing can be said of the human mind. But I for one should react strongly against any suggestion that we are, let alone must forever remain, in our mental qualities, animals and nothing more" (p. 66). Cf. a similar utterance by Thorpe in his *Learning and Instinct in Animals*, pp. 469–470. See also in this book, pp. 132–133, 175–176; 391–393, 467.

11. Lorenz stresses the fact that the

> "purely innate signal code of an animal species differs fundamentally from human language, every word of which must be learned laboriously by the human child. Moreover, being a genetically fixed character of the species—just as much as any bodily character—this so-called language is, for every individual animal species, ubiquitous in its distribution. Obviously though this fact may seem, it was, nevertheless, with something akin to naive surprise that I heard the jackdaws in northern Russia 'talk' exactly the same, familiar 'dialect' as my birds at home in Altenberg. The superficial similarity between these animal utterances and human language diminishes further as it becomes gradually clear to the observer that the animal, in all these sounds and movements expressing its emotions, has in no way the conscious intention of influencing a fellow-member of its species. This is proved by the fact that even geese or jackdaws reared and kept singly make all these signals as soon as the corresponding mood overtakes them. Under these circumstances the automatic and even mechanical character of these signals becomes strikingly apparent and reveals them as entirely different from human words" (*King Solomon's Ring*, pp. 76–77; see also *ibid.*, pp. 77–91).

In the light of these observations, let us examine once more Thorpe's statement that "although no animal appears to have a language which is (i) propositional, (ii) syntactic, and at the same time (iii) clearly expressive of intention, yet all these features can be found separately (to at least some degree) in the animal kingdom" (roman numerals added). Apart from the dance language of the honey bee, which is purely instinctive and so is utterly incomparable with human language, no evidence is offered to support points (i) and (ii) in the sphere of animal communication; nor is there any evidence for (iii); quite the contrary, according to Lorenz. Hence if having a true language means having a mode of communication that involves (i), (ii), and (iii), then only man has a true language that is also a learned language, and no aspect of such language is to be found in the animal kingdom as a learned performance.

12. See Osgood, *Method and Theory in Experimental Psychology*, pp. 681–682; Hebb, *A Textbook of Psychology*, pp. 207–209; MacDonald Crichtley, "The Evolution of Man's Capacity for Language," in *Evolution After Darwin*, Volume II, pp. 291–293, 306–307; Leslie A. White, *The Science of Culture*, 1949, pp. 31–33.

13. *King Solomon's Ring*, p. 88. Cf. *ibid.*, pp. 83–88.

14. *Learning and Instinct in Animals*, p. 393. See also his *Science, Man and Morals*, pp. 100–101.

15. See Osgood, *op. cit.*, pp. 681–682; Lorenz, *King Solomon's Ring*, pp. 76–77.

16. See Julian Huxley, *Evolution in Action*, pp. 107–109; *Evolution, The Modern Synthesis*, pp. 570–574; Bernhard Rensch, *Evolution Above the Species Level*, pp. 306–307; pp. 332, 349, 352; Ernst Mayr, *Animal Species and Evolution*, pp. 634–635; T. Dobzhansky, *Mankind Evolving*, pp. 200–202; Washburn and Howell, "Human Evolution and Culture," in *Evolution After Darwin*, Volume II, pp. 50–53; Washburn and Avis, "Evolution of Human Behavior," in *Behavior and Evolution*, pp. 424–425; John Lilly, *Man and Dolphins*, pp. 278, 284–285; MacDonald Crichtley, *op. cit.*, pp. 303–305, 308; M. E. Bitterman, "The Evolution of Intelligence," in *Scientific American*, Volume 212, No. 1, January, 1965, pp. 98, 100; Donald Hebb, A *Textbook of Psychology*, p. 210; Charles E. Osgood, *Method and Theory in Experimental Psychology*, pp. 681–682; C. Judson Herrick, *The Evolution of Human Nature*, pp. 368, 386–387, 431, *The Brains of Rats and Men*, pp. 265–267; K. S. Lashley, "The Problem of Serial Order in Behavior," in *Cerebral Mechanisms in Behavior*, pp. 120–122; Leslie White, *The Science of Culture*, pp. 32–33.

NOTES TO CHAPTER 9

1. For references to relevant passages in the writings of the scientists mentioned, see the notes to Chapters 7 and 8.

2. For references to relevant passages in the writings of some of the scientists mentioned, see the notes to Chapters 6 and 8. In addition, see Kenneth J. W. Craik, *The Nature of Psychology*, 1966: Chapters 6 and 21; *The Nature of Explanation*, 1952: Chapters VI and VII; Jerome S. Bruner, J. J. Goodnow, and G. A. Austin, *A Study of Thinking*, 1956: pp. 9, 231; Earl B. Hunt, *Concept Learning*, 1962:

pp. 5–6; Heinrich Klüver, *Behavior Mechanisms in Monkeys*, pp. 326–328, 344–345; C. Ward Halstead, "Brain and Intelligence," in *Cerebral Mechanisms in Behavior*, pp. 254–255.

3. See Sir Charles Sherrington, *Man on His Nature*, 1941: Chapters XI–XII; W. Macneile Dixon, *The Human Situation*, 1938; Edmund W. Sinnott, *Matter, Mind, and Man*, 1957: Chapters 1, 2, 4, 7, 9, and 17; *The Bridge of Life*, 1966; Roger W. Sperry, "Mind, Brain, and Humanist Values," in *New Views of the Nature of Man*, ed. by John R. Platt, 1965: pp. 71–92; Hans Jonas, *The Phenomenon of Life*, 1966: pp. 108–134; 183–187; Wilder Penfield, "The Physiological Basis of the Mind," in *Control of the Mind*, ed. by Seymour Farber and Roger Wilson, 1961: pp. 3–17. Cf. Theodosius Dobzhansky, *The Biology of Ultimate Concern*, 1967.

4. William James, *Principles of Psychology*, 1891: Volume II, 354 ff.; Ernst Cassirer, *An Essay on Man*, 1944: pp. 25–26, 30, 67–68; Jonathan Bennett, *Rationality*, 1964: pp. 4–6, 90; MacDonald Crichtley, "The Evolution of Man's Capacity for Language," in *Evolution After Darwin*, Volume II, pp. 295, 307–308; Leslie White, *The Science of Culture*, p. 25; Wilfrid Sellars, *Science, Perception and Reality*, 1963: pp. 6–18. Professor Sellars' essay is distinguished from most of the writing in this field by its avowed and explicit aim to treat the question about man as a mixed question—one that requires us to combine common-sense opinion, traditional philosophy, and contemporary science. He takes the position that the traditional philosophical conception of man as different in kind, by virtue of man's exclusive possession of a propositional language and the power of conceptual thought, is indisputably sound; and he then tries to reconcile this view of man with the scientific view that attempts to reduce conceptual thought to neurophysiological processes. Hence, in the end, he interprets man's difference in kind as superficial, not radical.

5. *Reconstruction in Philosophy*, 1920: pp. 1–2. Cf. his *How We Think*, 1910: p. 14.

6. *The Two Sources of Morality and Religion*, 1935.

7. *Thinking and Experience*, 1953: p. 104.

8. *Ibid.*, p. 200. In the context of the passage quoted, Professor Price attributes concepts or abstract ideas to sub-human animals, without recognizing that doing so is manifestly inconsistent with his own distinction between sign-cognition and symbol-cognition, and with his distinction between perceptually-tied and conceptually-free thinking. If animals can respond only to signs, but never to symbols, and if all animal thinking is perceptually tied, whereas human thinking is mediated by symbols and transcends the perceptual environment, then concepts cannot be attributed to both men and sub-

human animals in a strictly univocal sense of that term: for it is man's possession of concepts that enables him to use symbols and to transcend the perceptual environment. The inconsistency results from Price's failure to recognize that he has allowed himself to use the word "concept" in an equivocal manner; it would be removed if, instead of concepts, he were to attribute perceptual abstractions or generalizations to sub-human animals in order to explain their sign-thinking. He seems to be aware of the distinction between perceptual abstraction (or generalization) and concept-formation (see pp. 43, 52–54, 73), but he also erroneously supposes that concept-formation is an abstractive process in the same way that perceptual generalization is, and this leads him to identify concepts with "abstract ideas." See Peter Geach, *Mental Acts*, 1957: pp. 18–44.

Other writers who distinguish between sign and symbol, attributing the latter exclusively to man, also make the error of attributing concepts to sub-human animals, even though doing so is inconsistent with their understanding of conceptual thought as inseparable from the use of symbols. See Leslie White, *The Science of Culture*, pp. 44–45; cf. *ibid.*, pp. 25–27, 30–31. See also his essay "Four Stages in The Evolution of Minding," in *Evolution After Darwin*, Volume II, esp. pp. 249–250. In the same volume, see the essay by MacDonald Crichtley, in which he says that the facts no longer justify us in restricting conceptual or abstract thinking to man alone (p. 299), though a little earlier he says that with the advent of human speech we have "the earliest mastery over purely perceptual thinking, the dawn of conceptual thought, and release from the shackles of time-present" (p. 297). In both White and Crichtley, as in Price, the root of the trouble lies in unclarity concerning the difference between perceptual abstraction and concept-formation. This subject is treated at length in Chapter 10.

9. See *op. cit.*, pp. 79–80, 85–86, 97–98.

10. See *op. cit.*, pp. 25–26, 41. Cf. *ibid.*, pp. 27–31. See also Erich Kahler, *Man the Measure*, 1943: pp. 7, 10, 14–16; Michael Polanyi, *The Study of Man*, 1963: pp. 59–69.

11. I have a number of reasons for electing to use the phrase "conceptual thought" for the intellectual power that is distinctive of man. In the first place, conceptual as distinct from perceptual thought is not limited to the temporally and physically present environment; and so the word "conceptual" connotes the autonomy of distinctively human thought—its independence or transcendence of the perceptual present. In the second place, the use of the term reminds us that human concept-formation must always be differentiated from perceptual abstraction or generalization in sub-human animals. In the third place, since concepts are exercised in acts of judgment and in processes of reasoning, the term "conceptual" has a connotation that includes "rational." And finally, if by "symbolic

thought" is meant that which is verbally expressed, then conceptual thought is broader in its connotation, for it covers not only that which is verbally expressed, but also that which can be but is not.

12. See *op. cit.*, Chapters VII–XII.

13. See Sellars, *op. cit.*, p. 6; Crichtley, *op cit.*, pp. 302–304; White, *The Science of Culture*, p. 32.

14. James, *op. cit.*, Volume II, p. 356; White, *op. cit.*, pp. 25, 29. Cf. Price, *op. cit.*, pp. 173, 180–181.

15. White, *op. cit.*, pp. 25–29; cf. his essay in *Evolution After Darwin*, Volume II, pp. 249–250; Crichtley, in *ibid.*, pp. 293, 300. If White's handling of the distinction between sign and symbol had had greater precision and clarity, it might have prevented the misunderstanding of his thesis by Herrick in his *The Evolution of Human Nature*, pp. 326, 329. Herrick's own position on this matter is equally unclear and self-refuting; see *ibid.*, pp. 401–405.

16. *Op. cit.*, p. 29.

17. *Ibid.*, p. 32.

18. See *op. cit.*, pp. 144–145, 160–161, 213–214, 231–233.

19. See *ibid.*, pp. 180–233. For the substance of Price's own theory of meaning, and for his understanding of the relation between concepts and symbols, see *ibid.*, pp. 298–358. Here he is much closer to Geach's analysis of concept-formation: see the latter's *Mental Acts*, pp. 11–17. For critiques of both Price and Geach from the viewpoint of more behavioristic philosophies, see A. J. Ayer, *Thinking and Meaning*, 1947: pp. 23–25. Ayer sides with Gilbert Ryle against Price, and so does G. J. Warnock in his essay "Logical Analysis and the Nature of Thought," in *Scientific Psychology*, pp. 474–487. On the other hand, for a penetrating critique of Ryle's *The Concept of Mind*, see C. A. Campbell's essay "Ryle on the Intellect" in *Clarity Is Not Enough*, ed. by H. D. Lewis, 1963: pp. 278–310.

20. *Conjectures and Refutations*, 1962: p. 295. Cf. Bennett, *Rationality*, pp. 56, 79, 82–83.

21. *Op. cit.*, Chapters XII and XXII.

22. See *op. cit.*, pp. 18–44, 130–131. For Geach's critique of the experimental work done on animals that claims to find concept-formation in rats in virtue of their being able to discriminate perceptually between squares and triangles, or between reds and blues, see *ibid.*, pp. 16–17, 42–44. Geach is not alone in his criticism of this misinterpretation of the experimental data: see Klüver, *op. cit.*, pp. 326–328, 344–345; Maier and Schneirla, *Principles of Animal Psychology*, pp. 455–458.

23. See *op. cit.*, pp. 56, 79–80, 82–83, 89–90, 104–112. Professor J. J. C. Smart takes a diametrically opposed view of reasons *versus* causes (or *because* as distinct from *cause*); see his *Philosophy and Scientific Realism*, pp. 126–130.

24. The following authors clearly assert that conceptual thought is the indispensable pre-requisite of propositional speech: Ernst Mayr, *Animal Species and Evolution*, p. 658; George Schaller, *The Year of the Gorilla*, p. 217, 228–229; Richard Carrington, *A Million Years of Man*, pp. 67–68.

The following clearly assert that man's propositional speech explains his power of conceptual thought: Bernhard Rensch, *Evolution Above the Species Level*, pp. 306–307; Harry Harlow, in *Behavior and Evolution*, pp. 278, 282; and in *Theoretical Foundations of Psychology*, pp. 493–496.

And the following authors appear to make both of the foregoing assertions, without attempting to reconcile them: T. Dobzhansky, *Mankind Evolving*, p. 207 versus *Evolution, Genetics, and Man*, p. 338; Donald Hebb, *A Textbook of Psychology*, pp. 29–30, 46–48 versus 207–209, 211; Julian Huxley, *Evolution in Action*, 107–109, esp. 109 versus *The Uniqueness of Man*, p. 3, 15.

25. See Geach, *op. cit.*, pp. 13, 44; Price, *Thinking and Experience*, pp. 305–311, 316–319. Cf. *Cerebral Mechanisms in Behavior*, ed. by L. A. Jeffress, pp. 112–133, 116–118, 120–122, 182–193, 259.

26. See Bennett, *op. cit.*, pp. 46–47, 86–87, 93–96. Cf. Geach, *op. cit.*, p. 18. With regard to the separability of words and concepts and the *priority* of concepts or intentions, see Roderick Chisholm in *Minnesota Studies in the Philosophy of Science*, 1958: Volume II, Appendix, pp. 532–533.

NOTES TO CHAPTER 10

1. Psychologists tend to use the words "stimulus" and "response" with maximum ambiguity. On the one hand, they use "stimulus" as physiologists and neurologists use the term: for the physical factor that activates a receptor. On the other hand, they use the term loosely for any *perceived or sensible object*; e.g., they speak of food or of a dangerous situation as a stimulus. Similarly, they use the word "response" as physiologists and neurologists do, to name the activation of specific effectors (muscles or glands); but they more frequently use "response" for any kind of action, and their naming of it often includes their interpretation of the purpose of the action, as when they speak of a "flight response," or a "fighting response," or a "food-seeking response." This loose use of the terms

"stimulus" and "response" permits them to cover much ground illicitly, and to conceal the psychological barrenness of strict S-R formulations. It allows them to think that they are being scientific and objective in ways that they are not.

2. I am indebted to Professor Wilfrid Sellars for the distinction between methodological and metaphysical, or what he calls "philosophical," behaviorism. See *Science, Perception and Reality*, pp. 22–25, 183–185.

3. For Aristotle, and for Aquinas who follows him in this regard, our knowledge of an animal's powers or abilities, its habits or dispositions, can be learned only from observation of its actions or operations. The same rule applies to our knowledge of man. It is only by observing what a man does that we obtain the data from which we are able to infer what, by innate ability, he can do or what, by acquired habit, he is disposed to do. See, for example, *Summa Theologica*, I, 77, 3; *ibid.*, I, 87, 2.

4. Thus, for example, Donald Hebb writes: "There are two theories of mind, speaking very generally. One is animistic, a theory that the body is inhabited by an entity—the mind or soul—that is quite different from it, having nothing in common with bodily processes. The second theory is physiological or mechanistic; it assumes that mind is a bodily process, an activity of the brain. Modern psychology works with this latter theory only. Both are intellectually respectable (that is, each has support from highly intelligent people, including scientists), and there is certainly no decisive means available of proving one to be right, the other wrong" (*A Textbook of Psychology*, p. 3). Cf. *ibid.*, pp. 260–262. See also Charles E. Osgood, *Method and Theory in Experimental Psychology*: "The term 'thought,' as it is used in everyday language, connotes vague, immaterial stuff, activity that takes place in the brain but is not strictly part of it. It falls in the same category as ideas and images, mentalistic constructs that Watson, as an early and forceful behaviorist, ejected from psychological science as 'ghosts.' Although we cannot deny that some processes warranting these labels exist, we must follow Watson in denying that they partake of something other than the material world. *Otherwise we should be unable to investigate them at all with scientific methods*" (p. 638, italics added). Cf. *ibid.*, pp. 680–681.

5. *A Textbook of Psychology*, p. 203.

6. See N. Tinbergen, *The Study of Instinct*, pp. 160–184; Konrad Lorenz, *King Solomon's Ring*, pp. 120–180; *On Aggression*, pp. 85–108; W. H. Thorpe, *Learning and Instinct in Animals*, pp. 404–437, 449–466. As used in the pages just cited, the terms "instinct" and

"instinctive" do not refer to observable behavior, but rather stand for a theoretical construct that is needed to explain behavior that is both unlearned and species-predictable. Thus, when an animal, without prior perceptual experience, recognizes another animal either as a hostile predator or as a member of its own species, it is exercising a perceptual abstraction that cannot be a perceptual attainment, and can only be explained as an innate or instinctive perceptual endowment that is common to all members of the species. Such instinctive perceptual recognitions in animals are the analogue of what were once thought to be innate ideas in man. The denial of innate ideas in man is tantamount to the denial that man has any perceptual abstractions or conceptual dispositions that are *innate endowments*; they are all *attainments*.

7. *Behavior Mechanisms in Monkeys*, pp. 4–10, 19–25, 326 ff.

8. The error of supposing that percepts and concepts are themselves knowable objects or inspectable occurrents in experience is pervasive in modern psychology from the seventeenth century on. When H. H. Price criticizes this error and calls it the "classical theory" of concepts, he obviously refers to its seventeenth century origins with Descartes and Locke (see *Thinking and Experience*, pp. 320–335; cf. *ibid.*, pp. 247–250, 260–263, 276–277, 301–304). It is not "classical" at all if that word is understood as referring to ancient and mediaeval thought, especially that of Aristotle and Aquinas. The theory of perceptual abstractions and concepts not as inspectable occurrents, but as functioning dispositions—not as objects which we know, but only as that by which we are able to know—is the ancient and truly classical theory, lately revived by Ryle, Price, and others without acknowledging its ancient lineage. For a comprehensive exposition of this theory of percepts and concepts as always the *id quo*, never the *id quod*, of knowing, see Jacques Maritain, *Les Degrés du Savoir*, 1932: pp. 769–819. The reader will find an adaptation of this analysis in Chapter 12, note 41, *infra.* He is also referred to my discussion of this point in *The Conditions of Philosophy*, pp. 266–270, where I indicate the serious consequences in modern thought that flow from the error made by Descartes and Locke.

Credit for the revival of the ancient theory must be given, in part at least, to the behavioristic psychologists from John B. Watson on, who, in the face of a long tradition of scientific opinion to the contrary, with admirable persistence denied that one can look into his own mind introspectively and find there any directly observable entities, such as percepts, images, concepts, or ideas. Unfortunately, some of them went further and converted this denial—the denial that what their predecessors in modern psychology had supposed to be the observable contents of the mind *existed as observable* (i.e., *introspectable*) *occurrents* in experience—into a denial that such things as percepts, images, or concepts *exist at all.* They failed to see that such things may exist as functioning dispositions, even though they do not exist as inspectable occurrents.

9. In *Thinking and Experience*, Professor Price quotes with approval Aristotle's account of the genesis of those concepts that are formed on the basis of perceptual abstractions, but he fails to see that not all our concepts are thus formed, and that even those which arise in this way are not formed by an abstractive process. The passage quoted is the famous one in Book II, Chapter 19, of the *Posterior Analytics*: "Though sense-perception is innate in all animals, in some the sense-impression comes to persist, in others it does not. So animals in which this persistence does not come to be either have no knowledge at all outside the act of perceiving, or no knowledge of objects of which no impression persists; animals in which it does come into being have perception and can continue to retain the sense-impression in the soul; and when such persistence is frequently repeated a further distinction arises between those which out of the persistence of such sense-impressions develop a power of systematizing them and those which do not. So out of sense-perception comes to be what we call memory, and out of frequently repeated memories of the same thing develops experience; for a number of memories constitute a single experience. From experience again—i.e., from the universal now stabilized in its entirety within the soul, the one beside the many which is a single identity within them all—originate the skill of the craftsman and the knowledge of the man of science" (99^b36–100^a8).

My interpretation of this passage is somewhat different from that offered by Price. Translated into modern idiom, the passage describes the process by which perceptual abstractions or generalizations develop from the residues or memory of repeated perceptions. What Aristotle calls the "single experience" in which the "universal" is "stabilized" is what I have called a "perceptual abstraction"—the acquired disposition to recognize a number of perceptible object as being the same or sufficiently similar in kind; thus, from many acts of perceiving dogs—this dog, and that dog, and that—develops, by an abstractive process, a generalized memory of dogs, and from this memory the power or disposition to perceive this animal, that animal, and that, as the same in kind. The "universal" to which Aristotle refers is not the one we have in mind when we understand conceptually what it is like to be a dog, but only the generalization that is implicit in our memory of dogs and in our perceptual discrimination between animals that are dogs and animals that are not dogs. When we form the concept of dog, we make that implicit universal explicit in our understanding of the kind of thing a dog is; but though the concept we form is *based* on our experience of dogs, we do not abstract it from that experience; we do not abstract if from our generalized memory of dogs or from our ability to discriminate between dogs and non-dogs. Cf. Price, *op. cit.*, pp. 60–61; also pp. 35, 43, 52–53, 56, 73, and 341–358; and see Peter Geach's argument against the identification of concept-formation with the process of abstraction—the kind of process that occurs in perceptual generalization and discrimination—in *Mental Acts*, pp. 18–44, 130–131.

10. See N. R. F. Maier and T. C. Schneirla, *Principles of Animal Psychology*, pp. 446–453; and R. S. Woodworth and H. Schlosberg, *Experimental Psychology*, pp. 589–613.

11. See Hebb, *A Textbook of Psychology*, pp. 204–205; Ernest R. Hilgard, "Methods and Procedures in the Study of Learning," in *Handbook of Experiemntal Psychology*, ed. by S. S. Stevens, p. 523.

12. See Hebb, *ibid.*, pp. 46–48, 52–58, 203–206, 260–263; Osgood, *op. cit.*, 638–639, 653–665.

13. See Hebb and Osgood as cited in note 12, *supra*; see also Harry Harlow, "Primate Learning," in *Comparative Psychology*, ed. by C. P. Stone, pp. 228–231; and his "Thinking," in *Theoretical Foundations of Psychology*, ed. by H. Helson, pp. 457–468. Cf. Jonathan Bennett, *Rationality*, pp. 88–89, 101–114.

14. Cf. Maier and Schneirla, *op. cit.*, pp. 452–453.

15. See Woodworth and Schlosberg, *op cit.*, pp. 576–601; Harry Harlow, "Primate Learning," in *Comparative Psychology*, ed. by Stone, pp. 183–235; "Thinking," in *Theoretical Foundations of Psychology*, ed. by Helson, pp. 469–476, 487–497; "The Evolution of Learning," in *Behavior and Evolution*, ed. by Roe and Simpson, 1958: pp. 279–283; K. U. Smith, "Discriminative Behavior in Animals," in *Compartive Psychology*, ed. by Stone, pp. 316–361; W. T. Heron, "Complex Learning Processes," in *Comparative Psychology*, ed. by F. A. Moss, pp. 267–274; Hebb, *A Textbook of Psychology*, pp. 29–30, 188–191; Maier and Schneirla, *op. cit.*, pp. 455–460; Klüver, *op. cit.*, pp. 326–329, 344–349.

16. The title of the essay by Warren S. McCulloch and W. Pitts is revealing: "How We Know Universals: The Perception of Auditory and Visual Forms" (in a collection of McCulloch's essays entitled *Embodiments of Mind*, 1965). The second part of the title, following the colon, indicates that the so-called "universals," the knowledge of which the authors are attempting to explain neurologically, are merely perceptible forms or shapes, auditory or visual, and hence the universals referred to are the generalizations implicit in perceptual abstractions, not the explicit universals that are apprehended in conceptual cognition. See note 9, *supra*. It is perfectly plain, from all the evidence offered, that perceptual abstraction and not concept–formation is the psychological counterpart of the theoretical construct employed by neurologists to explain the perception of shapes and the recognition of other patterns by animals and

by machines. If there are memory residues of perceptual abstractions, these should be called "mnemonic or imaginative abstractions," for the generalized memory-image is nothing but a residue of the generalized perception. Cf. Kenneth J. W. Craik, *The Nature of Explanation*, pp. 69–73.

17. See Harlow, Hebb, and Heron as cited in note 15, *supra*. In addition, see Osgood, *op. cit.*, pp. 655–672; Henry W. Nissen, "Axes of Behavioral Comparison," in *Behavior and Evolution*, ed. by Roe and Simpson, pp. 193–195; C. Judson Herrick, *The Evolution of Human Nature*, pp. 360–361, 402–403, 444–445; W. H. Thorpe, *Learning and Instinct in Animals*, pp. 132, 385–394.

18. See Maier and Schneirla, *op. cit.*, pp. 455–460; Klüver, *op. cit.*, pp. 326–328, 344–349; J. P. Scott, *Animal Behavior*, 1958: pp. 113–114; Konrad Lorenz, *King Solomon's Ring*, pp. 84–89; K. S. Lashley, "The Problem of Serial Order in Behavior," in *Cerebral Mechanisms in Behavior*, ed. by L. A. Jeffress, pp. 112–116, 118–120. Lashley points out that understanding what is the same in two inter-translatable sentences is quite different from recognizing a series of A's as the same letter: what is perceived as common to a series of different A's cannot be compared with the cognition of the same meaning in a German and an English sentence. The one is accomplished by a perceptual abstraction; the other requires conceptual thought. Lashley's point is that the conceptual universal is grasped quite apart from any sensible sameness whatsoever; whereas there is always a sensible sameness in the case of perceptual abstractions, and so they are not true universals. The same point is made by Peter Geach in the following passage:

> "Many psychologists, wishing to use the term 'concept' far more widely than I do . . . would say that an animal has acquired a concept if it has learned a discriminative response to some feature of its environment. If a rat or dog is trained to react in a certain way whenever it has a triangle shown to it (rather than some other shape), then they would say it has acquired a concept of *triangle*. . . . What is at issue here is not just the way the term 'concept' is to be used, but the desirability of comparing these achievements of rats and dogs with the performances of human beings who possess a concept of *triangle*; the psychologists I am criticizing want to play down the differences between human and animal performances, and I want to stress them. The life of brutes lacks so much that is integral to human life that it can only be misleading to say that they have concepts like us—as misleading as it would be to say that men have tails and women lay eggs . . . or to call the noises made by brutes 'language.' Experience in training dogs to 'recognize' triangles can be no guide in (let us say) teaching geometry" (*Mental Acts*, p. 17).

19. See Chapter 11, note 13 for a more explicit statement on this point, after it has been shown that we must attribute conceptual thought to man in order to explain his linguistic behavior.

NOTES TO CHAPTER 11

1. See Charles E. Osgood, *Method and Theory in Experimental Psychology*, pp. 655–665, 681–682; Donald Hebb, *A Textbook of Psychology*, pp. 46–48, 260–263; Harry Harlow, "Thinking," in *Theoretical Foundations of Psychology*, ed. by H. Helson, pp. 493–496; C. Judson Herrick, *The Evolution of Human Nature*, pp. 324–326, 329, 360–361, 401–405. The foregoing writers all use the one word "symbol" for signs that are merely signals, on the one hand, and for signs that are designators, on the other. The following writers distinguish between signals and designators, but they use the word "symbol" for designators, and the word "sign" for signals: MacDonald Crichtley, "The Evolution of Man's Capacity for Language," in *Evolution After Darwin*, Volume II, pp. 300–301; Leslie A. White, *The Science of Culture*, pp. 26–29; Ernst Cassirer, *An Essay on Man*, pp. 31–32. Much misunderstanding results from these divergent uses of the word "symbol"; see, for example, Herrick's misunderstanding of White, p. 401 of his book, cited above.

2. When I use the word "name" or speak of "naming," I always have in mind what is ordinarily called a common or general name, never a proper name, i.e., a common noun, such as "dog" or "mammal," not a proper name or definite description that designates one and only one object, such as "George Washington, the first President of the United States." As any student of modern logic knows, the meaning or significance of common names is much easier to explain than that of proper names or definite descriptions. Karl Popper seems to hold the contrary view, that the use of proper names is "by far the simplest case of a descriptive use of words." See *Conjectures and Refutations*, pp. 297–298. Cf. H. H. Price, *Thinking and Experience*, pp. 281–283.

3. See *Prior Analytics*, II, 27; *Posterior Analytics*, I, 6, 75^a28–35; *Rhetoric*, I 2, 1357^a23–1357^b24. Aristotle is concerned with inference, but what he calls a sign is identical with what I have called a signal; in fact, he uses the same illustrations: clouds are a fallible sign of rain; smoke, a fallible sign of fire. For an interesting variety of examples of signs that function as signals, see Price, *Thinking and Experience*, p. 106 ff.

4. This obvious fact is overlooked and transgressed by the behavioristic theory of the meaning of signs that function as signals. That theory makes the actual response or the disposition to respond that

is elicited by a signal or cue (and it treats the words used in human language as if they were nothing but signals or cues) the constitutive source of the signal's meaning. See note 5, *infra*, for a critique of the bankruptcy of behaviorism when it comes to the problem of accounting for the meaning of signs, either signals or designators.

5. Anyone who understands the analysis here given of the implicative meaning of signals and the denotative-connotative meaning of designators should be able to discern the utter speciousness of the stimulus-response theory of signs and their meaning. For prime examples of the theory in question, see Charles Morris, *Signs, Language and Behavior*, 1946; *Signification and Significance*, 1964; B. F. Skinner, *Verbal Behavior*, 1957; Charles E. Osgood, *Method and Theory in Experimental Psychology*, pp. 690–699; C. E. Osgood, G. Suci, and P. Tannenbaum, "The Logic of Semantic Differentiation," in *Psycholinguistics*, ed. by S. Saporta, 1961: pp. 286–289.

It must be remembered that the S-R theory is offered as an account of verbal signs in human linguistic behavior, and not merely as an explanation of the functioning of non-verbal signs in the behavior of non-linguistic animals. On the very face of it, it is apparent that the S-R formulation cannot account for the meaning of designators, since it claims that a word which elicits a particular response gets its meaning from the stimulus (*the perceived object*) to which that response is made or which arouses a disposition to respond in certain ways. This amounts to saying that a word naming an object gets its designative meaning from that *object-as-perceived*. As Section 5 of this chapter will clearly show, the designative significance of names cannot be thus explained.

The analysis presented in Section 4 will reveal that the S-R theory is equally befuddled in its attempt to explain the implicative or if-then meaning of signals *in human behavior*. Here the central error consists in deriving the meaning of the signal from the response or disposition to respond to which it gives rise instead of recognizing that the response is itself determined by the apprehended meaning of the signal. The fact that the same signal with the same meaning can give rise to opposite responses and to quite contingent and variable ones shows that these responses are a consequence of, not a source of, the signal's meaning. The picture presented by the S-R theory of signs in human behavior is a fictitious concoction that does not even have the relevance of a false scientific theory.

Professor Price's criticism of the behavioristic formulation centers on the point that it attempts to treat all signs (including designators) as if they were signals (see *Thinking and Experience*, pp. 185–187, 191, 194, 197–201). He refers to it as "the signal theory of meaning." Professor Price's criticism does not go far enough. The defect in the behavioristic or S-R theory is not only that it cannot explain the meaning of designators, but also that it is irrelevant to the way in which signals function in human behavior. On the other hand, the S-R formulation may go a long way toward accounting for the functioning of cues in animal behavior. (These cues may be verbal or non-verbal; but when they are verbal, they do not have the meanings that words have, either as designators or as signals.) Learned cues that, through conditioning, become operative as substitute stimuli function *meaninglessly*; that is, without any prior apprehension of the meaning of the signal on the part of the animal responding to the cue. If this is so, then in the behavior of non-linguistic animals, no signs at all—not even signals, much less designators—are operative; for if a sign is *always meaningful*, then the word "signal" is being used equivocally when it is used, on the one hand, for the *meaningless* cues that function in animal behavior and, on the other hand, for the *meaningful* signals, verbal or non-verbal, that function in human behavior. What I am saying, in short, is that, to whatever extent S–R formulations account for cue-functioning in animal behavior, they do so without any reference to meaning or significance; hence, these same formulations cannot account for the functioning of signs (signals or designators) in human behavior, because here the apprehension of meaning must be taken into account, which is precisely what the S-R formulations cannot do.

6. Cf. Price, *Thinking and Experience*, pp. 160–164, 213–214, 231–233.

7. See the references given in Chapter 10, note 17.

8. Professor Price, as already pointed out, erroneously supposes that concepts must be attributed to non-linguistic animals in order to explain their reactions to signals (see *Thinking and Experience*, pp. 90–94, 98, 103–104, 200–203). He would be mistaken even if the signals that function in animal behavior operated meaningfully, for the attainment of perceptual memories and abstractions would suffice to explain the apprehension of the generalized significance of signals. Concept-formation by non-linguistic animals would not have to be posited. See *supra*, Chapter 9, note 8, and cf. Chapter 10, note 9. But Professor Price is even more fundamentally in error if the learned cues that function in animal behavior operate meaninglessly, and so can be explained entirely in S-R terms and by reference to conditioning (see note 5, *supra*).

9. Cf. Price, *Thinking and Experience*, pp. 214–233, 268, 273–274. I cannot stress too much the point that the linked denotative and connotative meanings of a designator do not derive from a single concept, but from a whole set of related concepts. This point, it seems to me, is related to the point that Geach is making when he maintains that no one knows the designative meaning of a naming-word unless he can use it meaningfully in a sentence. As thus used, the single word's meaning involves a whole set of concepts—the set of concepts that confer meaning upon the sentence (see *Mental Acts*, pp. 11–16).

10. The triadic theory of the significance or meaning of words (more specifically, of names, or signs that are designators) was first stated by Aristotle in two sentences in the opening chapter of his treatise *On Interpretation* (16ª3–8). Both because of its brevity and because Aristotle was not concerned with the problem of meaning as later generations have come to face it, the statement is obscure and has been subject to misunderstanding. It is clear with regard to the three distinct elements that are involved (the verbal sign, the things that we use language to talk about, and our understanding or knowledge of these things); but it is imprecise about the relation of these three elements. The theory, as stated by Aristotle, simply points out that we cannot use words to talk about things of which we have no knowledge or undersanding at all; and so the significance of our words, when we do talk about things that we know or understand, involves our knowledge or understanding of those things. In sharp contrast to this triadic theory of meaning are a variety of dyadic theories that, in one way or another, try to explain the significance of names or designators without employing, as the pivotal element in the explanation, our knowledge or understanding of the things signified. It is my contention that all dyadic theories fail to solve the problem or, worse, fail to understand the problem for which they are offered as solutions. But I am not saying that all triadic theories succeed in solving the problem. There is a correct and an incorrect version of the triadic theory. The incorrect version of it, which had its origin in Locke, committed a fundamental error that not only prevented it from solving the problem, but also resulted in the rejection of the triadic theory itself and led to the effort to substitute one or another dyadic theory for it.

Only within the general context of a correct theory of knowledge can we find a correct statement of the triadic theory. Only when the concept is treated (as in Aristotle and Aquinas) as *that by which* we know or understand (*id quo*), never as *that which* we know or understand (*id quod*), does the correct version of the triadic theory result: the object known or understood is that which our designative words signify; the object as understood is that which is signified. Since our concepts are that by which we understand the objects we know, they are also that by which our words signify those objects as known; they are themselves never the objects signified.

Unfortunately, even in the correct version, the triadic theory has often been stated in a way that leads to misunderstanding. Not only are there three distinct elements in the theory (the verbal sign, the concept, and the significate or object signified); but there are also three distinct relations involved: (i) the relation, R_1, between verbal sign and concept; (ii) the relation, R_2, between concept and object understood; and (iii) the relation, R_3, between the verbal sign and the object signified as understood. In traditional statements of the correct version of the triadic theory, one word has often been used to name all three relations; thus, it is said that the verbal sign *signifies* the concept, that the concept *signifies* the object known, and that the verbal sign *signifies* the object as known. The philosophers who made such statements were not led into error by this triple use of the word "signifies" because within the general context of their theory of the concept as *id quo*, never *id quod*, they used that one word in quite distinct senses when they used it to relate the verbal sign to the concept, the concept to the object known, and the verbal sign to the object as known. They recognized that the verbal sign signifies the object-as-known through the medium of the concept as that by which the object known is understood. See, for example, Aquinas, *Summa Theologica*, I, 13, 1.

To prevent misunderstanding by contemporary readers who are not habituated to the distinction between *id quo* and *id quod*, I propose to use three distinct words to name the three distinct relations involved in the correct version of the triadic theory of meaning. I reserve the word "signifies" or "means" for the relation, R_3, between the verbal sign and its significate, the object signified. For the relation, R_1, between the verbal sign and the concept, I will use the word "evokes." And for the relation, R_2, between the concept of an object and the object understood, I will use the word "represents" or "makes known." Thus, the verbal sign "dog" evokes (R_1) the concept *dog*, which represents or makes known (R_2) the animal dog, and through the functioning of these two relations, the verbal sign "dog" signifies (R_3) the animal dog. When we say that the meaningless sound or mark becomes the meaningful name "dog" we are saying that it has acquired, through linkage with the concept *dog*, the power to evoke that concept and, through it, to signify the animal dog that is understood and made known by the concept *dog*. And when we say that the mark or sound "dog" *has thus acquired* the meaning which makes it a designative sign or name, and that the concept of dogs *is* the meaning that it has acquired, we must observe that, in using the word "meaning" itself twice, we have used it in two distinct ways. A current distinction between sense and reference helps us to clarify this point. The meaning which *is* the concept *dog* is the sense of the word "dog." The meaning which the word "dog" *has*, through evoking the concept by which the object is understood, is the reference of the word "dog"; i.e., the significate or object signified is its referent. Hence when we speak of the meaning of the word "dog," we must always distinguish its sense (meaning_1) and its reference (meaning_2). And when we say that concepts *are* meanings, whereas verbal signs only *have* meanings, we must always be clear that concepts *as* meanings give sense to our words, but are never its referents; and that the meaning which our words *have* is always twofold—their sense, on the one hand, and their reference, on the other..

I said earlier that the incorrect version of the triadic theory originated with John Locke. It does so in the context of a theory of knowledge and ideas that makes ideas the objects (*id quod*) of the mind when the mind thinks. Hence when Locke comes to explain the meaning that words *acquire* and *have*, he cannot help but make ideas the objects that they signify—their significates or referents. "Words, in their primary or immediate signification," Locke writes, "stand for nothing but the ideas in the mind of him that uses them" (*Essay Concerning Human Understanding*, Book III, Chapter ii, Section 2). Cf. *ibid.*, Section 5. The distinction between sense and reference is lost; ideas or concepts are no longer treated as the medium through which words signify things known or understood, thus giving a word the sense by which it is able to refer to a thing. When the triadic theory of meaning is mentioned—and either embraced or rejected—by twentieth-century writers, it is always the incorrect Lockean version, never the correct Aristotelian version, of the theory that they have in mind. See C. K. Ogden and I. A. Richards, *The Meaning of Meaning*, 1923: pp. 49 ff.; Stephen Ullmann, *The Principles of Semantics*, 1963: pp. 71–72; N. E. Christensen, "A Proof That Meanings Are Neither Ideas Nor Concepts," in *Analysis*, Volume XVII, No. 1, October, 1956, pp. 10–13. Christensen's proof that words do not signify concepts or ideas amounts to no more than a showing that concepts are not the referents or significates of verbal signs, which is precisely what the correct version of the triadic theory maintains. Only the incorrect version makes the mistake against which Christensen argues; he does not seem to be aware of the Aristotelian version of the theory.

The Institute for Philosophical Research is currently engaged in the study of the whole discussion of language and thought and especially the problem of meaning. We have examined most of the major twentieth-century treatments of this subject. We have found only two contemporary writers who indicate some awareness of the correct version of the triadic theory of meaning: J. N. Findlay (see "Use, Usage, and Meaning," in *Clarity Is Not Enough*, pp. 429–441, esp. pp. 440–441); and R. Chisholm (see the reference to him in note 11, *infra*). Others among contemporaries who comment on the triadic theory are either unacquainted with the Aristotelian version or so misunderstand it that they treat that version and the Lockean version as if they were identical, e.g., Ogden and Richards and those who have criticized Ogden and Richards. The rest manifest no awareness at all of the triadic theory in its correct version and, in addition, do not seem to understand the problem that it tried to solve and succeeded in solving.

Professor Findlay's article, cited above, first appeared as a reply to a paper presented by Gilbert Ryle in an Aristotelian Society Symposium on meaning and use (see *Proceedings of the Aristotelian Society*, Supplementary Volume XXXV, 1961: pp. 223–230). Findlay clearly showed the inadequacy of the Wittgensteinian theory that the meaning of words in ordinary language is *nothing but* their use. That theory is, in its own terms, unable to explain how originally meaningless marks or sounds acquire meaning; rules of usage or conventions of use cannot adequately explain this, for the role they play needs to be explained; and as Findlay points out, the explanation presupposes the existence of meanings as intentions of the mind. (Compare Findlay's criticism of the theory that meaning is use with the criticism offered by J. N. Mohanty in *Edmund Husserl's Theory of Meaning*, 1963: pp. 38–41.)

Among the leading advocates of the "meaning is use" theory are Ludwig Wittgenstein, *Philosophical Investigations*, 1953; Gilbert Ryle, "The Theory of Meaning," in *British Philosophy in Mid-Century*, ed. by C. A. Mace, 1957; N. E. Christensen, *On the Nature of Meanings*, 1961; and William Alston, *Philosophy of Language*, 1964. Among those writers who advance a dyadic theory of meaning are W. V. Quine, *Word and Object*, 1960; Charles Morris, *Signification and Significance*, 1964; and B. F. Skinner, *Verbal Behavior*, 1957. For critical discussions of diverse theories of meaning, see L. Antal, *Questions of Meaning*, 1963, and *Content, Meaning, and Understanding*, 1964; L. J. Cohn, *The Diversity of Meaning*, 1963; N. E. Christensen, *On the Nature of Meanings*, 1961; A. J. Ayer, "Meaning and Intentionality," in *Proceedings of the 12th International Congress of Philosophy*, Volume 1, 1958; P. Henle, "The Problem of Meaning," in *Proceedings of the American Philosophical Association*, Volume XXVII, 1953–54; James W. Cornman, *Metaphysics, Reference and Language*, 1966.

One writer who appears to state the triadic theory in a way that very roughly corresponds to the correct version rejects it for a reason that completely begs the question. See C. E. Osgood, *Method and Theory in Experimental Psychology*, pp. 691–692. Earlier Professor Osgood concedes the fact that, in order to explain man's linguistic behavior, "meaning must be brought into the picture somehow," and then he adds "here's the rub—meaning has no accepted material correlate. If we are to hold to our materialistic moorings, we must *postulate material events for meanings*" (*ibid.*, p. 681). In a later essay, Osgood, in collaboration with Suci and Tannenbaum, again presents the triadic theory, attributing the best statement of it to Ogden and Richards, and calling it the "mentalistic view" of meaning; and concludes by saying: "If a dualistic view [i.e., a non-materialistic view] is harmonious with the truth, then the Ogden and Richards theory is the most tenable one available" ("The Logic of Semantic Variation," in *Psycholinguistics*, ed. by S. Saporta, pp. 285–286). The question whether concepts as meanings can or cannot be adequately explained in neurophysiological terms is posterior to the question whether concepts as meanings must be posited in order to give a satisfactory explanation of man's linguistic behavior. If they must be posited in order to explain man's use of names or designators, then they must be posited whether or not an adequate neurophysiological explanation can be given of the power and process of conceptual thought; and whether or not the materialistic position is sustained or infirmed as a result. To assume the truth of metaphysical behaviorism as Osgood does, and then to make that assumption the reason for rejecting the triadic theory of meaning, is to beg the question in a most flagrant fashion. (There is no conflict between the triadic theory of meaning and methodological behaviorism; Aristotelian psychology is methodologically behaviorist.) If the triadic theory of meaning is the only one that solves the problem of how originally meaningless marks or sounds acquire meaning and become meaningful names or designators, then it must be adopted no matter what consequences it may have for the issue concerning the adequacy of neurophysiological explanations of conceptual thought. The procedure followed in this book does not beg that question. Having established man's psychological difference in kind from other animals by virtue of his having the power of conceptual thought that they totally lack, we must still face the question whether that difference in kind is superficial or radical—whether the action of the brain is the sufficient cause of conceptual thought, or only a necessary but not the sufficient cause of it.

11. The statement that concepts *are* meanings will be understood only by those who also understand that concepts are *that by which* (*id quo*) we understand or know whatever we understand or know, never *that which* (*id quod*) we understand or know. See *supra*, Chapter 10, note 8 and *infra*, Chapter 12, note 41. That which is understood or known by means of our concepts (i.e., the object known or understood) is also that which is meant by the words we use designatively (i.e., the object signified). The concept that functions as the means whereby we understand the kind of thing a dog is also functions as the means whereby we are able to use the word "dog" to signify this particular conceived in a certain way or to signify a certain class or kind to which particulars conceived in this way belong. The meaning of the designative sign is an object that we understand or conceive in a certain way; that object—the thing signified or the significate—is that which the designative sign or signifier means; the concept is that by which the sign means the object, never that which the sign means.

Hence to say that concepts *are* meanings is not to say that concepts are the significates of signs, but rather to say that concepts are the *tertium quid* through which signs mean their significates. The word "dog" does not mean the concept *dog*; the word "dog" means the perceived particular understood in a certain way or the class to which it belongs; the concept through which the perceived particular is understood is the meaning through which the word "dog" means the perceived particular conceived as a dog.

Just as concepts, as the *id quo* of our knowing or understanding, are not inspectable entities in our experience, so neither are the meanings whereby signs signify their significates. Hence to say that we apprehend the meaning of a sign is not to say that we apprehend *that whereby it means* (the meaning itself which *is* a concept), but rather to say that we apprehend *that which it means* (the object it signifies through the concept by which we understand that object). It is of the utmost importance to distinguish these two ways in which we use the word "meaning" when we speak of the meaning of a sign: (a) on the one hand, for *that which* is meant—the significate or object signified; (b) on the other hand, for *that by which* or *that through which* the sign signifies its significate. As we saw earlier (see note 10, *supra*), the meaning of "meaning" which is (a) above is the *referent* of the verbal sign, the meaning of "meaning" which is (b) above is its *sense*. It is only as the sense of a verbal sign that the meaning *is* a concept; as the reference of a verbal sign, the meaning is never a concept, but always an object conceived or understood. Cf. Jacques Maritain, *Ransoming the Time*, 1941: pp. 222–223.

A letter written by Professor Chisholm to Professor Sellars covers many of the points in the foregoing analysis of meaning. See *Minnestota Studies in the Philosophy of Science*, Volume II, p. 533. In this letter, Professor Chisholm enunciates seven theses. Instead of quoting them here, I am going to paraphrase them in order to avoid confusion, because where I use the word "concepts," Chisholm uses the word "thoughts," and where I use the word "meaning," Chisholm uses the word "intentional." The seven theses, paraphrased accordingly, are as follows.

(1) Concepts are meanings: they are that whereby something is meant.

(2) Linguistic entities (names, sentences) are meaningful, i.e., have meanings.

(3) Nothing else is a meaning or meaningful. (This thesis, in my judgment, requires qualification, for non-verbal signs can be meaningful.)

(4) Concepts would be meanings even if there were no meaningful linguistic entities (or signs, verbal or non-verbal, that have meaning).

(5) But for man's having concepts, linguistic entities would not be meaningful. If there were no men, then the mark or noise "hund"—if somehow occasionally it got produced—would not mean dog.

(6) Concepts, through being meanings, are the source of the meanings possessed by meaningful signs; i.e., nothing would be meaningful or have meaning were it not for the fact that concepts are meanings.

(7) Hence concepts are peculiar in that they have an important characteristic which nothing else in the world has, namely, the characteristic described in (6) above.

12. Notwithstanding Locke's fundamental mistake in treating ideas as the objects signified by names, it is to his credit that he so clearly

recognized that the signification of our general or common names cannot be explained without reference to our possession of what he sometimes calls "general or universal ideas," and sometimes "abstract ideas." See *Essay Concerning Human Understanding*, III, i, 3; III, iii, 6–11. Where Locke succeeds in some measure, Berkeley and Hume, confronting the same problem (the problem of explaining the signification of general names) fail signally; see Berkeley's *Principles of Natural Knowledge*, Introduction, paragraphs 10–18; and Hume's *Enquiry Concerning Human Understanding*, Part I, Section XII, Part 1, 122. The nominalism of Berkeley and Hume, which prevents them from explaining how common names signify kinds or classes, was probably caused in part by the influence on them of Locke's own confusion of the process of concept-formation (by which "general or universal ideas" are formed) and the process of perceptual generalization which gives rise to perceptual abstractions (i.e., generalized images), but not concepts (i.e., general ideas). Even if Berkeley and Hume had been empirically correct in denying generalized or abstract images, they would still be wrong; their basic failure stems from their blindness to the distinction between perceptions, memories, and images, on the one hand, and concepts, on the other. Like Locke, they used the word "idea" primarily for sensations or perceptions and lacked a word for conceptual thought as something quite distinct from all perceptual processes. Locke's awareness of the distinction could not help but be obscured by his treatment of general and universal ideas as if they were the same as abstract ideas. In a section headed "*Brutes abstract not*," he writes: "We observe no footsteps in them of making use of general signs for universal ideas; from which we have reason to imagine that they have not the faculty of abstracting, or making general ideas, since they have no use of words, or any other general signs" (*op. cit.*, II, xi, 10). The section should have been headed: "*Brutes do not form concepts*"; for, through perceptual generalization and discrimination, brutes do attain perceptual abstractions. On this confusion in Locke, which, unfortunately, he shares to some extent, see Price, *Thinking and Experience*, pp. 43, 98, 200; and on Locke's superiority to Berkeley and Hume in dealing with the problem of verbal signs and their meanings, see *ibid.*, pp. 288–289, 291, 296, 302, 327–332, 354, 357.

13. If animals had the power of conceptual thought and could understand, for the things they were able to perceive, the kind of thing each was, then, given the equipment to make sounds which many animals have, they should be able to name things and make sentences. The fact that they do not name things and make sentences is fairly weighty evidence that they are not able to do so. This, in turn, forces us to the conclusion that they do not have the power of conceptual thought. This conclusion can hardly be negatived by saying that animals do have the power of conceptual thought, which

enables them to name things and make sentences, but, for reasons known only to them, they do not choose to exercise the power and engage in propositional speech.

14. If animals do not have concepts at all, then their perceptual experience is not of the same order as human perceptual experience, for the latter is always or for the most part illuminated by an understanding of the objects perceived that is totally absent from the perceptual experience of animals. Without concepts operative at the moment of perception, all that animals perceive in a set of similar objects is what is sensibly common to them. They do not perceive a set or series of similar objects—all functioning as equivalent stimuli in Klüver's sense of that term—as particular instances of a class or kind that they understand. In short, when rats react to different triangles in terms of their sameness as triangles, they do not perceive this set or series of visible forms as particular instances of triangularity, for they have no concept of triangle, no understanding of triangularity *as such.* Hence the perceptual abstractions attained by animals cannot be regarded as functionally the same kind of cognitive dispositions as the perceptual abstractions attained by men; for, in the human case, the perceptual abstractions always or for the most part function in conjunction with concepts, so that when the object is perceived, the perception is infused with an understanding of the kind of thing it is. Unless one understands what a triangle is, one cannot perceive this visible shape as a triangle, even though, by means of a perceptual abstraction, one may be able to recognize this shape and that shape as being of the same kind.

NOTES TO CHAPTER 12

1. See John Beloff, "The Identity Hypothesis: A Critique," in *Brain and Mind*, ed. by J. R. Smythies, 1965: p. 50; see also *ibid.*, p. 194; and H. H. Price, "Some Objections to Behaviorism," in *Dimensions of Mind*, ed. by S. Hook, 1960: p, 84, Cf. C. E. M. Hansel, *ESP, A Scientific Evaluation*, 1966.

2. The contemporary philosophers to whom general reference is here made include C. A. Campbell, R. Chisholm, R. B. Brandt, A. C. Ewing, H. D. Lewis, S. C. Pepper, M. Polany, K. R. Popper, H. H. Price, and A. Danto. Specific references to their works will be given, where relevant, in notes that follow.

3. See *Minnesota Studies in the Philosophy of Science*, Volume II, pp. 483–497.

4. See Gilbert Ryle, *The Concept of Mind*, 1949; H. Feigl, "The 'Mental' and the 'Physical,' " in *Minnesota Studies in the Philosophy*

of Science, Volume II, pp. 370–483; and "Mind-Body, *Not* a Pseudo-problem," in *Dimensions of Mind*, pp. 24–36; W. Sellars, *Science, Perception, and Reality*, 1963: pp. 1–40, 127–196; J. J. C. Smart, *Philosophy and Scientific Realism*, 1963: pp. 64–120; K. J. W. Craik, *The Nature of Explanation*, 1952; *The Nature of Psychology*, 1966; Hilary Putnam, "Minds and Machines," in *Dimensions of Mind*, pp. 148–179; U. T. Place, "Is Consciousness a Brain Process?" in *The Philosophy of Mind*, ed. by V. C. Chappell, 1962: pp. 101–109; S. Pepper, "A Neural Identity Theory of Mind," in *Dimensions of Mind*, pp. 37–55; A. Quinton, "Mind and Matter," in *Brain and Mind*, pp. 201–233. See also M. Scriven, "The Complete Robot: A Prolegomena to Androidology," in *Dimensions of Mind*, pp. 118–142; "The Mechanical Concept of Mind," in *Minds and Machines*, ed. by A. R. Anderson, pp. 31–42; Donald M. McKay, "From Mechanism to Mind," in *Brain and Mind*, pp. 163–191. For excellent and concise summaries of the identity hypothesis, see V. C. Chappell, Introduction to *The Philosophy of Mind*, and Bruce Aune, "Feigl on the Mind–Body Problem," in *Mind, Matter, and Method*, ed. by P. K. Feyerabend and G. Maxwell, 1966: pp. 17–39.

5. See Feigl, in *Minnesota Studies*, pp. 429, 482–483; Smart, "Sensations and Brain Processes," in *The Philosophy of Mind*, ed. by V. C. Chappell, pp. 160–172; W. Sellars, "The Identity Approach to the Mind-Body Problem," in *Philosophy of Mind*, ed. by Stuart Hampshire, 1966; V. C. Chappell, *op. cit.*, Price, in *Dimensions of Mind*, p. 78; C. D. Broad, *The Mind and Its Place in Nature*, 1925: pp. 622–623; Beloff, *op. cit.*, pp. 44–46; McKay, *op. cit.*, p. 190; B. B. Wolman, "Principles of Monistic Transitionism," in *Scientific Psychology*, 1965: pp. 563–593.

6. See Feigl, in *Minnesota Studies*, p. 461, and in *Dimensions of Mind*, pp. 30–34; V. C. Chappell, *op. cit.*, pp. 19–21; Bruce Aune, in *Mind, Matter, and Method*, pp. 30, 38; Smart, in *The Philosophy of Mind*; Beloff, in *Brain and Mind*, pp. 36, 39, 42.

7. See Feigl, in *Minnesota Studies*, pp. 461, 463, 471–473. Cf. R. B. Brandt, "Doubts About the Identity Theory," in *Dimensions of Mind*, pp. 60–63; and J. Beloff, in *op. cit.*, pp. 36–38.

8. See R. B. Brandt, in *op. cit.*, pp. 57–67; H. H. Price, in *Dimensions of Mind*, pp. 78–84; A. Danto, "On Consciousness in Machines," in *ibid.*, pp. 180–187; A. C. Ewing, "Professor Ryle's Attack on Dualism," in *Clarity Is Not Enough*, pp. 311–338; M. Polanyi, "The Structure of Consciousness," in *Brain*, Volume 89, Part 4, 1966, pp. 799–810; J. Beloff, in *op. cit.*; Bruce Aune, in *op. cit.*

9. See Feigl, in *Minnesota Studies*, pp. 479–482; and Smart, in *The Philosophy of Mind*, pp. 164–172; cf. *Philosophy and Scientific Realism*, pp. 92–99.

10. *Science, Perception and Reality*, pp. 30–31.

11. *Ibid.*, pp. 33–34. Cf. Smart, *Philosophy and Scientific Realism*, pp. 103–105.

12. *The Nature of Explanation*, p. 52. Cf. *ibid.*, pp. 53, 58–60.

13. *Ibid.*, p. 63. Cf. *ibid.*, pp. 98–99.

14. *The Nature of Psychology*, pp. 151, 166.

15. See *Conjectures and Refutations*, p. 298. Cf. his "Note on the Body-Mind Problem," in *ibid.*, pp. 299–303, in which Professor Popper discusses his interchanges with Professor Sellars on this subject.

16. See *Brain and Mind*, p. 234. Cf. *ibid.*, p. 59.

17. See *Minnesota Studies in the Philosophy of Science*, Volume II, Appendix, pp. 507–539.

18. *Ibid.*, pp. 536–537.

19. Professor Sellars writes: "Characteristic of thoughts is their *intentionality*, *reference*, or *aboutness*, and it is clear that semantical talk about the meaning or reference of verbal expressions has the same structure as mentalistic discourse concerning what thoughts are about. It is therefore all the more tempting to suppose that the intentionality of *thoughts* can be traced to the application of semantic categories to overt verbal performances, and to suggest a modified Rylean account according to which talk about so-called 'thoughts' is shorthand for hypothetical and mongrel categorical-hypothetical statements about overt verbal and non-verbal behavior, *and* that talk about the *intentionality* of these 'episodes' is correspondingly reducible to semantical talk about the verbal components" (*Science, Perception and Reality*, p. 180). For a recent discussion of Professor Sellars' views on intentionality, see R. J. Bernstein, "Sellars' Vision of Man-in-the-Universe," in *The Review of Metaphysics*, Volume XX, No. 1, September, 1966, pp. 120 ff. As Bernstein points out, what distinguishes Sellars from other contemporary writers, such as Chisholm and Price, who make use of Brentano's theory of the intentionality of mental acts, is that Sellars, unlike the others, restricts intentionality to thoughts alone and does not extend it to sensations and feelings. In taking this position, Sellars departs not only from the theory of intentionality as revived in a somewhat corrupt form by Brentano, but also from it in its earlier and better statement by Aristotle and Aquinas (see Sellars' "Aristotelian Philosophies of Mind," in *Philosophy for the Future*, p. 556). The critical difference between the Aristotelian-Thomistic theory of the intentionality of mental acts and the recrudescence of that theory in Brentano and Husserl, is discussed in Section 6 of this chapter.

20. In *op. cit.*, p. 174. "Machine performances," Putnam writes, "may be wholly analogous to language, so much so that the whole of lin-

guistic theory can be applied to them. If the reader wishes to check this, he may go through a work like Chomsky's *Syntactic Structures* carefully, and note that *at no place is the assumption employed that the corpus of utterances studied by the linguist was produced by a conscious organism.* Then he may turn to such pioneer work in empirical semantics as Ziff's *Semantic Analysis* and observe that the same thing holds true for *semantical* theory" (*ibid.*, pp. 173–174). If the objection were raised that such works as Chomsky's and Ziff's, which are representative of behavioristic linguistics and empirical semantics, treat all linguistic operations and processes without any reference whatsoever to the meaning of the linguistic elements as signs (especially designators), Professor Putnam would reply by saying, as he does: "Of course, the objection to 'behavioristic' linguistics might *really* be an objection to all attempts at *scientific* linguistics. But this possibility I feel justified in dismissing" (*ibid.*, p. 174). See Warren McCulloch's comment on Chomsky's "analysis of context-free, phrase-structured language," as inapplicable to the linguistic behavior of man, because, as McCulloch points out, "no natural language is ever context-free, even when it is written carefully" (in *The Great Ideas Today*, 1966: p. 332).

21. In *op. cit.*, pp. 224–225. Cf. *ibid.*, pp. 220–224. And see Price's critique of contingent identity, in *ibid.*, pp. 234–235.

22. In *Minnesota Studies*, pp. 416–418.

23. Aristotle and Aquinas reject the psychophysical dualism of Plato and Descartes (involving a duality of substance—body and mind, *res extensa* and *res cogitans*) because it abrogates the existential unity of man: for them, man is one substance, not a composite of two. See Aristotle, *On the Soul*, II, 1; Aquinas, *Summa Theologica*, I, 75, 76. They also reject psychophysical interactionism on the same ground advanced by the proponents of the identity hypothesis; namely, that in positing a many-one and one-many relationship between the acts or states of the mind and acts or states of the body, it disregards the weight of empirical evidence that there is a one-one relationship between the psychical and the physical.

24. On the one hand, the reductive materialists go to the extreme of denying the analytical or logical separability of mind and body. On the other hand, the extreme immaterialists deny the existential inseparability, i.e., the empirical and contingent inseparability, of mind and body. The two moderate positions—the one advanced by proponents of the identity hypothesis and the one held by Aristotle and Aquinas—agree in rejecting both of these extremist denials; i.e., they affirm both the logical separability of mind and body, and also the empirical and contingent existential inseparability of mind and body (i.e., a one-one relationship between them, the assertion of which is tantamount to the assertion that bodily action is *at least* a necessary condition of mental acts).

25. See Price's discussion of Quinton's paper in *Brain and Mind*, pp. 234–235; see Beloff in *ibid.*; and Brandt, in *op. cit.*, pp. 60–63. Cf. Michael Polanyi, *The Study of Man*, 1963: pp. 53–70.

26. See passages referred to in notes 15, 16, and 17, *supra.*

27. In his Inaugural Lecture at Oxford in 1947, dedicated to Gilbert Ryle, Professor A. J. Ayer writes as follows: " 'What do you see with?' 'My eyes.' 'What do you hear with?' 'My ears.' 'What do you touch with?' 'My hands.' 'What do you walk with?' 'My legs.' 'What do you think with?' The proper answer is there is no 'with' in this case, and that this is just one of the ways in which it differs from the others. But because it is assumed that every activity must have its special organ, a mythical entity is brought in to do the work. And so to the misleading question, 'What do you think with?' we get the even more misleading answer, 'With my mind.' A very much less misleading answer is that I think with my brain. For at least the brain can be identified as a physical existent, and there is good empirical evidence that a certain condition of the brain is *causally necessary, if not sufficient*, for the occurrence of any process of thought. But equally, there is good empirical evidence that a certain condition of the brain is *causally necessary* for the occurrence of any perceptual activity. And the only reason I can find why the brain should be regarded as specifically the organ of thought, as opposed to perception, is that in the case of thought no other organ conspicuously intervenes" (*Thinking and Meaning*, p. 5, italics added).

The moderate immaterialists would agree with Professor Ayer that the brain is a necessary condition of thought, and they would be more precise than he is in his statement about perception, for with regard to perception they would say that the sense-organs *and* the brain *together* are not only a necessary, but the sufficient condition. The question in issue—whether the brain is *only a necessary*, or is also *the sufficient*, condition of thought—is unanswered by Ayer, though there are ample indications that he, like Ryle, would be inclined to answer: *sufficient as well as necessary*. With regard to Ayer's position on the question in issue, the best indication is, perhaps, to be found in this Inaugural Lecture itself, where he argues against Professor Price's theory of the intentionality of mental acts and tries to solve the problem of the meaning of signs without reference to concepts or their objects (see *ibid.*, pp. 20–25). For a discussion of Ayer's views *vis-a-vis* those of Price, see J. N. Mohanty, *Edmund Husserl's Theory of Meaning*, 1964: pp. 5–7.

28. See Aristotle, *On the Soul*, II, 1–2; Aquinas, *Summa Theologica*, I, 76, 8; I, 77, 4, Resp. and ad 3; I, 78, 3–4.

29. See Aristotle, *On the Soul*, II, 2, 413b23–30; III, 3–5, and 7, 431a14–19. And see Aquinas, *Summa Theologica*, I, 84, 6–8.

30. See Aquinas, *ibid.*, I, 75, 3–5.

31. See Aristotle, *On the Soul*, III, 2; Aquinas, *Summa Theologica*, I, 12, 4; I, 14, 1; I, 14, 2 ad 1; I, 18, 3; I, 85, 1.

32. See John Locke, *Essay Concerning Human Understanding*, IV, iii, 6. Here Locke declares that, apart from Divine revelation, we cannot be certain that an omnipotent power did not give a fitly disposed system of matter the power to think as well as to perceive. Cf. *ibid.*, IV, x, 9; and II, xxiii, 13.

33. The argument that I regard as fallacious is the one concerning contraries; namely, that contrary qualities are never co-present in sensation or perception, and cannot be, because sensation and perception are bodily acts, and matter does not admit of the simultaneous presence of contraries; whereas contraries are sometimes co-present in our intellectual apprehensions (see Aquinas, *Summa Theologica*, I, 76, 6). Even if this were true, it would not establish the immateriality of the intellect; for a number is, as such, an immaterial entity, and it does not admit of simultaneous contraries: an integer cannot be both odd and even.

The other argument is based on what is claimed to be an empirically observed difference between the senses and the intellect. Aristotle writes: "After strong stimulation of a sense we are less able to exercise it than before, as, e.g., in the case of a loud sound we cannot hear easily immediately after, or in the case of a bright color or a powerful order we cannot see or smell; but in the case of the mind, thought about an object that is highly intelligible renders it more and not less able afterwards to think about objects that are less intelligible: the reason is that while the faculty of sensation is dependent upon the body, mind is separable from it" (*On the Soul*, III, 4, 429^a31–429^b4). If the facts are as claimed, this argument might have the force assigned to it by Aristotle and Aquinas (see *Summa Theologica*, I, 75, 3, Resp. and ad 2). But while the observation concerning the temporary impairment of the sense-organs by intense stimulation is well-authenticated, we have no equally well-established empirical evidence concerning the invigoration of our mind by objects of thought that would be comparable, in the sphere of intellection, to intense lights and sounds in the sphere of vision and hearing.

34. In *Mind, Matter, and Method*, pp. 92–102.

35. *Ibid.*, p. 101. Matson cites Feigl's enumeration of the isms generated by the mind-body problem: "materialism, mentalism, mind-body interactionism, evolutionary emergence theories, psychoneurophysiological parallelism (epiphenomenalism, isomorphism, double aspect theories), and neutral monism"; and then adds: "Aristotle would have been baffled by all this" (*ibid.*, p. 96).

36. *Ibid.*, p. 93.

37. The relevant passages in Aristotle's treatise *On the Soul* are cited in notes 28, 29, and 31 *supra.*

38. See *On the Soul*, III, 4, 429^a18–429^b23.

39. In addition to the passages in the *Summa Theologica* cited in notes 28–31 *supra*, see the following for other and more extended presentations of arguments for the immateriality of the intellect: *Summa Contra Gentiles* trans. by J. F. Anderson under the title, "On the Truth of the Catholic Faith," Book II, 1956: Chapters 49 (4), (8); 50 (3), (7); 51 (4); 59 (3), (4); 62 (4); 66 (3)–(6); 69; 75 (8), (13); 79 (7), (15). See also Aquinas treatise *Disputed Questions on the Soul*, trans. by J. B. Rowan, 1949: pp. 180–182.

40. For example, in their introduction to *Computers and Thought*, 1963, E. A. Feigenbaum and J. Feldman raise the question about the prospects of carrying experiments with artificial or machine intelligence to the point where a manufactured robot will be able to do everything that a human mind can do. "Is there any reason to suppose that we shall never get there?" they ask; and their answer is: "None whatever. Not a single piece of evidence, no logical argument, no proof or theorem has ever been advanced which demonstrates an insurmountable hurdle along the continuum" (p. 8). Either they are totally unaware of the arguments advanced by Aristotle and Aquinas, or they have studied them carefully and rejected them as not logical or not demonstrative. Of these two alternatives, my guess is that the first is more likely. What is true of Feigenbaum and Feldman and their colleagues in the field of computer technology is equally true of most, if not all, of the twentieth-century philosophers who have been cited in this chapter either as proponents or as opponents of the identity hypothesis. In spite of the fact that philosophical behaviorists who are moderate materialists have much in common with Aristotle, they fail to recognize and profit from that affinity. One is inclined to wonder what effect *The Concept of Mind* might have had upon contemporary thought if Ryle, in taking his strong stand against the Cartesian dualism that has pervaded modern thought, had seen himself, not as standing in Aristotle's shoes, but as standing on his shoulders.

41. The argument briefly summarized on pages 220–222 deserves expansion for those who may be interested in its details. The argument rests on two controlling principles, both metaphysical: one with respect to the metaphysics of knowledge (*note*: the metaphysics, not the psychology, of knowledge); the other with respect to the metaphysics of existence relative to knowing and things known. I will first expound these two principles, and I will then state the argument that puts them to use.

(1) *The metaphysics of knowledge: the relation of knower and known.* The process of knowing is such that there must be some-

thing in the knower whereby he knows that which he knows. Let us call *that by which* the knower knows whatever it is that he knows the "quo" of knowing. Let us call *that which* the knower knows in any act of knowing, the "quod" of knowing.

To deny the *quod* of knowing is to assert that there is knowledge without an object known; which is impossible. Nothing is here being assumed about the manner of existence of the object known. All that is being asserted is that for every act of knowing there is an object known.

To deny the *quo* of knowing is to assert that there is knowledge without any factor in the knower that accounts for his knowing that which he knows. Nothing is here being assumed about the manner of existence of that cognitive factor—the *quo* of knowing —whatever it is. All that is being asserted is that for every act of knowing there is a cognitive factor in the knower—that whereby he knows whatever it is that he knows.

To this distinction between the *quod* and the *quo* of knowing, it may be objected that they are one and the same thing. To say this is to say that *knowing is like eating*. Just as the thing to be eaten becomes the thing being eaten by entering into the body of the eater, so the thing to be known becomes the thing being known by entering into the mind of the knower. According to this view of knowledge, there is no *quo* of knowing, for the *quod* of knowing—that which is known—is itself in the knower, just as the food is itself in the eater. The falsity of this view can be seen as follows. The physical and chemical properties of the thing to be eaten are present in the process of that thing's being eaten, and enter into the explanation of its nutritive value. But if the physical and chemical properties of the thing to be known were present in the process of that thing's being known, then fire perceived would burn the perceiver, which is not the case.

It may also be objected that, although the *quod* of knowing never enters into the constitution of the knower, as food enters into the constitution of the eater, knowing involves nothing more than the attention of the knower to that which is known. To say this is to say that *knowing is like illumination*. The act of knowing is like a beam of light thrown on the knowable, thereby making it known. According to this view of knowledge, there may be a *quo* of knowing, but it is not something in the knower, any more than the beam of light that illuminates an object is *in* the source of the illumination. The act of knowing, like the act of illuminating, is a transitive action by the knower on the knowable, rendering it known, without there being anything in the knower whereby he knows that which he knows.

The falsity of this view can be seen as follows: If the act of knowing were a transitive act merely changing the object from the knowable to the known, then the known object would always be present to the knower exactly as it is, and there could be no explanation of how we make errors in our knowledge of things, or assert false claims to knowing that which does not exist at all or does not exist as we claim to know it. The evidence of illusions and hallucinations in the field of perception is sufficient to dismiss this view of knowing which makes it analogous to "lighting up" the object known.

We are, therefore, left with a real distinction between the *quod* and the *quo* of knowing—between that which we know and that whereby we know that which we know. In addition, we can now assert two things about the *quo*. (a) It is something that exists in the knower—exists in some manner, but, in any case, exists apart from the existence of the *quod*. (In the case of hallucinations, it is the existence of the *quo* unaccompanied by the existence of the *quod* which accounts for the perceptual error that is made by the subject of the hallucination.) (b) Since the *quo* is not identical with *quod* as something present in or present to the knower, the *quo* is representative of the *quod*. This second point requires a word of further explanation. To speak of the *quo*—the cognitive factor in the knower—as a representation of the *quod* (that which is known) is to assert two things, one negative, the other positive. The negative point is simply the assertion of the non-identity of *quod* and *quo*. The positive point is the assertion of a similitude between *quod* and *quo*.

If the *quod* and the *quo* of knowing are not identical, which means that they are two distinct entities, then either there is some relation between them, or none. But knowledge is a relation between knower and known; hence it cannot be the case that there is no relation between the *quo* and the *quod* of knowing. Now, if there is some relation between the *quo* and *quod* of knowing, it is either a relation of similitude or some other type of relation. The only other type of relation that could explain the act of knowing is a causal relation. That the *quod*—the object known—is in some way a cause of knowing need not, and probably cannot, be questioned; but that does not explain how the *quo*—that whereby we know that which we know—is the cause of our knowing. So far as I can see, the only explanation of the efficacy of the *quo* as somehow a cause of our knowing that which we know lies in its having a similitude to the *quod*—that which is known. This can be tested by a *reductio ad absurdum*. Try to conceive the *quo* as having no similitude whatsoever to the *quod*, and still try to understand how it functions as that whereby we know that which we know. If you find this impossible, as I do, you will conclude, as I do, that the *quo* of knowing is something in the knower that, by virtue of its similitude to the *quod* of knowing, represents the latter and so can function as that whereby we know that which we know.

One point of explanation is necessary. The similitude between *quo* and *quod*, by virtue of which the *quo* is representative of the *quod*, is not itself knowable, i.e., it cannot be an object of knowledge. Another way of saying this is that the *quo* is self-effacing: being that whereby we know, its whole being consists in its functioning to make the *quod* known. This is the meaning of "representation." It makes something other than itself present; namely, the object known, the *quod*. That is why, traditionally, the *quo* of knowing is called an "intentional being," something whose whole being consists in intending another. To function as a representation is to function intentionally.

In order not to beg, at this point, any questions about conceptual thought, let me illustrate the foregoing analysis of knowledge by applying it to perceptual processes, and especially to what contemporary psychologists, neurologists, and computer technologists, call "perceptual abstractions"—that whereby the machine or the animal (non-human as well as human) reacts to sensible shapes or patterns in such a manner that the animal or machine can be said to *cognize* or *apprehend* the pattern. To explain a cognition or apprehension of this sort, the scientists try to construct, theoretically at least, the pattern that must exist in the brain or in the electrical network of the machine, and that must have sufficient similitude to the pattern being cognized or apprehended, in order that it may function as the *quo* of knowing. The work done by Warren McCulloch in this field, especially his famous essay on the perception of auditory and visual forms, together with the work on the Perceptron and similar devices, perfectly exemplify the point I am here making. To say that there must be, in the nervous system or in the network of the Perceptron, a pattern that bears some resemblance to the pattern being cognized or at least being reacted to in a discriminating way, is to assert the need for a *quo* in the cognitive agent that has some resemblance to the *quod* being cognized.

(2) *The metaphysics of existence as applied to the quod and quo of knowing*. Let us begin by considering only that which can be known or that which is known; for the moment, let us omit any reference to that in us whereby we know whatever we know. And, in order to avoid begging questions at this point in the argument, let us also exclude reference to any type of known object a particular instance of which cannot be perceived by the senses.

With these restrictions in force, it can be asserted that all the particulars we know or can know exist materially; that is, have the physical properties of material things. This can be explained as follows. We never perceive *chair as such* or *tree as such*, but always *this particular chair*, or *that particular tree*. The particular thing perceived is always a unique individual thing, non-identical with any other instance of the same kind of thing, even though it is also a particular instance of the same kind in those respects which do not make it this one unique individual. Things that are otherwise alike as instances of the same kind have certain features that distinguish them as individuals and make them so many different particular instances of the same kind. Principal among these individuating marks or features are the unique spatio-temporal determinations of the individual thing.

Since the spatio-temporal determinations of a thing are physical properties of it, it can be asserted (a) that whatever exists as an individual exists physically, i.e., has a material mode of existence; (b) that whatever has a material mode of existence, exists as an individual, i.e., exists with certain individuating features that make it a unique existence as well as a particular instance of this or that kind of thing. *This equation of individual mode of existence with material mode of existence applies to everything we know perceptually*. The things we know perceptually we know as individuals and as particular instances of kind. In other words, the *quod* of perceptual knowledge always has the individuating marks or features that betoken its material mode of existence. Now let us ask about the *quo* of perceptual knowledge—the representative factor in us whereby we perceive this or that individual thing or particular instance. Applied to this question, the principle of similitude between the *quo* and the *quod* of knowing yields the following answer: to be that whereby we know something as an individual, the *quo* must itself have individuating marks or features. But it can have such marks or features only if it has a material mode of existence. Hence we are brought to the conclusion which, from other relevant evidence, we have every reason to believe is the case; namely, that the *quo* in us that represents the perceptually known object, and is that whereby we know it as an individual, exists materially in us, specifically as a state or pattern of our central nervous system.

(3) We are now in a position to state the argument for the immateriality of conceptual thought. First, let us recall that the inference from man's possession of propositional language to his possession of the power of conceptual thought involves the following points. The sentences of propositional language are composed, in part, of names or designators having denotative and connotative significance. The originally meaningless physical marks or sounds that are designators or names only when they have such significance cannot get their meaning either from the object designated or from our perception of the object designated. To understand this, we need only remember that the particular object named "poodle," "dog," "mammal," etc.—each name with a different denotative and connotative significance—is the same individual thing under all these designations, and that our perception of it as that individual thing remains the same as we

apply different designations to it. This leads us to the conclusion that, since it is not the object itself nor our perception of it that bestows meaning on the marks or sounds we use as designators, the only thing left that can bestow meaning is our conception or understanding of the objects we name. Hence, in contradistinction to percepts, concepts must be that whereby we know classes as such. If we did not have percepts, whereby we know individuals as such, we could not use proper names significantly to designate this or that individual thing. So, if we did not have concepts, whereby we know classes or kinds as such, we could not use common or general names significantly to designate the class or kind to which this and that individual belong as individually particular instances.

Before we take the next and last step in the argument, let us observe a certain parallelism between percepts and concepts. Percepts and concepts function as the *quo* of knowing: they are that in us whereby we know that which we know: in the one case, the individual as such; in the other case, the various classes or kinds to which the individual belongs. Percepts and concepts are also the *quo* of meaning (that whereby our words get their significance as designators): in the one case, our proper names; in the other, our common or general names. They could not be the second without being the first; that is, they could not be that by which we use words meaningfully as proper or as common names, if they were not, first of all, that by which we know that which we know—either individuals as such or the classes of which they are particular instances. The parallelism extends to one further point; whatever is a *quo* of knowing must be a representation or intention of the object known, existing in us; and, as a representation whereby we know that which we know, it must have an appropriate similitude to that which we know by means of it.

This brings us to the final step in the argument. We saw a little earlier that perceptual representation, in order to function as the *quo* of our knowing individuals as such, must have a mode of existence akin to the mode of existence of that which is known as an individual. If the latter exists materially under individuating conditions, so must the perceptual representation whereby we know it. Now if conceptual representations were also to exist in the same way that perceptual representations do (i.e., materially, as definite states of the central nervous system), they could not function as the *quo* of our knowing classes or kinds as such. Hence we must face the question: "How do classes or kinds—traditionally called 'universals'—exist?"

One answer to this question is that they exist as such quite apart from knowers. This answer carries with it the attribution to the existent universal of a non-physical or immaterial mode of existence. Another answer to this question is that they exist as that which is common to a number of individuals, all of which are, by virtue of their common characteristic, particular instances of the universal. But, according to this answer, the universal does not exist *actually* as a universal when it exists only as that which is common to so many individuals; and it does not then exist actually as a universal because it exists in matter, under individuating conditions. A third answer to this question is that universals exist, and now *actually* as universals, in the knower. They are, in the knower, that whereby he knows what is common to a number of individuals; or, in other words, the classes or kinds of which individuals are particular instances. But they could not, as the *quo* of knowing kinds or classes, be actual universals if they existed materially, for then they would exist under individuating conditions.

All these answers to the question about how universals exist make the same point, namely, that a material mode of existence, which entails individuating conditions, precludes the existence of *actual universals, either* in the knower *or* apart from the knower. We can see in passing that the nominalist who denies the existence of universals, in the knower as well as apart from the knower, must either be a materialist, as in the case of Hobbes, or must, as in the case of Berkeley and Hume, maintain that all knowledge is by means of perceptions or perceptual residues. Since Berkeley and Hume do not give a neurological account of perceptual knowledge or thought, they fail to explain why our perceptual representations cannot be universal (in their words, cannot be "abstract or general ideas").

Thus we reach the conclusion that conceptual representations, which function as the *quo* of our knowing classes or kinds, cannot exist in us in a material mode of existence. Perceptual representations, which function as the *quo* or our knowing individuals as such, do exist in us materially—as states of our nervous system. To deny that conceptual representations have a material mode of existence in us is to deny that they exist as states of our nervous system (or as brain patterns). This, in turn, is tantamount to saying that man's power of conceptual thought cannot be entirely explained in terms of neurological mechanisms. Or, in other words, the brain is not by itself the sufficient condition of conceptual thought. Some other factor—and, necessarily, an immaterial or non-physical factor—must be posited to explain conceptual thought.

Here, then, is the nerve of the direct argument in four propositions. (a) Our concepts are that in us whereby we apprehend the universal aspects of the things we think and talk about. (b) To perform that cognitive function, our concepts must be actual universals. (c) But for anything to be an actual universal, its mode of existence must be immaterial. (d) Hence, the existence in man of conceptual thought cannot be adequately explained by the action of a material organ, such as his brain, but requires the presence and operation of an immaterial factor.

There is one difficulty intrinsic to the argument, which must be faced. That which is known conceptually is always a universal, never an individual. But unless we affirm that universals actually exist, in the manner of Platonic ideas, we must recognize that the object of conceptual knowledge does not exist as such; namely, as an actual universal. Hence, we must say that existent individual things are known conceptually when they are known, not in their individuality, but in their universal aspects, i.e., in those respects in which they, as individuals, have common characteristics or traits. But if this is so, then it would appear that the mode of existence of the actual thing that is known is material, whereas the mode of existence of that whereby it is known in its universal aspects is immaterial; and hence, the principle of similitude between *quo* and *quod* would appear to be violated.

This difficulty is resolved, so far as it can be resolved, by the distinction that was made, in the course of the argument, between the potential and actual existence of the universal. It exists potentially in individual things insofar as they have common characteristics or traits, in virtue of which they belong to classes or kinds. It exists actually in the knower as that whereby he knows individual things in their universal aspects. There is a similitude here between the *quod* and the *quo* in that the one is potentially what the other is actually. In addition, it should be pointed out that the similitude between the *quod* and the *quo* of conceptual knowing is different from the similitude between the *quod* and *quo* of perceptual knowing; for in the latter case both exist actually in a material mode of existence, i.e., under individuating conditions. The acknowledgement of this difference between perceptual and conceptual knowing does not invalidate the argument. Failure to acknowledge this difference leads to the Platonic error of attributing actual existence to that which is known conceptually, by a false parallelism to the actual existence of that which is known perceptually. In addition, acknowledging this difference enables us to account for the fact that our conceptual knowledge extends to the non-sensible aspects of things that have a material mode of existence; for example, our concept of inertia or valence, or our concept of justice or of freedom, is that whereby we understand a universal aspect of things, but a universal of which particular instances cannot be directly perceived by means of our senses.

42. See *Summa Theologica*, I, 84, 7–8.

43. For relevant discussions of aphasia and agnosia, see *Cerebral Mechanisms in Behavior*, ed. by L. A. Jeffress, pp. 184 ff., and 259; J. M. Nielsen, *Agnosia, Apraxia, Aphasia*, 1936: esp. pp. 255–256; W. Penfield and L. Roberts, *Speech and Brain Mechanisms*, 1959: pp. 117, 127; K. Goldstein, *Language and Language Disturbances*,

1948: pp. 22–26, 56, 63; G. Humphrey, *Thinking*, 1951: pp. 236–256; *Brain Function*, Volume III, ed. by E. C. Carterette, 1966: pp. 67–92, 141–172.

44. For brain growth in the first two years of human life in relation to the appearance and development of human speech in the infant, see J. C. Lilly, *Man and Dolphin*, Appendix Two, pp. 278–286, and especially Table VI, p. 285.

45. See Warren S. McCulloch, *Embodiments of Mind*, pp. 46–66; also in *ibid.*, pp. 1–17, 72–156, 307–318; K. M. Sayre, *Recognition*, 1965; and "Human and Mechanical Recognition," in *The Modeling of Mind*, ed. by K. M. Sayre and F. J. Crosson, 1963: pp. 166–170; N. Sutherland, "Stimulus Analyzing Mechanisms," in *ibid.*, pp. 174–175; D. McKay, "Mindlike Behavior in Artefacts," in *ibid.*, pp. 228–229, 232–233, 237–241; O. G. Selfridge and U. Neisser, "Pattern Recognition by Machine," in *Computers and Thought*, ed. by E. A. Feigenbaum and J. Feldman, 1963: pp. 237–238, 250; L. Uhr and C. Vossler, "A Pattern–Recognition Program That Generates, Evaluates, and Adjusts Its Own Operators," in *ibid.*, pp. 251–252, 267–268; M. Minsky, "Steps Toward Artificial Intelligence," in *ibid.*, pp. 407–408, 411–413; W. Sluckin, *Minds and Machines*, 1960: pp. 143, 195. See also "The Relevance of Neurophysiology for Anthropology," in *Cross-Cultural Understanding*, ed. by F. S. C. Northrop and H. H. Livingston, 1964: pp. 339–355; and W. McCulloch, "A Historical Introduction to the Postulational Foundations of Experimental Epistemology," in *ibid.*, pp. 180–193.

46. Without concepts, we would only perceive, as animals do, the individual thing; and if we reacted to a number of individually differing things in the same way, we would not be cognizing what is common to them or knowing them in their universal aspects; we would only be reacting to them as functionally equivalent stimuli. By means of concepts, and only by means of concepts, we understand kinds or classes as such, entirely apart from perceived particulars and even though no particular instances exist. By means of percepts alone—*if that ever occurs in human cognition*—we would apprehend individual things without any understanding of them. This is the meaning of Kant's statement that percepts without concepts are blind, and concepts without percepts are empty. Hence, if we are right in thinking that men have and other animals lack the power of conceptual thought, then we must also assert a difference in kind between perceptual processes in animals which are blind in Kant's sense, and perceptual processes in man which are enlightened by concepts. Cf. Chapter 11, note 14, *supra*.

47. In my judgment, the correct interpretation of the phenomena is that given by Professor Heinrich Klüver in *Behavior Mechanisms in Monkeys*, pp. 4–10, 326–330, 344–349. According to Klüver, the experimental data shows that the animal can be trained, just as

machines can be built, to discriminate between equivalent and non-equivalent stimuli. Such discrimination—as, for example, between triangular and non-triangular shapes—does not show that the animal or the machine understands this individual stimulus as a particular instance of the class of triangular things. Neither the rat nor the machine understands triangularity as such. To understand the individual as a particular instance of a class is possible only if there is some understanding of the class—the universal—as such. But it is precisely an understanding of the class—the universal—as such that is the work of conceptual thought. Hence if animals had such understanding, they would have the power of conceptual thought; and if they had the power of conceptual thought, they would also have the power of propositional speech. As Locke pointed out, the lack of propositional speech on the part of animals is adequate reason for denying to them the power of conceptual thought (see *supra*, Chapter 11, notes 12 and 13). Hence, when animals, lacking this power, react in the same way to a number of individually differing instances of the same shape, their behavior indicates *only* the functional equivalence of the stimuli *and nothing more*. For the views of the computer technologists and neurologists on the reaction of machines to equivalent and non-equivalent stimuli, see the works cited in note 45 *supra*; and also M. A. Arbib, *Brains, Machines, and Mathematics*, 1964: pp. 33, 41–49, 108, 112–113, and A. Rapoport, "Technological Models of the Nervous System," in *The Modeling of Mind*, pp. 30 ff. The best statement that I have found in the current literature concerning the distinction between perceptual abstraction and concept-formation (between perceptual generalization and discrimination and the cognition of kinds or universals) is the one made by Aron Gurwitsch in the paper "On the Conceptual Consciousness" in *ibid.*, see pp. 199–205, esp. 202–204.

NOTES TO CHAPTER 13

1. See N. Chomsky, *Syntactic Structures*, 1957; P. Ziff, *Semantic Analysis*, 1960; Cf. W. S. McCulloch and W. M. Brodey, in *The Great Ideas Today*, 1966: pp. 296–297, 331–333.

2. *The Philosophical Works of Descartes*, ed. by E. S. Haldane and G. R. T. Ross, Volume I, p. 116.

3. *Ibid.*, pp. 116–117.

4. *Ibid.*, pp. 117–118.

5. *Ibid.*, pp. 116–117.

6. Pointing out that, other than man, there is no animal "however perfect and fortunately circumstanced it may be," that can utter

statements by which it makes known its thoughts, Descartes adds: "It is not the want of organs that brings this to pass, for it is evident that magpies and parrots are able to utter words just like ourselves, and yet they cannot speak as we do, that is, so as to give evidence that they think of what they say" (*ibid.*).

7. See John von Neumann, *The Computer and the Brain*, 1958: pp. 60–68; W. S. McCulloch and W. M. Brodey, in *The Great Ideas Today, 1966*, pp. 307–313; K. S. Lashley, in *Cerebral Mechanisms in Behavior*, p. 72; and P. Weiss, in *ibid.*, pp. 75–77, 89–91. Professor Weiss points out that the critical role played by brain chemistry tends to invalidate computer models of the brain's action, because the latter are entirely electronic in their functioning, whereas brain processes are electro-chemical. On the role played by RNA in the biochemistry of memory, see Karl H. Pribram, "Proposal for a Structural Pragmatism," in *Scientific Psychology*, pp. 433–438. All of these findings relate solely to information storage and retrieval —the retention of learned patterns of behavior—*not to memory as knowledge of the past.*

8. "The Problem of Serial Order in Behavior," in *Cerebral Mechanisms in Behavior*, pp. 112–118, 120–133; and cf. P. Weiss, in *ibid.*, p. 140–142.

9. See *Agnosia, Apraxia, Aphasia*, 2nd ed., 1965: p. 22. Cf. W. Penfield and L. Roberts, *Speech and Brain Mechanisms*, 1959: pp. 228–234.

10. See *Mind, Perception, and Science*, 1951: p. 30; and cf. *ibid.*, pp. 23–30, 40–41, 86. See also his "Speech and Thought, in *The Physical Basis of Mind*, 1957; Sir Charles Sherrington, *Man on his Nature*, 1941: Chapters IX, XI, XII; Roger W. Sperry, "Mind, Brain, and Humanist Values," in *New Views of the Nature of Man*, ed. by J. R. Platt, 1965: pp. 71–92. For involvement of the neurologists in the discussion of the identity hypothesis, see *Brain and Mind*, ed. by J. R. Smythies, pp. 54–55, 60; and *The Philosophy of Mind*, ed. by V. C. Chappell, pp. 107–108.

11. See K. S. Lashley, *op cit*, pp. 134–135; M. A. Arbib, *Brains, Machines and Mathematics*, pp. 47–48; W. McCulloch, *Embodiments of Mind*, Chapters 1, 7, 17, 19; W. C. Halstead, *Brain and Intelligence*, Chapters I, IV, XVII; J. C. Eccles, *The Neurophysiological Basis of Mind*, Chapter VIII.

12. *Science, Perception and Reality*, p. 30.

13. See McCulloch and Brodey, in *The Great Ideas Today, 1966*, p. 330.

14. See *Man and Dolphin*, pp. 255–278.

15. See *ibid.*, Chapters 1 and 12, esp. p. 204 ff.

16. See the "second objection and reply" in Chapter 12, *supra*, pp. 224.

NOTES TO CHAPTER 14

1. See A. M. Turing, "Computing Machinery and Intelligence," in *Computers and Thought*, ed. by E. A. Feigenbaum and J. Feldman, 1963: pp. 30–35; P. Armer, "Attitudes Toward Intelligent Machines," in *ibid.*, pp. 392–393; M. Minsky, "Steps Toward Artificial Intelligence," in *ibid.*, p. 407; M. Scriven, "The Mechanical Concept of Mind," in *The Modeling of Mind*, ed. by K. M. Sayre and F. J. Crosson, 1963: pp. 243, 248–249; D. A. Bell, *Intelligent Machines*, 1962: pp. 61–67, 88–90. Many writers who dismiss programmed computers as incomparable with human minds fail to take cognizance of the basic distinction between a programmed computer and a random network robot with no more than "infant" programming: see, for example, Jonathan Cohn, "Can There Be Artificial Minds?" in *Analysis*, Volume 16, No. 2, N.S. No. 50, pp. 36–41. With regard to the conception of infant programming see Turing, *op. cit.*, pp. 31–32.

2. See John von Neumann, *The Computer and the Brain*, pp. 46–50; M. Scriven, *op. cit.*, pp. 248–249; J. J. C. Smart, *Philosophy and Scientific Realism*, pp. 107–111.

3. See F. Crosson and K. Sayre, "Modeling: Simulation and Replication," in *The Modeling of Mind*, pp. 4, 13, 18–23; E. A. Feigenbaum and J. Feldman, in *Computers and Thought*, pp. 269–270; P. Armer, in *ibid.*, pp. 397–398; M. Taube, *Computers and Common Sense*, 1961: pp. 72, 75–76. For criticisms by neurologists and others of the computer technologists' efforts to replicate brain processes, see von Neumann, *op. cit.*, pp. 41, 81–82; M. A. Arbib, *Brains, Machines, and Mathematics*, pp. 5–7, 93–117; Lord Russell Brain, *Mind, Perception, and Science*, p. 86; P. Weiss, in *Cerebral Mechanisms and Intelligence*, pp. 75–79, 89–91, 140; C. J. Herrick, *The Evolution of Human Nature*, pp. 431–448; W. H. Thorpe, *Learning and Instinct in Animals*, pp. 175–176; cf. his *Science, Man and Morals*, p. 51; E. B. Hunt, *Concept Learning*, pp. 212–218. In this connection see also Feigl's comment on the lack of proteins in Scriven's "androids," in *Minnesota Studies in the Philosophy of Science*, Volume II, p. 451; and cf. p. 423.

4. See W. Sluckin, *Minds and Machines*, revised edition, 1960: pp. 159, 174–177; D. A. Bell, *op. cit.*, 1962: pp. 61–67, 88–90; M. Taube, *op. cit.*, pp. 47–49; Herbert A. Simon, in *Control of the Mind*, ed. by S. M. Farber and R. H. L. Wilson, pp. 222–231, and cf. *ibid.*,

pp. 282–285; P. Ziff, "The Feelings of Robots," in *Minds and Machines*, ed. by A. R. Anderson, pp. 98–103; J. J. C. Smart, "Professor Ziff on Robots," in *ibid.*, pp. 104–105; Ninian Smart, "Robots Incorporated," in *ibid.*, pp. 106–108; A. Newell, J. C. Shaw, and H. A. Simon, "Chess-Playing Programs and the Problem of Complexity," in *Computers and Thought*, pp. 39–70; H. Gelernter, "Realization of a Geometry-Theorem Proving Machine," in *ibid.*, pp. 158–159; A. Newell and H. A. Simon, "GPS, A Program That Simulates Human Thought," in *ibid.*, pp. 279, 292–293; E. A. Feigenbaum, "The Simulation of Verbal Learning Behavior," in *ibid.*, pp. 297–309; M. Minsky, "Steps Toward Artificial Intelligence," in *ibid.*, pp. 425, 435, 446–450; and editorial summaries in *ibid.*, on pp. 269–270, 272–273, 275–276. See also A. Hormann, "Gaku: An Artificial Student," in *Behavioral Science*, Volume 10, No. 1, January, 1965, pp. 88–107.

5. See M. Taube, *op. cit.*, *passim*, esp. pp. 60, 120. Extravagant claims are made by W. McCulloch, *Embodiments of Mind*, 1965: *passim*; J. J. C. Smart, *Philosophy and Scientific Realism*, 1963: pp. 111–116, 119–125; M. Scriven, "The Mechanical Concept of Mind," in *The Modeling of Mind*, pp. 243–254; "The Complete Robot: A Prolegomena to Androidology," in *Dimensions of Mind*, pp. 118–142; Hilary Putnam, "Minds and Machines," in *ibid.*, pp. 148–179; D. McKay, "Mindlike Behavior in Artefacts," in *The Modeling of Mind*, pp. 225–241, "From Mechanism to Mind," in *Brain and Mind*, p. 190; A. Newell and H. A. Simon, *op. cit.*, p. 293; E. A. Feigenbaum, *op. cit.*, p. 308; M. Minsky, *op. cit.*, p. 447; Much more moderate claims, together with confessions of present inadequacies or of the slightness of present achievements are to be found in K. M. Sayre, "Human and Mechanical Recognition," in *The Modeling of Mind*, pp. 157–170; N. Sutherland, "Stimulus Analyzing Mechanisms," in *ibid.*, pp. 171–197; J. Lucas, "Minds, Machines and Gödel," in *ibid.*, pp. 255–271; M. Minsky, *op. cit.*, pp. 406, 408; see also editorial summaries in *Computers and Thought*, pp. 7–8, 275–276; E. B. Hunt and C. I. Hovland, "Programming a Model of Human Concept Formulation," in *ibid.*, pp. 319–325; J. O. Wisdom, "Mentality in Machines," in *Proceedings of the Aristotelian Society*, Supplementary Volume XXVI, 1952, p. 26.

A delightful discussion of these claims and counter-claims will be found in *The New Yorker*, June 11, 1966, Notes and Comments, pp. 27–28. It quotes H. A. Simon as saying several years ago that "there are now in the world machines that think, that learn, and that create. Moreover, their ability to do these things is going to increase rapidly until—in a visible future—the range of problems they can handle will be co-extensive with the range to which the human mind can be applied." Against this, it cites Professor H. L. Dreyfus of M.I.T. as saying in 1966 that computers cannot do these things and won't do them. Dreyfus, according to *The New Yorker*, compared the pertinacity and extravagant claims of the computer technologists to that of the alchemists. "By defining 'progress' as displacement toward the ultimate goal, today's alchemists, the cognitive-simulation workers, obscure the prospects for artificial intelligence. According to this definition, Dreyfus points out, the first man to climb a tree could claim progress toward flight to the moon."

6. See W. Sluckin, *op. cit.*, p. 129; J. von Neumann, *op. cit.*, pp. 46–50; W. S. McCulloch, *Embodiments of Mind*, pp. 72–87.

7. See A. N. Turing, *op. cit.*, pp. 19–20; A. Newell and H. A. Simon, *op. cit.*, pp. 2–3; P. Armer, *op. cit.*, pp. 390–393; M. Minsky, *op. cit.*, pp. 407–408, 425, 446–450; W. Sluckin, *op. cit.*, pp. 196–201; 215–216; D. A. Bell, *op. cit.*, p. 67; D. McKay, "From Mechanism to Mind," in *Brain and Mind*, pp. 163–191; and cf. *ibid.*, pp. 193–195, 199–200.

8. See A. N. Turing, *op. cit.*, pp. 11–12, 20, 21–29, 30–35; and for a characterization of Turing and his work, see Jeremy Bernstein, *The Analytical Engine*, 1963: pp. 96–103.

9. For espousal of the hypothesis and prediction developed in terms of Turing machines, see Hilary Putnam, *op. cit.*, pp. 148–158, 175–176; M. Scriven, Postscript to "The Mechanical Concept of Mind," in *The Modeling of Mind*, pp. 253–254; J. J. C. Smart, *op. cit.*, pp. 128–130. For adverse comments on claims made for Turing machines, see J. Lucas, *op. cit.*, pp. 270–271; and K. Gunderson, "The Imitation Game," in *Minds and Machines*, pp. 62–64, 69–71.

With regard to the currently debated problem concerning the possibility that a machine can either be programmed to use or can, by learning, acquire the use of a natural language, such as English, see J. Pfeiffer, *The Thinking Machine*, 1962: pp. 147–150; M. Taube, *op. cit.*, Chapters 3 and 5; B. F. Green, A. K. Wolff, N. Chomsky, and K. Laughery, "Baseball: An Automatic Question Answerer," in *Computers and Thought*, p. 207, 214–216; R. K. Lindsay, "Inferential Memory as the Basis of Machines Which Understand Natural Language," in *ibid.*, pp. 217–220, 223–224, 233; M. Minsky, "Steps Toward Artificial Intelligence," in *ibid.*, pp. 412–413; editorial comment, in *ibid.*, p. 8; Hilary Putnam, in *Dimensions of Mind*, pp. 173–175. See also Jan Srzednicki, "Could Machines Talk?" in *Analysis*, Vol. 22, No. 5, N.S. No. 89, April, 1962, pp. 113–117. This last is offered as a demonstration that they cannot be programmed to talk, using a natural language such as English. But even if the demonstration is sound, that leaves open the question whether a Turing machine, with only infant programming, could learn to use English. Turing and his confreres think that it can be mathematically shown to be, *in principle*, possible.

10. For statements of the materialist position, as that is now expressed with faith in the prospects for critical advances in neurophysiology and in computer technology, see W. Sluckin, *op. cit.*, pp. 230–232; J. J. C. Smart, *Philosophy and Scientific Realism*, pp. 94–130 *passim*; M. Scriven, Postscript to "The Mechanical Concept of Mind," in *The Modeling of Mind*, pp. 253–254; cf. Addendum to *ibid.*, in *Minds and Machines*, p. 42; P. Armer, *op. cit.*, p. 399; M. Minsky, *op. cit.*, p. 449; W. Sellars, *Science, Perception and Reality*, pp. 69–71; S. Toulmin, reviewing Arthur Koestler's *Act of Creation*, in *Encounter*, Volume XXIII, No. 1, July, 1964, pp. 69–70.

NOTES TO CHAPTER 15

1. In my judgment, being able to play the Turing game successfully is an all-or-none affair. A robot either passes the conversational test or fails. Among human conversationalists, some are more articulate, more versatile, wittier, cleverer, more resourceful, and so on. They can be ranked on a scale of degrees. So too, perhaps, there may be, among future generations of Turing machines, manifestations of lower and higer degrees of conversational ability. But between the first robot that manifests such an ability to the slightest degree (i.e., a degree just sufficient to pass the conversational test) and all earlier machines that do not manifest any conversational ability whatsoever, there is a difference in kind, not of degree.

It may be thought, however, that before that happens, improvements in machine intelligence may be made that will give the technologist the impression that he will eventually succeed in building a Turing machine that can pass the conversational test. With regard to this point, I would like to quote the comments of a correspondent:

> "If in 1980 a machine is built that can perform all the feats of today's machines, plus the added feat of paraphrasing English sentences, it would rank higher on the scale of accomplishment than today's machines. All these attempts would still score zero in Turing's game. But it is plain that, with a more advanced machine at hand, there is more hope for achieving the minimum passing score in the future than there would be with less advanced machines at hand. Thus we must take into account the possibility of building machines that are ever more advanced on the scale of how much they accomplish, but all of which fail decisively on the conversational test. Under these circumstances, a reasonable person could still argue that the probability of eventual success in Turing's game has increased in spite of every trial's still being a failure."

If one concedes that, what effect does it have on the statement that, with repeated trials and failures, the relative truth of the materialist hypothesis diminishes and the relative truth of the immaterialist hypothesis correspondingly increases? My answer to this question is contrary to the one that my correspondent had in my mind. He thought that one would have to say that, as the probability of eventual success in the Turing test increased, we would become more and more assured of the truth of the materialist hypothesis. The opposite seems to me to be the case. If, with technological advances being made, it becomes more and more probable that a Turing machine will eventually be built, successive failures to build a machine that can pass the conversational test tend to weaken our confidence that one will ever be produced. The more probable it is that something can happen, the more disappointing is its failure to happen.

NOTES TO CHAPTER 16

1. The distinction made here between reasons of expediency and reasons of principle needs a word of further explanation. I have used the phrase "reasons of expediency" as it is often used in everyday speech to cover those *ad hoc* justifications of action that recommend the action solely on the ground that it serves the purpose at hand. It suits us to treat our pets as if they were persons, while slaughtering other animals to satisfy our wants. The justification of these opposite lines of conduct is *ad hoc*: each serves a different purpose. To say this and no more is to offer a reason of expediency. In contrast, if I could establish, *as a matter of fact*, that my household pet differs in kind from the pigs and steers that are butchered for my table; and if, in addition, I could defend the *principle* that different kinds of treatment are appropriate to things that differ in kind, then I could justify my opposite lines of conduct in a fashion that is not *ad hoc* and that does not appeal merely to the purpose that the action serves.

I have used the phrase "reasons of principle" for those justifications of conduct that appeal to antecedent facts and principles, not merely to consequences (i.e., purposes to be served). Reasons of principle, as the foregoing example indicates, never consist of principles alone, but always of principles combined with assertions of fact; and the principles involved are always normative rules or prescriptions (i.e., statements about what ought or ought not be done). I have called such statements principles in order to distinguish them from the statements of fact with which we associate the given reasons for action, not in order to elevate them to the level of indubitable or incorrigible truth. This use of the word "principle" conforms to everyday usage. When we say, in view of a person's conduct or character, that he is a "man of principle," or when we say that "it is not the money, but the principle that matters," the kind of principles that we have in mind are moral principles, that is, normative or prescriptive statements about what ought or ought not to be done or sought. In line with this use of words, when I refer to principled conduct, I mean conduct that is justified by reasons of principle (reasoning that appeals to a normative principle in conjunction with an assertion of fact); and when I refer to unprincipled conduct, I mean conduct that is justified only by *ad hoc* reasons of expediency (by reference only to the purpose the conduct serves or the desirable consequences that one expects from it).

If no empirical evidence were available that could help us to decide whether human and non-human animals differ in kind or only in degree, men might still make *ad hoc* differentiations that suited their purposes. In an essay entitled "Slaves and Machines" (in *Analysis*, Volume 22, No. 5, N.S. No. 89, April, 1962, pp. 118–120), Amelie O. Rorty argues that that is all they can ever do. In her view, when we call some entity a slave, a brute animal, or a machine, the designation merely expresses how we *want* to treat the entity so designated—specifically, *not* as a man or a person. We assert to be a matter of fact that which we wish to believe, because the belief in question is the basis for our acting in a certain way, and what is ultimately decisive is the way in which we want to act toward this or that entity. Rorty's argument proceeds without any regard for the logic involved in the process of determining whether two things differ in degree or in kind, and without any cognizance of the wealth of empirical evidence that is now available to decide how men differ from other things. It is historically true, of course, that men have in the past treated other men *as if* they were not different in kind from brute animals or from inanimate machines; in many parts of the world, they still do so today. There is nothing here to condemn, according to Rorty; and she would be right if there were no facts to show that all men are the same in kind, by virtue of commonly possessing the trait (the power of conceptual thought) which makes them different in kind from other animals and from any machines that now exist.

Other writers make the same mistake that Rorty does—the mistake of thinking that the decision whether an entity under consideration (be it a man or a machine) is a person or a thing depends entirely on how we act with respect to it, how we wish to treat it, or how we talk about it. This puts the cart before the horse and totally ignores the possibility that the question can be decided entirely by an appeal to observed behavioral facts. See Peter T. Manicas, "Men, Machines, Materialism, and Morality," in *Philosophy and Phenomenological Research*, Volume XXVII, No. 2, December, 1966, pp. 238–246; Hilary Putnam, "Robots: Machines or Artificially Created Life?" in *Philosophy of Mind*, ed. by Stuart Hampshire, 1966; and Edward Shils, "The Sanctity of Life," in *Encounter*, Volume XXVIII, No. 1, January, 1967, pp. 39–49. If a robot were to succeed in passing the Turing test, or to manifest a mind of its own in answering questions and carrying on a conversation, then the immaterialist hypothesis would be falsified. In that case, the refusal to call the robot a person while still calling men persons would have no justification in fact and could only be interpreted as an expression of self-serving bias or discrimination. If having the power of conceptual thought were the only factual criterion of being a person, then the conversational robot would be no less a person than a man is. But if, as I will argue in Chapter 17, the presence of an immaterial factor is indispensable to being a person, because indispensable to freedom of choice, then should we find that both men and robots have the power of conceptual thought, but that neither have freedom of choice because neither have the immaterial or non-physical power requisite for such freedom, then we must, in accordance with the facts, concede that neither men nor conversational robots are persons, and that there is nothing wrong with treating them as things.

2. What is called the naturalistic fallacy in moral reasoning or argumentation consists in attempting to draw normative conclusions from assertions of fact. I commit this fallacy if the only grounds or reasons that I offer for my recommendation that this or that ought or ought not to be done consist of the views I hold concerning the nature of things, i.e., assertions I make concerning the way things are. The nature of things—the way things are—does not by itself validly support any normative conclusions, i.e., any statements about what ought or ought not to be done. I do not commit the fallacy of supposing that the nature of things leads to moral conclusions when I employ moral principles in my reasoning and combine these moral principles with statements of fact about the nature of things (i.e., when I combine an ought-premise with an is-premise to arrive at an ought-conclusion). See my discussion of this point in *The Conditions of Philosophy*, pp. 188–195.

It is a misunderstanding of the naturalist fallacy to hold that facts have no normative consequences at all. While it is true that facts by themselves (unaccompanied by appeal to normative principles) do not have normative consequences, they do have such consequences when they are subsumed under normative rules; e.g., the fact that A ignored a red light leads to a normative judgment about A's driving only when it is subsumed under the rule that red lights ought to be heeded by drivers. As Professor Smart points out, "no account of scientific facts about the world can *by themselves* determine what we should do. Some philosophers and scientists have tried to deduce ultimate ethical precepts from the conclusions of evolutionary biology . . . Scientific facts *alone* cannot give us a precept. This is not to say that scientific facts are not of the greatest importance for ethics. It is simply that scientific facts do not *by themselves* determine any ethical system" (*Philosophy and Scientific Realism*, p. 154; italics added). In the context of this passage, Professor Smart also writes: "What ethical precepts we recommend depends in the last analysis on what we *want*" (italics his). The truth of this statement depends in the last analysis on what the writer means by "wants." It is false if he means merely the purpose to be served in a particular case by a particular action; for then, as indicated in note 1, *supra*, the recommendation that this or that line of conduct be pursued to serve our needs is not an ethical, or normative, precept at all. When Professor Smart himself enunciates the ethical precept that those who give or receive arguments, as scientists in fact do, ought to be respected as persons (see *ibid.*, p. 155), that ought-statement does not depend on whether, in a particular case, we *want* to achieve a certain result or have a certain purpose in mind.

3. Consider the person who maintains that it makes no practical difference whether man differs from other things only in degree or in kind as well, *because*, without any reference to the facts of the matter, we can justify any line of conduct that we wish to pursue in our treatment of men, on the one hand, and of animals and machines, on the other. If we examine this attitude (it is one that I have met not only in scientists but also in professors of law and of political science), we find that it rests on two errors: (1) the error of supposing that because facts *by themselves* do not support normative recommendations, they have no relevance whatsoever to normative problems; and (2) the error of supposing that, given the same state of facts, quite opposite practical policies or courses of action can be justified by reference to the purpose at hand. Such *ad hoc* justification shifts from time to time, and from case to case, as our purposes change. No consistency is to be expected in our policies. We can excuse ourselves for doing what we condemn in others on the ground that, even though the facts are the same in both cases, our conduct served the purpose of the moment, whereas the conduct of others worked in the opposite way so far as we were concerned. But if the justification of conduct requires us to subsume the facts of the case under a normative principle that applies to all cases without regard to who the parties are and what their momentary purposes may be, then opposite courses of conduct can be justified only by appealing to opposite normative principles; and then the question of which of the conflicting principles is the right one must be faced. When our conduct is *principled*, we must be prepared to defend the soundness of the principles on which we act and if we act on a certain principle in one case, we cannot justify acting in an opposite way in another case in which the facts are the same and the same principle applies. But when our conduct is *unprincipled*, we may concoct a "justification" or explanation of our conduct, if one is called for, and we seldom find insuperable difficulties in the way of rationalizing opposite policies or courses of action, even when the facts are the same in the cases in which, to serve our purposes, we act in opposite ways.

In this connection, the following example of inconsistency is instructive. In his "Apology for Raimond de Sebonde," Montaigne claims that the observable facts of human and animal behavior lead to the conclusion that animals are man's equals, if not superiors. Nevertheless, in his essay "Of Cruelty," he criticizes those tribes or cultures which admit animals to human status and associate with them on the same plane of conduct that applies to human beings (see *Essays of Montaigne*, trans. by Charles Cotton, revised by W. C. Hazlett: Volume 4, pp. 163–166). Spinoza, on the other hand, maintains, as a matter of fact, that men are rational and brutes are not, and therefore they differ in kind; accordingly, he says that "the law against killing animals is based upon an empty superstition and womanish tenderness rather than upon sound reason. A proper regard, indeed, to one's own profit teaches us to unite in friendship with men, and not with brutes, nor with things whose nature is different from human nature" (*Ethics*, Part IV, Prop. 37, Scholium 1). Cf. Kant's exposition of the thesis that it is wrong to treat men and not wrong to treat other animals merely as means: *Critique of Practical Reason and Other Works on Ethics*, trans. by T. K. Abbott, 6th ed., pp. 46–53; *Critique of Teleological Judgment*, trans. by J. C. Meredeth, pp. 99–100.

NOTES TO CHAPTER 17

1. See *Man and Dolphin*, Chapters 1 and 12. Cf. Lilly's more recent book: *The Mind of the Dolphin: A Nonhuman Intelligence*, 1967.
2. *Ibid.*, pp. 211–212. Considering Dr. Lilly's prediction that, if dolphins and humans engage in conversation and thus appear to share a common intellectual power, some groups of men will probably advocate that we treat them as we treat human beings, a reader of this book in manuscript suggested to me that the opposite result might also occur. It is just as likely, he wrote, that some group of men "will take the view that a large part of the human race is *no better* than dophins, and should therefore cease to have the rights currently accorded to human beings. In effect, this was the argument of the Germans with respect to Poles and Jews. Without denying that the Poles and Jews were biologically human, the Nazis maintained that they were in other respects sub-human, and more like animals or things. In short, the effect of the discovery that men do not differ in kind from animals is just as likely to promote malevolence toward some human groups as benevolence toward dolphins or other animals that are found not to differ in kind from men."

   I have nothing to say about the relative probability of Dr. Lilly's prediction or my friend's prediction of the actual consequences that might follow from the discovery that men and dolphins do not differ in kind. I have no way of estimating which guess is shrewder or more likely to be true. When, in this chapter I consider the practical consequences of man's being different in kind from other animals—or, in the case of the dolphins, perhaps the same in kind —I am concerned *only with what ought or ought not to be the result of one or another state of facts, not with predictions of what might or might not actually result.* In other words, by *practical* consequences, I mean *normative consequences*—consequences in the form of the normative conclusions that we reach in the light of the facts as ascertained, not consequences in the form of actions taken, regardless of whether or not they can be justified in the light of the facts and sound normative principles (see *supra*, Chapter 16, notes 1 and 2).

My friend obviously understood Dr. Lilly to be doing no more than making a prediction. I understood him to be considering the legal and ethical problem that the human race will have to face if and when dolphins show themselves to have the power of conceptual thought. I, therefore, read him as taking the position that if and when it is ascertained, as a matter of fact, that dolphins and men do not differ psychologically in kind, justice will require us to treat dolphins as persons and accord to them the same rights that we accord to men as persons. The action predicted by my friend would not be justified by the facts as ascertained, if they were subsumed under the normative principle that all persons (i.e., all living organisms that have the power of conceptual thought *in any degree*) ought to be treated in the same way—as persons, not as things. Nazi policies with regard to Poles and Jews, or similar policies with regard to Negroes, which have longed prevailed and are still not eradicated, cannot be justified by the facts (that all human beings have the power of conceptual thought to some degree, and that every human being, even the least, therefore differs psychologically from the most intelligent animal) when those facts are subsumed under the correct normative principle that, as a matter of right or justice, all human beings ought to be treated in the same way (as persons rather than as things), and accorded the rights of persons. If the facts were otherwise—if men and other animals differ only in degree, and if some men are superior to other men in degree, as much as if not more than some men are to some animals—then Nazi policies in the treatment of Poles and Jews, or segregationist policies in the treatment of Negroes, would not be, *prima facie*, wrong as a matter of principle; the only question to be determined would be the question of fact about the inferiority of Jews or Poles to Germans, or Negroes to white men.

3. *Op. cit.*, in *The Modeling of Mind*, p. 254.

4. *Ibid.* Cf Hilary Putnam, "Minds and Machines," in *Dimensions of Mind*, pp. 175–176; Donald M. McKay, "From Mechanism to Mind," in *Brain and Mind*, pp. 180–190.

5. *Science, Perception and Reality*, pp. 39–40.

6. For Professor Smart's views, see *Philosophy and Scientific Realism*, pp. 153–154; and cf. *ibid.*, pp. 93–105, 111–116, 119–125. For Professor Sellars' views, see *Science, Perception and Reality*, pp. 6, 15–17, 30–34.

7. *Philosophy and Scientific Realism*, p. 155.

8. In a brilliant essay, Jacques Maritain outlines the importance of the question of man's difference for the conception of human equality, showing how divergent conceptions of the equality of men stem from divergent views of man as a species and how they give rise to divergent normative recommendations (see "Human Equality," in *Ransoming the Time*, 1941: pp. 1–32). Among its other current projects, the Institute for Philosophical Research is engaged in the dialectical clarification of the idea of equality in Western thought. Even at this early stage of the work, it has become clear that the central and controlling issue in the whole discussion is constituted by conflicting views about the specific equality of men as persons in relation to all the inequalities that arise from their individual differences, and that these views are resolvable into conflicting views of the difference of man.

9. *Critique of Practical Reason and Other Works on Ethics*, trans. by T. K. Abbott, 6th ed., p. 180. Cf. *ibid.*, pp. 46–53; and *Critique of Teleological Judgment*, trans. by J. C. Meredith, pp. 99–100. The Christian conception of personality, like Kant's, involves an element of immateriality. The Christian dogma that man is made in the image of God, Who is pre-eminently a person, attributes personality to man as reflecting the divine being in this respect, i.e., immateriality.

10. I have treated these problems at greater length in another book of much earlier date (see *A Dialectic of Morals*, 1941, Chapter IV, esp. pp. 58–59). While I would revise what is there said in many respects were I to address myself anew to the problems of moral philosophy, as I hope to do in a book I am now working on, the points made there would remain essentially unchanged, at least so far as they bear on the relevance to morality of the way that man differs from other animals.

11. See Robert Ardrey, *The Territorial Imperative*, 1966; and also his *African Genesis*, 1961. Both books are engaging popularizations of the findings of ethology, full of fascinating stories of animal behavior; but both are also flagrant examples of special pleading for the questionable thesis that instinct governs human life exactly as it does animal life. The truth of that thesis depends upon how man differs from other animals; if man differs even superficially in kind from other animals, it is in important respects false; if man

differs radically, it is wholly false. In his zeal to explain human behavior and human life in terms of animal instincts, Ardrey does not pause to consider the facts bearing on the question of how man differs. He assumes the truth of the answer that suits his *ad hoc* rhetoric. The fact that books of this sort are dismissed for what they are by the scientific community does not prevent them from bemusing and misleading the laymen who read them for the enjoyable animal stories they contain and uncritically swallow the thesis along with the stories.

12. *Op. cit.*, trans. by J. Riviere, 1930: p. 63. Cf. Chapter III, *passim.*

13. *The Future of an Illusion*, trans. by W. D. Ronson-Scott, 1928: p. 93.

14. Freud's attribution of an intellectual power to man that is not possessed to any degree by other animals is all of one piece with his theory of distinctively human erotic love, as contrasted with the sexuality of other animals, a sexuality that is devoid of love even when it involves the instinctive inhibition of aggressive behavior and so gives the *appearance* of tenderness and benevolence. Nevertheless, for Freud every form of human love is erotic, either overtly sexual or a sublimation of sexuality. But if the human intellect has the autonomy that it would have to have in order to control the instincts and to sublimate them, and if that, in turn, depends on the intellect's transcendence of physical causality, then, contrary to Freud's theory of love, the non-erotic forms of human love (such as the *amor intellectualis dei* of Spinoza, the appetitive character of which takes its special form from intellectual cognition rather than from sense-perception) would be explicable without reference to sex, sensuality, or sublimation.

15. *On Aggression*, pp. 238 ff. Though Lorenz discusses free will in relation to "the laws of natural causation" governing human and animal behavior, he shows little or no understanding of free choice (see *ibid.*, Chapter 12, esp. pp. 225, 228–229, 231–232). An excellent critical review of the book by S. A. Barnett points out the illicit use that Lorenz makes of superficial analogies between human and animal behavior, and also the inconsistencies into which he falls by his effort to plead a case beyond what the acknowleged facts will support (see *Scientific American*, Volume 216, No. 2, February, 1967, *ibid.*, pp. 135–137).

16. *Ibid.*, p. 254. Cf. *ibid.*, pp. 240–254.

17. See *ibid.*, Chapter 7, esp. p. 110.

18. *Ibid.*, p. 248. In another place, Lorenz refers to "the functions of reason and moral responsibility which first came into the world with man and which, provided he does not blindly and arrogantly

deny the existence of his animal inheritance, give him the power to control it" (*ibid.*, p. 215).

19. *Ibid.*, p. 247.

20. See especially Lorenz' concluding chapter, "Avowal of Optimism," in *ibid.*, pp. 275 ff.

NOTES TO CHAPTER 18

1. See *Honest to God*, 1963: esp. Chapter 2, "The End of Theism"; and *The New Reformation*, 1965: esp. Appendix II, "Can a Truly Contemporary Person *Not* Be an Atheist?"

2. For a fair sample of the bourgeoning literature of the "new theology," see T. J. J. Altizer and W. Hamilton, *Radical Theology and the Death of God*, 1966; T. J. J. Altizer, *The Gospel of Christian Atheism*, 1966; W. Hamilton, *The New Essence of Christianity*, 1966; G. Vahanian, *No Other God*, 1966; *The Death of God*, 1957; P. Van Buren, *The Secular Meaning of the Gospel*, 1953; H. Cox, *The Secular City*, 1965; *New Theology*, ed. by M. E. Marty and D. G. Peerman, Nos. 1, 2, 3, and 4, 1964–1967; K. Hamilton, *God is Dead, The Anatomy of a Slogan*, 1966; Austin Farrer, *God Is Not Dead*, 1966; D. E. Jenkins, *Guide to the Debate About God*, 1966; *The Secular City Debate*, ed. by D. Callahan, 1966; Leslie Dewart, *The Future of Belief*, 1966.

   If all the oratory, repetition, loose-talk, double-talk, and plain nonsense were removed from the thousands of pages cited above, they could be boiled down to less than a hundred pages of solid substance. The puzzling question, not satisfactorily answered, is why these "new theologians," who implicitly and inconsistently espouse a completely naturalistic materialism, continue to call themselves theologians and persist in trying to give some meaning to the term "God." Better the honest if also somewhat rhetorical atheism of Nietzsche, who coined the phrase "death of God," and of Feuerbach, whose *Essence of Christianity* replaced theology with anthropology and initiated the "religion of humanism."

   The works cited above would be better described as representing the death of theology. However, there is a lively contemporary debate going on between theists and atheists that shows how far from dead theology is. See, for example, Martin Buber, *Eclipse of God*, 1952; J. Lacroix, *The Meaning of Modern Atheism*, 1965; J. C. Murray, *The Problem of God*, 1964; E. L. Mascall, *The Secularization of Christianity*, 1965; W. Earle, J. M. Edie, and J. Wild, *Christianity and Existentialism*, 1963; *New Essays in Philosophical Theology*, ed. by A. Flew and A. MacIntyre, 1965; *The Meaning of the Death of God*, ed. by Bernard Murchland, 1967.

3. See Étienne Gilson, *Reason and Revelation in the Middle Ages*, 1938, esp. Chapter 1.

4. See *ibid.*, Chapter 3. See also Aquinas, *Summa Theologica*, Part I, Q. 1, AA. 1–2, 5–6, 8.

5. See "Vatican Council II, Declaration on Religious Freedom," #2, p. 269, in *The Documents of Vatican II*, 1966.

6. See encyclical of Pius XII, *Humani Generis*, no. 36, 1950: pp. 16–17.

7. See "Vatican Council II, *Constitution of the Church in the Modern World*," #14, p. 212 in *op. cit.*

8. See in *ibid.*, #17, p. 214.

9. See Bernard Ryan, *The Evolution of Man*, 1965: pp. 138–139, 151–156; P. Schoonenberg, *God's World in the Making*, 1964: Chapter 2; J. Donceel, "Teilhard de Chardin," in *Thought*, Volume XL, No. 158, 1965: esp. pp. 383–389. Cf. David Lack, *Evolutionary Theory and Christian Belief*, 1961. Two contemporary Protestant writers claim to see no conflict between a completely naturalistic materialism, on the one hand, and Christian doctrines about the spirituality of man and the immortality of the soul, on the other: see C. W. Kegley, "Problems in the Contemporary Understanding of Man," in *Lutheran World*, Volume XII, No. 1, 1965: pp. 28–33; and D. M. McKay, "From Mechanism to Mind," in *Brain and Mind*, pp. 186–190. Commenting on McKay's essay, John Beloff writes: "It would indeed be a presumption on the part of an agnostic like myself to challenge McKay on points of Christian doctrine or biblical exegesis. If he assures me that Christianity is quite compatible with the truth of Mechanism or Materialism, I am quite happy to take his word for it but he must not complain if he has increased my suspicion that Christianity (at least as professed by someone at McKay's level of sophistication) is compatible with anything at all" (in *ibid.*, pp. 194–195).

10. See P. Weiss, *Nature and Man*, 1947; *Man's Freedom*, 1950; M. Capek, "The Doctrine of Necessity Re-Examined," in *The Review of Metaphysics*, Volume V, No. 1, September, 1951; C. Hartshorne, "Causal Necessities: An Alternative to Hume," in *The Philosophical Review*, Volume LXIII, No. 3, October, 1954; "Freedom Requires Indeterminism and Universal Causality," in *The Journal of Philosophy*, Volume LV, No. 19, September, 1958. For a critical summary of the position taken by these three writers, see *The Idea of Freedom*, Volume II, 1961: pp. 362–368; and cf. *ibid.*, pp. 640–642.

11. Between 1953 and 1961, the Institute for Philosophical Research carried on an extensive study of the discussion of freedom in the tradition of Western thought, in the course of which it undertook

to reconstruct and clarify the controversy concerning the freedom of the will. The Institute's findings and formulations were published in the two volumes of *The Idea of Freedom*, Volume I in 1958, Volume II, in 1961. It is in the light of the work done by the Institute that I here report the finding that, with few exceptions, the philosophers who affirm the freedom of the will understand free choice in terms of a mode of causality that is non-physical: in their view, the denial of a non-physical or immaterial factor in the constitution of man would entail a denial of free choice. This is confirmed by the correlative finding that the philosophers who deny free will do so on the ground that the only mode of causality that is operative in man as well as in the rest of nature is one that has its model in the action and reaction of bodies: for them as well as for their opponents, to affirm mechanism and materialism in the case of man is to deny what has come to be called the "contra-causal" freedom of the will (where "contra-causal" means not the absence of causality, but the presence of a mode of causality that is not found in the actions and reactions of physical things). See *The Idea of Freedom*, Volume I, pp. 423–494; Volume II, pp. 221–463.

12. For a dialectical examination of opposite views on this subject, see *The Idea of Freedom*, Volume II, pp. 488–525.

13. For the statement of Kant's doctrine on this point, see the passages cited in Chapter 17, note 3.

14. See W. Sellars, *Science, Perception and Reality*, pp. 25–30, 34–37; J. J. C. Smart, *Philosophy and Scientific Realism*, pp. 64–105. Cf. my statement of this challenge as it applies to classical materialism from antiquity to the end of the nineteenth century, in *The Conditions of Philosophy*, pp. 155–156, and Chapter 12; see esp. fn. 28 on p. 224.

15. If the existence of man as a person, i.e., as a physical being with a non-physical or immaterial element in his constitution, cannot be accounted for by the operation of the same natural causes that account for the origin of all other species of living things, then either the origin of man is inexplicable, or the operation of a supernatural cause must be posited to explain man's existence. The line of reasoning indicated here might constitute the strongest and simplest form of *a posteriori* argument for the existence of God as the indispensable cause of the *coming to be* of a being known to exist; and it would reinforce the much more difficult and debatable form of *a posteriori* argument that posits the existence of God as the indispensable cause of the being, *not the coming to be*, of anything that is known to exist and is known to be capable of either existing or not existing. The reason why the inference from the existence of man to the existence of God has seldom, if ever, been employed in natural theology is that the establishment of the

premise (the proposition concerning a non-physical or immaterial element in the constitution of man) has always rightly been regarded as no less difficult than the establishment of the conclusion; perhaps much more so. The reader who examines the statement of the traditional argument for the immateriality of the human intellect, as summarized in Chapter 12, note 41, will find this much more complicated and subtle than the traditional argument for the existence of God as the creative cause of whatever exists that can also not exist. But if the failure of repeated efforts to build a Turing machine able to pass the conversational test has the effect of weakening the materialist hypothesis and of strengthening the opposite view that the brain is not the sufficient cause of conceptual thought in man, then the premise required may be sufficiently established by empirical evidence, so that the subtle and complicated argument for the immateriality of the intellect need not be exclusively relied on; in which case, the positing of God's causality to explain the origin of man would become the strongest and simplest form of *a posteriori* argument for God's existence.

16. See *The Conditions of Philosophy*, Chapter 12.

17. If the science fiction writers and the scientific speculators are anywhere in the neighborhood of the truth, the future is also likely to include, as a result of space exploration, the discovery of intelligent beings elsewhere in the cosmos. As far as I can see or think, the alternatives set forth in this book concerning the difference of man from everything else on earth would apply to the difference of man from such extra-terrestrial beings. If these extra-terrestrial beings are corporeal and animate, and, either by propositional speech or in some other way, manifest their possession of the power of conceptual thought, then we must be prepared for the following alternatives: we will find either (a) that they differ only in degree from man or (b) that they differ superficially in kind. The first alternative needs no explanation; men differ from one another in the degree to which they possess the power of conceptual thought. The second alternative can be explained by analogy. If Aristotle and other conservative thinkers were correct in their hypothesis that some men are by nature born slaves and some are by nature born to be free, that would divide the human group, all members of which possess the power of conceptual thought, into two kinds —a superior kind and an inferior kind. This difference in kind would be a superficial difference in kind if it resulted from a critical threshold in the continuum of degrees of conceptual power, the superior men being able to perform certain functions because their degree of conceptual power is above this critical threshold, and the inferior men totally unable to perform these functions because their degree of conceptual power is below it. Now, the future possibility we face is that the extra-terrestrial intelligent beings that we dis-

cover may be our superiors in kind, but only superficially, by virtue of having a degree of conceptual power that lies above a critical threshold below which falls the conceptual power of terrestrial mankind. In that case, these extra-terrestrial intelligent beings will be able to perform certain functions that we cannot perform at all to any degree. The science fiction writers envisage two other possibilities. One is that we may find corporeal but inanimate intelligences, i.e., intelligent machines, possessing the power of conceptual thought; in which case, the alternatives just considered would still apply. The other possibility can only be described as incorporeal intelligences having the power of conceptual thought or a power superior to that, such as the power of non-discursive intuitive thought that is attributed to the angels in the tradition of Western theology. Such beings, if they existed, would be radically different in kind from men; in fact, it can be argued that any being that was radically different in kind from man by virtue of having an intellectual power not possessed to any degree by him would have to be an angel, i.e., a totally incorporeal being, not just a physical organism with an immaterial or non-physical power. Whether such beings can or do exist is a highly disputable philosophical question, but it should be beyond dispute that, if such beings do exist, they cannot be discovered by space exploration or by means of scientific investigation.

18. See *The Conditions of Philosophy*, pp. 174–177; and Chapter 17: "Philosophy's Future."

19. The decisive confirmation of materialism in the near future by the success of a Turing machine in passing the conversational test would cause little shock or embarrassment in learned circles if they continue to move in the direction that characterizes their doctrinal predilections in the twentieth century. I am including here not only the leading representatives of the natural and the social sciences, but also all forms of *avant-garde* thought in philosophy, theology, and religion. Only a few scientists who persist in raising questions that they think science cannot answer, only a few philosophers who stubbornly hold onto doctrines generally regarded as out-moded, and only a few orthodox theologians, mainly Roman Catholics, would be seriously challenged by such confirmation. But a progressive strengthening of the immaterialist hypothesis by repeated failures in the effort to build a Turing machine that can pass the conversational test would have earth-shaking effects throughout the learned world of the future. And to whatever extent the attitudes that now prevail among those laymen who, in some degree, are touched by the world of learning, reflect the naturalistic materialism and atheism of the learned, then a reversal in those attitudes might also be anticipated as a consequence of an altered state of mind on the part of the learned.

References

References

ADLER, MORTIMER J.: *Problems for Thomists: The Problems of Species*, Sheed and Ward, New York, 1940.

———. *A Dialectic of Morals*, Frederick Ungar Publishing Company, New York, 1941.

———. *The Idea of Freedom*, Volumes I and II, Doubleday & Company, Inc., Garden City, 1958 and 1961.

———. *The Conditions of Philosophy*, Atheneum, New York, 1965.

ALTIZER, T. J. J.: *The Gospel of Christian Atheism*, The Westminster Press, Philadelphia, 1966.

ALTIZER, T. J. J. and WILLIAM HAMILTON: *Radical Theology and the Death of God*, The Bobbs-Merrill Company, Inc., Indianapolis, 1966.

ALSTON, WILLIAM P.: *Philosophy of Language*, Prentice-Hall, Englewood Cliffs, 1964.

ANDERSON, ALAN ROSS (ed): *Minds and Machines*, Prentice-Hall, Inc., Englewood Cliffs, 1964.

ANTAL, L.: *Questions of Meaning*, Mouton & Co., The Hague, 1963.

———. *Content, Meaning, and Understanding*, Mouton & Co., The Hague, 1964.

AQUINAS, THOMAS: *Summa Theologica; Summa Contra Gentiles*, trans. by J. F. Anderson under the title, "On the Truth of the Catholic Faith"; *Disputed Questions on the Soul.*

ARBIB, M. A.: *Brains, Machines, and Mathematics*, McGraw-Hill, New York, 1964.

ARDREY, ROBERT: *African Genesis*, Atheneum, New York, 1961.

———. *The Territorial Imperative*, Atheneum, New York, 1966.

ARISTOTLE: *On Interpretation; Prior Analytics; Posterior Analytics; Metaphysics; On the Soul; On Plants; History of Animals; Parts of Animals; Generation of Animals; Nichomachean Ethics; Politics; Rhetoric.*

ARMER, PAUL: "Attitudes Toward Intelligent Machines," in *Computers and Thought*, ed. by E. A. Feigenbaum and J. Feldman.

AUGUSTINE: *Confessions; City of God; On Christian Doctrine; Immortality of the Soul.*

AUNE, BRUCE: "Feigl on the Mind-Body Problem," in *Mind, Matter and Method*, ed. by P. K. Feyerabend and G. Maxwell.

AURELIUS, MARCUS: *Meditations.*

AYER, A. J.: "Meaning and Intentionality," in *Proceedings of the American Philosophical Association*, Volume XXVII, 1953–1954.

———. *Thinking and Meaning*, H. K. Lewis & Co. Ltd., London, 1947.

BARNETT, S. A.: Review of *On Aggression* by Konrad Lorenz, in *Scientific American*, Volume 216, No. 2, February, 1967.

BEADLE, GEORGE and MURIEL: *The Language of Life*, Doubleday & Company, Inc., Garden City, 1966.

Behavior and Evolution, ed. by Anne Roe and George Gaylord Simpson, Yale University Press, New Haven, 1958.

BELL, D. A.: *Intelligent Machines*, Random House, Inc., New York, 1962.

BELOFF, JOHN: "The Identity Hypothesis: A Critique," in *Brain and Mind*, ed. by J. R. Smythies.

BENNETT, JONATHAN: *Rationality*, Humanities Press, New York, 1964.

BERGSON, HENRI: *The Two Sources of Morality and Religion*, Henry Holt & Company, New York, 1935.

BERKELEY, GEORGE: *Principles of Natural Knowledge.*

BERNSTEIN, JEREMY: *The Analytical Engine*, Random House, Inc., New York, 1963.

BERNSTEIN, R. J.: "Sellars' Vision of Man-in-the-Universe," in *The Review of Metaphysics*, Volume XX, No. 1, pp. 113–143, September, 1966.

BITTERMAN, M. E.: "The Evolution of Intelligence," in *Scientific American*, Volume 212, No. 1, pp. 92–100, January, 1965.

BONNET, CHARLES: *Contemplation de la Nature*, 1764–65; 2nd edition, 1769.

Brain and Mind, ed. by J. R. Smythies, Humanities Press, New York, 1965.

BRAIN, LORD RUSSELL: *Mind, Perception, and Science*, Blackwell Scientific Publications, Oxford, 1951.

———. "Speech and Thought," in *Physical Basis of Mind*, ed. by P. Laslett, Basil Blackwell, Oxford, 1957.

BRANDT, RICHARD, B.: "Doubts About the Identity Theory," in *Dimensions of Mind*, ed. by S. Hook.

BROAD, C. D.: *The Mind and Its Place in Nature*, Kegan Paul, Trench, Trubner & Co., Ltd., London, 1925.

BRONOWSKI, J.: *The Identity of Man*, The Natural History Press, New York, 1965.

BRUNER, JEROME S., J. J. GOODNOW, G. A. AUSTIN: *A Study of Thinking*, John Wiley & Sons, Inc., New York, 1956.

BUBER, MARTIN: *Eclipse of God*, Harper & Row, New York, 1952.

BUFFON, GEORGES, L. L.: *Histoire Naturelle*, 1749.

CAIN, A. J.: *Animal Species and Their Evolution*, Harper & Brothers, New York, 1954.

Callahan, Daniel (ed.): *The Secular City Debate*, Macmillan, New York, 1966.

Campbell, C. A.: "Ryle on the Intellect," in *Clarity Is Not Enough*, ed. by H. D. Lewis.

Capek, M.: "The Doctrine of Necessity Re-Examined," in *The Review of Metaphysics*, Volume 5, No. 1, Sept., 1951.

Carlson, A. J.: "Dynamics of Living Processes," in *Nature of the World and Man*, ed. by H. H. Newman, 1926.

Carrington, Richard: *A Million Years of Man*, World Publishing Company, Cleveland, 1963.

Carterette, E. C. (ed.): *Brain Function*, Volume III, University of California Press, Berkeley, 1966.

Cassirer, Ernst: *An Essay on Man*, Yale University Press, New Haven, 1944.

Cerebral Mechanisms in Behavior, ed. by L. A. Jeffress, John Wiley & Sons, Inc., New York, 1951.

Chappell, V. C. (ed.): *The Philosophy of Mind*, Prentice-Hall, Inc., Englewood Cliffs, 1962.

Chisholm, Roderick: in *Minnesota Studies in the Philosophy of Science*, Volume II, ed. by H. Feigl, M. Scriven, and G. Maxwell.

Chomsky, N.: *Syntactic Structures*, Mouton & Co., The Hague, 1957.

Christensen, N. E.: "A Proof that Meanings are Neither Ideas Nor Concepts," in *Analysis*, Volume XVII, No. 1, pp. 10–13, October, 1956.

———. *On the Nature of Meanings*, Munskgaard, Copenhagen, 1961.

Clarity is Not Enough, ed. by H. D. Lewis, George Allen & Unwin, Ltd., London, 1963.

Clark, W. E. Le Gros: *The Antecedents of Man*, Quadrangle Books, Inc., Chicago, 1960.

———. *History of the Primates*, University of Chicago Press, Chicago, 1961.

———. *Man-Apes or Ape-Men?*, Holt, Rinehart and Winston, New York, 1967.

Cohn, L. J.: *The Diversity of Meaning*, Herder and Herder, New York, 1963.

Cohen, Jonathan: "Can there be Artificial Minds?" in *Analysis*, Volume 16, No. 2, pp. 36–41, December, 1955.

Comparative Psychology, ed. by F. A. Moss, Prentice-Hall, Inc., New York, 1942.

Comparative Psychology, 2nd edition, ed. by C. P. Stone, Prentice-Hall, Inc., Englewood Cliffs, 1955.

Computers and Thought, ed. by E. A. Feigenbaum and J. Feldman, McGraw-Hill, New York, 1963.

Control of the Mind, ed. by S. M. Farber and R. H. L. Wilson, McGraw-Hill, New York, 1961.

Cornman, James W.: *Metaphysics, Reference and Language*, Yale University Press, New Haven, 1966.

Cox, Harvey: *The Secular City*, Macmillan, New York, 1965.

CRAIK, KENNETH J. W.: *The Nature of Psychology*, Cambridge University Press, Cambridge, 1966.

———. *The Nature of Explanation*, Cambridge University Press, Cambridge, 1952.

CRICHTLEY, MACDONALD: "The Evolution of Man's Capacity for Language," in *Evolution After Darwin*, Volume II, ed. by Sol Tax.

Cross-Cultural Understanding, ed. by F. S. C. Northrop and H. H. Livingston, Harper & Row, New York, 1964.

CROSSON, F J. and K. M. SAYRES: "Modelling: Simulation and Replication," in *The Modelling of Mind*, ed. by K. M. Sayre and F. J. Crosson.

DANTO, ARTHUR: "On Consciousness in Machines," in *Dimensions of Mind*, ed. by S. Hook.

DART, RAYMOND: *Adventures with the Missing Link*, Viking Press, New York, 1959.

DARWIN, CHARLES: *Origin of Species and The Descent of Man*, Modern Library edition, Random House, Inc., New York, n.d.

DESCARTES, RENÉ: *Philosophical Works*, 2 volumes, trans. by E. S. Haldane and G. R. T. Ross, Cambridge University Press, Cambridge, 1931.

DEWEY, JOHN: *How We Think*, D. C. Heath & Co., New York, 1910.

———. *Reconstruction In Philosophy*, Henry Holt & Company, New York, 1920.

DEWART, LESLIE: *The Future of Belief*, Herder and Herder, New York, 1966.

Dimensions of Mind, ed. by Sidney Hook, New York University Press, New York, 1960.

DIXON, W. MACNEILE: *The Human Situation*, Longmans, Green & Company, New York, 1938.

DOBZHANSKY, THEODOSIUS: *Genetics and the Origin of Species*, Columbia University Press, New York, 1937.

———. *Mankind Evolving*, Yale University Press, New Haven, 1962.

———. *Evolution, Genetics, and Man*, John Wiley & Sons, Inc., New York, 1961.

———. *The Biology of Ultimate Concern*, New American Library, New York, 1967.

Documents of Vatican II, Guild Press, New York, 1966.

DONCEEL, JOSEPH: "Teilhard de Chardin," in *Thought*, Volume XL, No. 158, Autumn, 1965.

DUNCAN, G. M. (trans.): *The Philosophical Works of Leibniz*, The Tuttle, Morehouse and Taylor Company, New Haven, 1908.

EARLE, W., J. M. EDIE, and J. WILD: *Christianity and Existentialism*, Northwestern University Press, Evanston, 1963.

ECCLES, J. C.: *The Neurophysiological Basis of Mind*, The Clarendon Press, Oxford, 1952.

EIBL-EIBESFELDT, IRENAUS: "Experimental Criteria for Distinguishing

Innate from Culturally Conditioned Behavior," in *Cross-Cultural Understanding*, ed. by F. S. C. Northrop and H. H. Livingston.

EISELEY, LOREN: *Darwin's Century*, Doubleday & Company, Inc., Garden City, 1958.

EMILIANI, CESARE: "Dating Human Evolution," in *Evolution After Darwin*, Volume II, ed. by Sol Tax.

ENGELS, FRIEDRICH: "German Ideology," in *Handbook of Marxism*, ed. by E. Burns, pp. 210–213, Random House, New York, 1935.

EPICTETUS: *Discourses*.

Evolution After Darwin, Volume II, ed. by Sol Tax, University of Chicago Press, Chicago, 1960.

EWING, A. C.: "Professor Ryle's Attack on Dualism," in *Clarity Is Not Enough*, ed. by H. D. Lewis.

FALCKENBURG, RICHARD: *History of Modern Philosophy*, Henry Holt & Company, New York, 1893.

FARBER, S. M. and R. H. L. WILSON, (eds.): *Control of the Mind*, McGraw-Hill, New York, 1961.

FARRER, AUSTIN: *God Is Not Dead*, Morehouse-Barlow Co., New York, 1966.

FEIGENBAUM, E. A.: "The Simulation of Verbal Learning Behavior," in *Computers and Thought*, ed. by E. A. Feigenbaum and J. Feldman.

FEIGENBAUM, E. A. and J. FELDMAN, (ed.): Computers and Thought, McGraw-Hill, New York, 1963.

FEIGL, H., M. SCRIVEN, and G. MAXWELL, (ed.): *Minnesota Studies in the Philosophy of Science*, Volume II, University of Minnesota Press, Minneapolis, 1958.

FEIGL, H.: "The 'Mental' and the 'Physical,'" in *Minnesota Studies in the Philosophy of Science*, Volume II, ed. by H. Feigl, M. Scriven, G. Maxwell.

———. "Mind-Body, Not a Pseudoproblem," in *Dimensions of Mind*, ed. by S. Hook.

FEUERBACH, LUDWIG: *Essence of Christianity* (1841), trans. by George Eliot, reprinted by Harper & Row, New York, 1957.

FEYERABEND, P. K. and G. MAXWELL, (ed.): *Mind, Matter, and Method*, University of Minnesota Press, Minneapolis, 1966.

FINDLAY, J. N.: "Use, Usage, and Meaning," in *Clarity Is Not Enough*, ed. by H. D. Lewis.

FLEW, ANTONY and ALASDAIR MACINTYRE (ed.): *New Essays in Philosophical Theology*, (1955), Macmillan Paperbook edition, Macmillan, New York, 1964.

FREEDMAN, L. Z. and A. ROE: "Evolution and Human Behavior," in *Behavior and Evolution*, ed. by A. Roe and G. G. Simpson.

FREUD, SIGMUND: *The Future of an Illusion*, trans. by W. D. Ronson-Scott, Liveright, New York, 1928.

———. *Civilization and its Discontents*, trans. by J. Riviere, Jonathan Cape & Harrison Smith, New York, 1930.

GEACH, PETER: *Mental Acts*, Humanities Press, New York, 1957.
GELERNTER, H.: "Realization of a Geometry-Theorem Proving Machine," in *Computers and Thought*, ed. by E. A. Feigenbaum and J. Feldman.
GILSON, ETIENNE: *Reason and Revelation in the Middle Ages*, Charles Scribner's Sons, New York, 1938.
GOLDENWEISER, ALEXANDER: *Anthropology*, Harrap, New York, 1937.
GOLDSTEIN, KURT: *Language and Language Disturbances*, Grune & Stratton, Inc., New York, 1948.
GRAHAM, WILLIAM: *The Creed of Science*, Arnold, Ltd., London, 1881.
Great Ideas Today, 1965, 1966, ed. by R. M. Hutchins and M. J. Adler, Encyclopaedia Britannica, Inc., Chicago, 1965, 1966.
GREEN, B. F., A. K. WOLFF, N. CHOMSKY, and K. LAUGHERY: "Baseball: An Automatic Question Answerer," in *Computers and Thought*, ed. by E. A. Feigenbaum and J. Feldman.
GUNDERSON, KEITH: "The Imitation Game," in *Minds and Machines*, ed. by A. R. Anderson.
GURWITSCH, ARON: "On the Conceptual Consciousness," in *The Modeling of Mind*, ed. by K. M. Sayre and F. J. Crosson.

HALSTEAD, WARD C: *Brain and Intelligence*, University of Chicago Press, Chicago, 1947.
———. "Brain and Intelligence," in *Cerebral Mechanisms In Behavior*, ed. by L. A. Jeffress.
HAMPSHIRE, STUART (ed.): *Philosophy of Mind*, Harper & Row, New York, 1966.
Handbook of Experimental Psychology, ed. by S. S. Stevens, John Wiley & Sons, New York, 1964.
Handbook of Marxism, ed. by E. Burns, Random House, New York, 1935.
HANKINS, F. H.: *Introduction to the Study of Society*, rev. ed., Macmillan, New York, 1935.
HANSEL, C. E. M.: *ESP, A Scientific Evaluation*, Charles Scribner's Sons, New York, 1966.
HAMILTON, KENNETH: *God is Dead, The Anatomy of a Slogan*, William B. Eerdmans Publishing Company, Grand Rapids, 1966.
HAMILTON, WILLIAM: *The New Essence of Christianity*, Association Press, New York, 1966.
HARLOW, HARRY F.: "The Evolution of Learning," in *Behavior and Evolution*, ed. by A. Roe and G. G. Simpson.
———. "Thinking," in *Theoretical Foundations of Psychology*, ed. by H. Helson.
———. "Primate Learning," in *Comparative Psychology*, ed. by C. P. Stone.
HARTSHORNE, C.: "Causal Necessities: An Alternative to Hume," in *The Philosophical Review*, Volume LXIII, No. 3, October, 1954.
———. "Freedom Requires Indeterminism and Universal Causality,"

in *The Journal of Philosophy*, Volume LV, No. 19, September 11, 1958.

HARVEY, WILLIAM: *The Works of William Harvey*, trans. by Robert Willis, Edward Brothers, Inc., Ann Arbor, 1943.

HEBB, DONALD: *The Organization of Behavior, A Neuropsychological Theory*, John Wiley & Sons, New York, 1949.

———. *A Textbook of Psychology*, W. B. Saunders Company, Philadelphia, 1958.

HEGEL, GEORG W. F.: *Philosophy of Right*, trans. by T. M. Knox, The Clarendon Press, Oxford, 1942.

———. *The Philosophy of History*, trans. by J. Sibree, Willey Book Co., rev. ed., New York, 1944.

HELSON, HARRY (ed.): *Theoretical Foundations of Psychology*, D. Van Nostrand Company, Inc., New York, 1951.

HERON, W. T.: "Complex Learning Processes," in *Comparative Psychology*, ed. by F. A. Moss.

HERRICK, C. JUDSON: *The Brains of Rats and Men*, University of Chicago Press, Chicago, 1926.

———. *The Evolution of Human Nature*, University of Texas Press, Austin, 1956; Harper Torchbooks, New York, 1961.

HILGARD, ERNEST R.: "Methods and Procedures in the Study of Learning," in *Handbook of Experimental Psychology*, ed. by S. S. Stevens.

———. "Psychology After Darwin," in *Evolution After Darwin*, Volume II, ed. by Sol Tax.

HOBBES, THOMAS: *Leviathan*, The Clarendon Press, Oxford, 1909.

HOOK, SIDNEY (ed.): *Dimensions of Mind*, New York University Press, New York, 1960.

HORMANN, A.: "Gaku: An Artificial Student," in *Behavioral Science*, Volume 10, No. 1, pp. 88–107, January, 1965.

HOWELLS, WILLIAM H.: "Homo Erectus," in *The Scientific American*, Volume 215, No. 5, November, 1966.

HUME, DAVID: *Enquiry Concerning Human Understanding.*

HUMPHREY, GEORGE: *Thinking*, John Wiley & Sons, Inc., New York, 1951.

HUNT, EARL B.: *Concept Learning*, John Wiley & Sons, Inc., New York, 1962.

HUNT, E. B. and C. I. HOVLAND: "Programming a Model of Human Concept Formation," in *The Modeling of Mind*, ed. by K. M. Sayre and F. J. Crosson.

HUTCHINS, R. M. and M. J. ADLER, (ed.): *The Great Ideas Today 1965; The Great Ideas Today 1966*, Encyclopaedia Britannica, Inc., Chicago, 1965, 1966.

HUXLEY, THOMAS HENRY: *Man's Place in Nature and Other Anthropological Essays*, D. Appleton and Company, New York, 1898.

HUXLEY, JULIAN: *Evolution, The Modern Synthesis*, Harper & Brothers, New York, 1942.

———. *The Uniqueness of Man*, Chatto & Windus, London, 1943.

———. *Evolution in Action*, Chatto & Windus, London, 1953.

JAMES, WILLIAM: *The Principles of Psychology*, Volumes I and II, Henry Holt & Company, New York, 1891.

JEFFRESS, L. A. (ed.): *Cerebral Mechanisms in Behavior*, John Wiley & Sons, Inc., New York, 1951.

JENKINS, D. E.: *Guide to the Debate about God*, The Westminster Press, Philadelphia, 1966.

JONAS, HANS: *The Phenomenon of Life*, Harper & Row, New York, 1966.

KAHLER, ERICH: *Man the Measure*, Pantheon Books Inc., New York, 1943.

KANT, IMMANUEL: *Critique of Practical Reason and Other Works on Ethics*, trans. by T. K. Abbott, 6th ed., Longmans, Green and Co., London, 1909.

———. *Critique of Aesthetic Judgment*, trans. by James C. Meredith, The Clarendon Press, Oxford, 1911.

———. *Critique of Teleological Judgment*, trans. by James C. Meredith, The Clarendon Press, Oxford, 1928.

———. *Critique of Pure Reason*, trans. by J. M. D. Meiklejohn, rev. ed., Willey Book Co., New York, 1943.

KEGLEY, C. W.: "Problems in the Understanding of Man," in *Lutheran World*, Volume XII, No. L, pp. 28–33, 1965.

KLÜVER, HEINRICH: *Behavior Mechanisms In Monkeys*, University of Chicago Press, Chicago, 1933; Phoenix paperback ed., 1961.

KÖHLER, WOLFGANG: *The Mentality of Apes*, 2nd rev. ed., Routledge & Kegan Paul, Ltd., London, 1927.

KORNILOV, K. N.: "Psychology in the Light of Dialectic Materialism," in *Psychologies of 1930*, ed. by C. Murchison.

LACK, DAVID: *Evolutionary Theory and Christian Belief*, Methuen, London, 1961.

LACROIX, JEAN: *The Meaning of Modern Atheism*, Macmillan, New York, 1965.

LA METTRIE: *L'Homme Machine*, critical edition with an introductory monograph and notes by Aram Vartanian, Princeton University Press, Princeton, 1960.

LANGE, FREDERICK ALBERT: *History of Materialism*, 3rd ed. trans. by E. C. Thomas, Harcourt, Brace & Co., New York, 1925.

LASHLEY, K. S.: "The Problem of Serial Order in Behavior," in *Cerebral Mechanisms in Behavior*, ed. by L. A. Jeffress.

LASLETT, P. (ed.): *The Physical Basis of Mind*, Basil Blackwell, Oxford, 1957.

LATTA, R. (trans.): *Leibniz: The Monadology and Other Philosophical Writings*, Oxford University Press, New York, 1925.

LEAKEY, L. S. B.: *Adam's Ancestors: The Evolution of Man and His Culture*, Harper & Row, New York, 1960.

———. "The Origin of the Genus Homo," in *Evolution After Darwin*, Volume II, ed. by Sol Tax.

———. *The Progress and Evolution of Man in Africa*, Oxford University Press, New York, 1961.

LEEPER, ROBERT: "Cognitive Processes," in *Handbook of Experimental Psychology*, ed. by S. S. Stevens.

LEIBNIZ, GOTTFRIED WILHELM: *The Monadology and Other Philosophical Writings*, trans. by R. Latta, Oxford, 1925.

———. *Philosophical Writings*, trans. by M. Morris, Everyman edition, E. P. Dutton & Co., Inc., New York, 1934.

———. *Selections*, ed. by P. P. Wiener.

———. *Discourse on Metaphysics*, trans. by G. R. Montgomery.

———. *New Essays Concerning Human Understanding.*

———. *The Philosophical Works of Leibniz*, trans. by G. M. Duncan.

LENIN, V. I.: "The Teachings of Karl Marx," in *A Handbook of Marxism*, pp. 537–570, ed. by E. Burns, Random House, Inc., New York, 1935.

LEWIS, H. D. (ed.): *Clarity Is Not Enough*, George Allen & Unwin, Ltd., London, 1963.

LILLY, JOHN C.: *Man and Dolphin*, Doubleday & Company, Inc., Garden City, 1961.

———. *The Mind of the Dolphin: A Nonhuman Intelligence*, Doubleday, New York, 1967.

LINDSAY, R. K.: "Inferential Memory as the Basis of Machines Which Understand Natural Language," in *Computers and Thought*, ed. by E. A. Feigenbaum and J. Feldman.

LINTON, RALPH: *The Study of Man*, Appleton-Century, New York, 1936.

LOCKE, JOHN: *Essay Concerning Human Understanding.*

LORENZ, KONRAD: *King Solomon's Ring*, Thomas Y. Crowell Company, New York, 1952.

———. *Evolution and the Modification of Behavior*, University of Chicago Press, Chicago, 1965.

———. *On Aggression*, Harcourt, Brace & World, New York, 1966.

LOVEJOY, ARTHUR O.: *The Great Chain of Being*, Harvard University Press, Cambridge (Mass.), 1948.

LUCAS, J.: "Minds, Machines and Godel," in *The Modelling of Mind*, ed. by K. M. Sayre and F. J. Crosson.

LYELL, SIR CHARLES: *The Antiquity of Man*, Everyman Edition, E. P. Dutton & Co., Inc., New York, 1927.

MACE, C. A. (ed.): *British Philosophy in Mid-Century*, 2nd edition, George Allen & Unwin Ltd., London, 1966.

MAIER, N. R. F. and T. C. SCHNEIRLA: *Principles of Animal Psychology*, McGraw-Hill, New York, 1935.

MANICAS, PETER T.: "Men, Machines, Materialism, and Morality," in *Philosophy and Phenomenological Research*, Volume XXVII, No. 2, December, 1966.

MARITAIN, JACQUES: *Les Degrés du Savoir*, Desclée De Brouwer et Cie., Paris, 1932.

———. *Ransoming the Time*, Charles Scribner's Sons, New York, 1941.

Mascall, E. L.: *The Secularization of Christianity*, Darton, Longman & Todd, London, 1965.

Matson, Wallace I.: "Why Isn't the Mind-Body Problem Ancient?" in *Mind, Matter, and Method*, ed. by P. K. Feyerabend and G. Maxwell.

Mayr, Ernst: *Animal Species and Evolution*, Harvard University Press, Cambridge (Mass.), 1963.

McCulloch, Warren S.: *Embodiments of Mind*, the M.I.T. Press, Cambridge (Mass.), 1965.

———. "A Historical Introduction to the Postulational Foundations of Experimental Epistemology," in *Cross-Cultural Understanding*, ed. by F. S. C. Northrop and H. H. Livingston.

McCulloch, W. S. and W. M. Brodey: "The Biological Sciences," in *The Great Ideas Today, 1966*, ed. by R. M. Hutchins and M. J. Adler.

McCulloch, W. S. and W. Pitts: "How We Know Universals: The Perception of Auditory and Visual Forms," in W. S. McCulloch, *Embodiments of Mind.*

McKay, Donald M.: "Mindlike Behavior in Artefacts," in *The Modeling of Mind*, ed. by K. M. Sayre and F. J. Crosson.

———. "From Mechanism to Mind," in *Brain and Mind*, ed by J. R Smythies.

Meaning of the Death of God, ed. by B. Murchland, Random House, New York, 1967.

Mind, Matter, and Method, ed. by P. K. Feyerabend and G. Maxwell, University of Minneapolis Press, Minneapolis, 1966.

Minds and Machines, ed. by Alan Ross Anderson, Prentice-Hall, Inc., Englewood Cliffs, 1964.

Minsky, Marvin: "Steps Toward Artificial Intelligence," in *Computers and Thought*, ed. by E. A. Feigenbaum and J. Feldman.

The Modeling of Mind, ed. by K. M. Sayre and F. J. Crosson, University of Notre Dame Press, Notre Dame, 1963.

Mohanty, J. N.: *Edmund Husserl's Theory of Meaning*, Mouton & Co., The Hague, 1964.

Montaigne: "Apology for Raimond de Sebonde," in *Essays of Montaigne*, Volumes 4 and 5, trans. by Charles Cotton, rev. by W. C. Hazlett; Edwin C. Hill, New York, 1910.

———. "Of Cruelty," in *Essays of Montaigne*, Volume 4, trans. by Charles Cotton, rev. by W. C. Hazlett; Edwin C. Hill, New York, 1910.

Montesquieu: *The Spirit of Laws.*

Montgomery, G. R. (trans.): *Leibniz: Discourse on Metaphysics*, Open Court Publishing Company, Chicago, 1931.

Morgan, Lloyd: *Animal Behavior*, Arnold, Ltd., London, 1900.

———. *Introduction to Comparative Psychology*, Scott, London, 1894, 2nd ed. 1909.

MORRIS, CHARLES: *Signs, Language and Behavior*, Prentice-Hall, Inc., New York, 1946.

———. *Signification and Significance*, M.I.T. Press, Cambridge (Mass.), 1964.

MOSS, F. A. (ed.): *Comparative Psychology*, Prentice-Hall, Inc., New York, 1942.

MURCHISON, C. (ed.): *Psychologies of 1930*, Clark University Press, Worchester, 1930.

MURCHLAND, BERNARD (ed.): *The Meaning of the Death of God*, Random House, New York, 1967.

MURRAY, J. C.: *The Problem of God*, Yale University Press, New Haven, 1964.

New Essays in Philosophical Theology, ed. by Antony Flew and Alasdair MacIntyre (1955), Macmillan Paperbook Edition, Macmillan, New York, 1964.

NEWMAN, H. H. (ed.): *Nature of the World and Man*, University of Chicago Press, Chicago, 1926.

NEWELL, A. and J. C. SHAW, and H. A. SIMON: "Chess-Playing Programs and the Problem of Complexity," in *Computers and Thought*, ed. by E. A. Feigenbaum and J. Feldman.

NEWELL, A. and H. A. SIMON: "GPS, A Program that Simulates Human Thought," in *Computers and Thought*, ed. by E. A. Feigenbaum and J. Feldman.

New Theology, Nos. 1, 2, 3, and *4*, ed. by Martin Marty and Dean Peerman, Macmillan, New York, 1964, 1965, 1966, and 1967.

New Views of the Nature of Man, ed. by J. R. Platt, University of Chicago Press, Chicago, 1965.

NIELSEN, J. M.: *Agnosia, Apraxia, Aphasia*, Hafner Publishing Company, Inc., New York, 1936, 2nd edition, 1965.

NISSEN, HENRY W.: "Axes of Behavioral Comparison," in *Behavior and Evolution*, ed. by A. Roe and G. G. Simpson.

———. "Phylogenetic Comparison," in *Handbook of Experimental Psychology*, ed. by S. S. Stevens.

NORTHROP, F. S. C. and H. H. LIVINGSTON, (ed.): *Cross-Cultural Understanding*, Harper & Row, New York, 1964.

OAKLEY, KENNETH P.: *Man the Tool-Maker*, University of Chicago Press, Chicago, 1964.

OGDEN, C. K., and I. A. RICHARDS: *The Meaning of Meaning*, Harcourt, Brace & Co., New York, 1923.

OSGOOD, CHARLES E.: *Method and Theory in Experimental Psychology*, Oxford University Press, New York, 1953.

OSGOOD, C. E., G. SUCI, and P. TANNENBAUM: "The Logic of Semantic Differentiation," in *Psycholinguistics*, ed. by S. Saporta.

PASCAL, BLAISE: *Thoughts; Treatise on the Vacuum.*

PENFIELD, WILDER: "The Physiological Basis of the Mind," in *Control of the Mind*, ed. by S. Farber and R. Wilson.

PENFIELD, W. and L. ROBERTS: *Speech and Brain Mechanisms*, Princeton University Press, Princeton, 1959.

PEPPER, STEPHEN: "A Neural Identity Theory of Mind," in *Dimensions of Mind*, ed. by S. Hook.

PFEIFFER, JOHN: *The Thinking Machine*, J. B. Lippincott Company, New York, 1962.

Philosophy for the Future, ed. by R. W. Sellars, V. J. McGill, M. Farber, Macmillan, New York, 1949.

Philosophy of Mind, ed. by V. C. Chappell, Prentice-Hall, Inc., Englewood Cliffs, 1962.

Philosophy of Mind, ed. by Stuart Hampshire, Harper & Row, New York, 1966.

Physical Basis of Mind, ed. by P. Laslett, Basil Blackwell, Oxford, 1957.

PIUS XII: *Humani Beneris*, No. 36, National Catholic Welfare Council, Washington, 1950.

PLACE, U. T.: "Is Consciousness a Brain Process?" in *The Philosophy of Mind*, ed. by V. C. Chappell.

PLATO: *Cratylus; Protagoras; Theaetetus; Timaeus.*

PLATT, J. R. (ed.): *New Views on the Nature of Man*, University of Chicago Press, Chicago, 1965.

PLEKHANOV, G. V.: *Essays in the History of Materialism*, trans. by R. Fox, The Bodley Head Ltd., London, 1934.

POLANYI, MICHAEL: *The Study of Man*, University of Chicago Press, Chicago, 1963.

———. "The Structure of Consciousness," in *Brain*, Volume 89, Part 4, 1966.

POPPER, KARL: *Conjectures and Refutations*, Basic Books, New York, 1962.

PORTMANN, ADOLF: *Animals as Social Beings*, Viking Press, New York, 1961.

PRIBRAM, KARL H.: "Proposal for a Structural Pragmatism," in *Scientific Psychology*, ed. by B. B. Wolman and E. Nagel.

PRICE, H. H.: *Thinking and Experience*, Hutchinson's University Library, London, 1953.

———. "Some Objections to Behaviorism," in *Dimensions of Mind*, ed. by S. Hook.

Psychologies of 1930, ed. by C. Murchison, Clark University Press, Worcester, 1930.

PUTNAM, HILARY: "Minds and Machines," in *Dimensions of Mind*, ed. by S. Hook.

———. "Robots: Machines or Artificially Created Life?" in *Philosophy of Mind*, ed. by Stuart Hampshire.

QUINE, W. V.: *Word and Object*, Harvard University Press, Cambridge (Mass.), 1960.

QUINTON, ANTHONY: "Mind and Matter," in *Brain and Mind*, ed. by J. R. Smythies.

RAPOPORT, ANATOL: "Technological Models of the Nervous System," in *The Modeling of Mind*, ed. by K. M. Sayre and F. J. Crosson.

RAZRAN, GREGORY: "Evolutionary Psychology: Levels of Learning—and Perception and Thinking," in *Scientific Psychology*, ed. by B. B. Wolman and E. Nagel.

RENSCH, BERNARD: *Evolution Above the Species Level*, Columbia University Press, New York, 1960.

ROBINET, JEAN BAPTISTE: *Considerations philosophique de la gradation naturelle des formes de l'être*, 1768.

———. *De la Nature*, 5 volumes, 1761–1768.

ROBINSON, BISHOP JOHN A. T.: *Honest To God*, The Westminster Press, Philadelphia, 1963.

———. *The New Reformation*, The Westminster Press, Philadelphia, 1965.

ROE, ANNE and GEORGE GAYLORD SIMPSON, (ed.): *Behavior and Evolution*, Yale University Press, New Haven, 1958.

RORTY, AMELIE, O.: "Slaves and Machines," in *Analysis*, Volume 22, No. 5, April, 1962.

ROUSSEAU, JEAN-JACQUES: *The Social Contract and the Discourses*, Everyman Edition, trans. by G. D. H. Cole, E. P. Dutton & Co., Inc., New York, 1913.

RUSSELL, BERTRAND: *A Critical Exposition of the Philosophy of Leibniz*, George Allen & Unwin Ltd., London, 1900.

RYAN, BERNARD: *The Evolution of Man*, Newman Press, Westminster, 1965.

RYLE, GILBERT: *The Concept of Mind*, Hutchinson, London, 1949.

———. "The Theory of Meaning," in *British Philosophy in Mid-Century*, ed. by C. A. Mace, 2nd edition, George Allen & Unwin Ltd., London, 1966.

———. "Use, Usage and Meaning," in *Proceedings of The Aristotelian Society*, Supplementary Volume XXXV, 1961.

SAPORTA, E. (ed.): *Psycholinguistics*, Holt, Rinehart & Winston, New York, 1961.

SAYRE, K. M.: "Human and Mechanical Recognition," in *The Modeling of Mind*, ed. by K. M. Sayre and F. J. Crosson.

———. *Recognition*, University of Notre Dame Press, Notre Dame, 1965.

SAYRE, K. M. and F. J. CROSSON, (eds.): *The Modeling of Mind*, University of Notre Dame Press, Notre Dame, 1963.

SCHALLER, GEORGE B.: *The Year of the Gorilla*, University of Chicago Press, Chicago, 1964.

SCHNEIRLA, T. C.: "Levels in the Psychological Capacities of Animals," in *Philosophy for the Future*, ed. by R. W. Sellars, V. J. McGill, M. Farber, 1949.

SCHOONENBERG, P.: *God's World in the Making*, Duquesne University Press, Pittsburgh, 1964.

Scientific Psychology, ed. by Benjamin B. Wolman and Ernest Nagel, Basic Books, New York, 1965.

SCOTT, JOHN PAUL: *Animal Behavior*, University of Chicago Press, Chicago, 1958; reprinted by Doubleday Anchor Books, New York, 1963.

SCRIVEN, MICHAEL: "The Complete Robot: A Prolegomena to Androidology," in *Dimensions of Mind*, ed. by S. Hook.

———. "The Mechanical Concept of Mind," in *Minds and Machines*, ed. by A. R. Anderson.

———. "The Mechanical Concept of Mind," in *The Modeling of Mind*, ed. by K. M. Sayre and F. J. Crosson.

———. *Primary Philosophy*, McGraw-Hill, New York, 1966.

SELFRIDGE, O. G. and U. NEISSER: "Pattern Recognition by Machine," in *Computers and Thought*, ed. by E. A. Feigenbaum and J. Feldman.

SELLARS, R. W., V. J. MCGILL, M. FARBER, (eds.): *Philosophy for the Future*, Macmillan, New York, 1949.

SELLARS, WILFRID: *Science, Perception and Reality*, Humanities Press, New York, 1963.

———. "Aristotelian Philosophies of Mind," in *Philosophy for the Future*, ed. by R. W. Sellars, V. J. McGill, and M. Farber, Macmillan, New York, 1949.

———. "The Identity Approach to the Mind-Body Problem," in *Philosophy of Mind*, ed. by Stuart Hampshire.

SHERRINGTON, SIR CHARLES: *Man On His Nature*, Macmillan, New York, 1941.

SHILS, EDWARD: "The Sanctity of Life," in *Encounter*, Volume XVIII, No. 1, January, 1967.

SIMPSON, GEORGE GAYLORD: *The Meaning of Evolution*, Yale University Press, New Haven, 1949.

———. *The Major Features of Evolution*, Columbia University Press, New York, 1953.

———. "The Biological Sciences," in *The Great Ideas Today, 1965*, ed. by R. M. Hutchins and M. J. Adler.

SINNOTT, EDMUND, W: *Mind, Matter, and Man*, Harper & Brothers, New York, 1957.

———. *The Bridge of Life*, Simon and Schuster, New York, 1966.

SKINNER, B. F.: *Verbal Behavior*, Appleton-Century Crofts, New York, 1957.

SLUCKIN, W.: *Minds and Machines*, rev. ed., Penguin Books, Baltimore, 1960.

SMART, J. J. C.: *Philosophy and Scientific Realism*, Humanities Press, New York, 1963.

———. "Professor Ziff on Robots," in *Minds and Machines*, ed. by A. R. Anderson.

———. "Sensations and Brain Processes," in *The Philosophy of Mind*, ed. by V. C. Chappell.

SMART, NINIAN: "Robots Incorporated," in *Minds and Machines*, ed. by A. R. Anderson.

SMITH, ADAM: *The Wealth of Nations*, Modern Library Edition, Random House, New York, 1937.

SMITH, K. U.: "Discriminative Behavior in Animals," in *Comparative Psychology*, ed. by C. P. Stone.

SMYTHIES, J. R. (ed.): *Brain and Mind*, Humanities Press, New York, 1965.

SPERRY, ROGER W.: "Mind, Brain, and Humanist Values," in *New Views on the Nature of Man*, ed. by J. R. Platt.

SPINOZA, BARUCH: *Ethics*.

SRZEDNICKI, JAN: "Could Machines Talk?" in *Analysis*, Volume 22, No. 5, April, 1962.

STEVENS, S. S. (ed.): *Handbook of Experimental Psychology*, John Wiley & Sons, New York, 1964.

STONE, C. P. (ed.): *Comparative Psychology*, 3rd edition, Prentice-Hall, Inc., Englewood Cliffs, 1955.

SUTHERLAND, N.: "Stimulus Analyzing Mechanisms," in *The Modeling of Mind*, ed. by K. M. Sayre and F. J. Crosson.

TAUBE, MORTIMER: *Computers and Common Sense*, Columbia University Press, New York, 1961.

TAX, SOL. (ed.): *Evolution After Darwin*, Volume II, University of Chicago Press, Chicago, 1960.

TEILHARD DE CHARDIN, PIERRE: *The Phenomenon of Man*, Harper & Row, New York, 1959.

———. *The Appearance of Man*, Harper & Row, New York, 1965.

A Textbook of Marxist Philosophy, prepared by The Leningrad Institute of Philosophy, trans. by A. C. Moseley, ed. by John Lewis, Victor Gollancz Limited, London, nd.

Theoretical Foundations of Psychology, ed. by Harry Helson, D. Van Nostrand Company, Inc., New York, 1951.

THOMPSON, W. R.: "Social Behavior," in *Behavior and Evolution*, ed. by A. Roe and G. G. Simpson.

THORPE, W H.: *Learning and Instinct in Animals*, Harvard University Press, Cambridge (Mass.), 1963.

———. *Science, Man and Morals*, Methuen, London, 1965.

TINBERGEN, N.: *The Study of Instinct*, The Clarendon Press, Oxford, 1951.

TINKLEPAUGH, OTTO, L.: "Social Behavior of Animals," in *Comparative Psychology*, ed. by F. A. Moss.

TOULMIN, S.: "Koestler's Act of Creation," in *Encounter*, Volume XXIII, No. 1, pp. 58–70, July, 1964.

TOULMIN, S. and J. GOODFIELD: *The Discovery of Time*, Harper & Row, New York, 1965.
TURING, A. M.: "Computing Machinery and Intelligence," in *Computers and Thought*, ed. by E. A. Feigenbaum and J. Feldman.

UHR, L. and C. VOSSLER: "A Pattern-Recognition Program that Generates, Evalutes, and Adjusts its Own Operators," in *Computers and Thought*, ed. by E. A. Feigenbaum and J. Feldman.
ULLMANN, STEPHEN: *The Principles of Semantics*, Barnes & Noble, New York, 1963.

VAHANIAN, GABRIEL: *The Death of God*, George Braziller, New York, 1957.
———. *No Other God*, George Braziller, New York, 1966.
VAN BUREN, PAUL: *The Secular Meaning of the Gospel*, Macmillan, New York, 1953.
VARTANIAN ARAM (ed.): *La Mettrie's L'Homme Machine*, Princeton University Press, Princeton, 1960.
VERCORS: *You Shall Know Them*, Little, Brown & Company, Boston, 1953.
VON FRISCH, KARL: *The Dancing Bees*, Harcourt, Brace and Company, New York, 1953.
VON KOENIGSWALD, G. H. R.: *The Evolution of Man*, University of Michigan Press, Ann Arbor, 1963.
VON NEUMANN, JOHN: *The Computer and the Brain*, Yale University Press, New Haven, 1958.

WALLACE, A. E.: *Contributions to the Theory of Natural Selection*, 2nd edition, Macmillan, London, 1871.
WARDEN, C. J., T. N. JENKINS, L. H. WARNER: *Introduction to Comparative Psychology*, Ronald Press, New York, 1934.
WARNOCK, G. J.: "Logical Analysis and the Nature of Thought," in *Scientific Psychology*, ed. by B. B. Wolman and E. Nagel.
WASHBURN, S. L. and V. AVIS: "Evolution of Human Behavior" in *Behavior and Evolution*, ed. by A. Roe and G. G. Simpson.
WASHBURN, S. L. and CLARK F. HOWELL: "Human Evolution and Culture," in *Evolution After Darwin*, Volume II, ed. by Sol Tax.
WATERS, R. H.: "The Historical Background of Comparative Psychology," in *Comparative Psychology*, ed. by F. A. Moss.
WEISS, P.: *Nature and Man*, Henry Holt & Company, New York, 1947.
———. *Man's Freedom*, Yale University Press, New Haven, 1950.
WHITE, LESLIE, A.: "Four Stages in the Evolution of Minding," in *Evolution After Darwin*, Volume II, ed. by Sol Tax.
———. *The Science of Culture*, Farrar, Straus and Cudahy, New York, 1949.

WIENER, P. P. (ed.): *Leibniz Selections*, Modern Students Library, Charles Scribner's Sons, New York, 1951.

WISDOM, J. O.: "Mentality in Machines," in *Proceedings of the Aristotelian Society*, Supplementary volume XXVI, 1952.

WITTENGENSTEIN, LUDWIG: *Philosophical Investigations*, Macmillan, New York, 1953.

WOLMAN, BENJAMIN B.: "Principles of Monistic Transitionism," in *Scientific Psychology*, ed. by B. B. Wolman and E. Nagel.

WOLMAN, BENJAMIN B. and ERNEST NAGEL, (ed.): *Scientific Psychology*, Basic Books, New York, 1965.

WOODWORTH, ROBERT S. and HAROLD SCHLOSBERG: *Experimental Psychology*, rev. ed., Holt, Rinehart & Winston, Inc., New York, 1954.

ZIFF, PAUL: *Semantic Analysis*, Cornell University Press, Ithaca, 1960.

"The Feelings of Robots," in *Mind and Machines*, ed. by A. R. Anderson.

Index

Index of Proper Names

About the Author

Mortimer J. Adler, director of the Institute for Philosophical Research in Chicago and a member of the board of editors of the Encyclopaedia Brittanica, is the distinguished author of many books, among them *The Conditions of Philosophy*, *A Dialectic of Morals*, *The Idea of Freedom*, *What Man Has Made of Man*, and the best-selling *How To Read A Book*.

Book Reviews:

Deely, John in *The Thomist*, 32, no 3 (July, 1968), 436-439

______. in *The New Scholasticism*, 42, no 2 (Spring, 1968), pp. 293-306 as Discussion Article II: "The Immateriality of the Intentional as Such." Adler replied to Deely's article in Discussion article: "Sense Cognition: Aristotle vs. Aquinas," in *The New Scholasticism*, 42, no 4 (Autumn, 1968), 578-5

Gerber, Rudolph J. in *America* (Dec 9, 1967) p 722a-c

in *Science* (April 5, 1968) 57a-

in *Modern Age* (Spring, 1968)

Book Reviews

Unknown - in *Time* (January 12, 1968), 60b-C9